SCIENCE 1

GRAHAM HILL AND JOHN HOLMAN

SCIENCE 1

GRAHAM HILL AND JOHN HOLMAN

Nelson

Thomas Nelson and Sons Ltd
Nelson House Mayfield Road
Walton-on-Thames Surrey
KT12 5PL UK

51 York Place
Edinburgh
EH1 3JD UK

Thomas Nelson (Hong Kong) Ltd
Toppan Building 10/F
22A Westlands Road
Quarry Bay Hong Kong

Thomas Nelson (Kenya) Ltd
P.O. Box 18123
Nairobi Kenya

Distributed in Australia by
Thomas Nelson Australia
480 La Trobe Street
Melbourne Victoria 3000
and in Sydney, Brisbane, Adelaide and Perth

First published 1986

ISBN 0-17-448075-X
NCN 21-KSC-3770-01

Illustration and Design by Gecko Limited

Printed in Hong Kong

Acknowledgements

Acknowledgement is due to the following for permission to use photographs:
B.T.A: 6, 9, 10, 40, 97, 104; Barnaby's Picture Library: 173; Penni Bickle: 69; Biofotos/Heather Angel: 14, 43, 63, 64; Biophotos: 21, 26; British Railway Board: 35; C.E.G.B: 127; Camera Press: 39, 289; Camerapix Hutchison: 136, 163; Bruce Coleman: 158; Gene Cox: 25 (2), 53; Daily Telegraph: 4; Daily Telegraph/NASA: 1; Daily Telegraph/Space Frontiers: 1, 59; Ford U.K: 41, 56; Gas Board: 153; Geological Institute: 37; Sally & Richard Greenhill: 5; Health Education Council: 169; London Fire Brigade: 160; S & O Mathews: 9 (2); Mexicolore: 141; Middlesex Hospital: 171; Mullard Ltd: 93; Nelson Picture Research Department: 13, 65, 100, 119, 122; Peebles: 129; Chris Perrett Photography: 12, 16, 20, 30; Picturepoint: 7, 8, 71, 107, 117, 140, 146, 148, 155; Rank Organisation: 35; Chris Ridgers Photography: 54, 61, 105, 112, 121, 124, 125, 139, 161, 172; Royal College of Surgeons: 52, 170; Science Photo Library: 63, 120, 141; Ronald Sheridan's Photo Library: 62; Sporting Pictures: 47, 60, 73; ZEFA: 6, 10, 46, 72, 83, 91, 132 (2), 146, 164.

Contents

Science 2 companion text to *Science 1* 0–17–448076–8

Science 2 Contents: Food; Micro-organisms and people; Heat and energy; Waves and energy; Hearing, sound and music; Seeing, light and colour; Senses and responses; Reproduction; Inheritance and evolution; Competitions; Industrial chemicals; Water all round; Atomic structure and radioactivity.

Preface

To the teacher

Why Integrated Science?

Two major trends have been dominant in science education in recent years: the call for Science for All and the move towards balanced science.

Along with these trends, and partly caused by them, has come growing interest in Integrated Science and in making science teaching more relevant to everyday life. Integrated Science courses are an effective way of enabling all pupils to study elements of all three major sciences without making excessive demands on curriculum time. Integrated Science is economical, not least because it removes the duplication of subject matter and the general lack of co-ordination that often accompanies the study of separate sciences. In any case, the *processes* and *methods* of science are the same whatever the subject area, and teachers are increasingly concerned to develop the processes of science, and to foster a scientific approach, rather than to concentrate on specific areas of content.

There is another sense in which integration can make the study of science more worthwhile. To make science relevant to pupils' lives, it is necessary to show its everyday applications and its social and technological implications. Far better to integrate these applications with the scientific principles to which they relate, than to add them on as an afterthought. In any case, real-life problems and applications have a tendency not to confine themselves conveniently to physics, chemistry or biology. Technology is no respecter of subject boundaries.

With these points in mind, we have planned a fully integrated text, starting from first principles rather than attempting to combine separate elements of physics, chemistry and biology. The social and technological aspects of the subject form an integrated part of the whole.

Who are the books for?

Science 1 and *Science 2* have been written to accompany single or double certificate GCSE courses in Integrated Science, particularly in years, 3, 4 and 5. They will also be useful accompaniments to single or double certificate Combined Science courses, and many teachers of separate subject sciences will find them valuable as core texts. They cover the National Criteria in science and most of the National Criteria in the separate subjects of physics, chemistry and biology.

Throughout the period of writing the books we have been guided by a team of advisers who have provided specialist knowledge from a wide variety of educational backgrounds. These advisers have checked both the accuracy of the subject matter and the level and readability of the text. They are also available as one volume, *Science*, combined edition.

Organisation of the books

The books are organised in chapters, divided into short sections. Chapters 1–14 are in the first book and chapters 15–27 are in the second one. Each chapter deals with an important scientific topic or theme. Inevitably, some chapters deal mainly with subject matter from a single subject area (e.g. chapter 10, Currents and Electricity). In others, elements of physics, chemistry and biology will all be found in a single chapter (e.g. chapter 12, Energy All Round).

We feel that wherever possible, reading should be an active rather than a passive process, with pupils thinking about and using the subject matter they are reading. We have therefore included, at frequent intervals, questions designed to probe and extend pupils' understanding of the text. The answers to most of these questions can be found on further reading, but we have included a number of more open-ended, speculative questions which will form a good basis for class discussion. Each chapter concludes with a range of Study

Questions, suitable for use in class or for homework. There is a Summary at the end of each chapter which brings together important facts and ideas.

The text is accompanied by many line diagrams, carefully designed to complement the written development of the subject matter. We have also selected a large number of photographs to illustrate the relevance of the scientific principles to the real world.

Some specific points to note

Nomenclature, Units and Symbols

We have been guided throughout by the latest recommendations of the Association for Science Education.

Electric current

We have used *the direction of electron flow* as our convention for electric current. We appreciate that this may seem unusual to physicists, accustomed to using conventional current flow from positive to negative. Nevertheless, we feel that in the context of an integrated text our treatment is justified because it makes a number of explanations (e.g. electrolysis) more straightforward.

Biological classification

We have adopted a classification based on the Five Kingdom system, which is gaining increasing acceptance among biologists.

Many friends, colleagues and pupils have helped and influenced us in writing these books. In particular we would like to thank our advisers, Christopher Hurst, Jean Mackie, Michael Roberts, Justine Coupland and Nikolas Coupland, for their guidance; our publishers and in particular Elizabeth Johnston and Fiona McGregor, for their faith and expertise, and our wives, Elizabeth and Wendy, for their tolerance and support.

To the student

These books are about science and the part that science plays in our lives, in industry and in society. They are specially written for the new GCSE courses and examinations in Science, Integrated Science and Combined Science. We hope that you will find them lively and interesting.

Science affects every aspect of our lives – our work, our health, our homes and our interests. Whenever possible, we have tried to show the *relevance of science* in our lives and to include topics which you will *need to know* about as you grow up in the twentieth century.

We have also tried to make the book as readable as possible by keeping the language and the sentences clear and concise.

The two books are divided into 27 chapters. Chapters 1–14 are in the first book and chapters 15–27 are in the second book. Each chapter is divided into several sections. There are questions in most of these sections to make you think and to help you to understand the topic being studied. Some of the questions are very easy, others are more difficult and you may want to discuss these with your teacher. At the end of each chapter, there are longer study questions to give you practice in answering examination questions. Try to answer as many as possible of these questions because this is a very good way of practising what you have learned. There is also a summary at the end of each chapter which draws together the key points from that area of science.

If you are looking for information on a particular topic remember to use the contents list at the beginning of the book as well as the index at the back.

Graham Hill
John Holman
August 1985

To our fathers, Harold and Leslie

1 Planet Earth

The surface of the Earth, where the Colorado River meets the sea in California, USA.

The Earth may seem large to us, but it is only a tiny speck in the whole universe.

1.1 The Earth and the universe

If you have gazed into the sky on a moonlit and cloudless night, you must surely have been filled with a sense of wonder. Looking out into the vastness of space you will see thousands of stars and planets. How large are these stars? How far away are they? Are there beings similar to ourselves on any other planets?

The universe, galaxies and stars

Stars are the units or **building blocks** of even larger star systems known as **galaxies**. Our own Sun is only one star in a huge galaxy containing over one hundred billion stars. And this is not all. Beyond our own galaxy there are billions of other galaxies which make up the building blocks of the **universe**.

Look at the photograph of the galaxy below.

(*Above*) The galaxy Andromeda is similar to our own. It is 10^{18} km across, and there are billions of other galaxies in the universe.

It contains millions and millions of stars. The distance across the galaxy is about one million million million (10^{18}) kilometres. The Earth may seem large to us, but its diameter of 13000 kilometres is tiny compared to the distances in space. In fact, astronomical distances are so large that they are not usually expressed in kilometres but in **light-years**. This is the distance that a beam of light can travel through space in one year. Light travels 300000 kilometres every second or about ten million million kilometres per year.

- Alpha Centauri, the nearest star in our own galaxy is about four light-years from the Earth. How many kilometres is that?

Building blocks

Galaxies are the building blocks for the universe, just as bricks are the building blocks for walls. Bricks themselves are made of even tinier building blocks, atoms and molecules. Building blocks are the units which make up larger groups or *higher levels of organisation*. Thus, molecules of proteins, carbohydrates and other substances are the building blocks for cells; and cells, in turn, are the building blocks for organisms.

Figure 1.1 shows some of the building blocks that we have mentioned, and the way in which each of these building blocks can be organised and arranged into larger units. Notice that each building block is 10^4 to 10^8 times smaller than the larger group of which it forms a small part.

- What do you understand by the term *building block*?
- What is (a) a light-year and (b) a galaxy?
- The Sun is eight light-minutes from the Earth. How many kilometres is this?
- How many building blocks can you find in the following address?
  Joe Bloggs,
  Amersham,
  Buckinghamshire,
  England,
  The Earth,
  The Solar System,
  The Galaxy,
  The Universe.

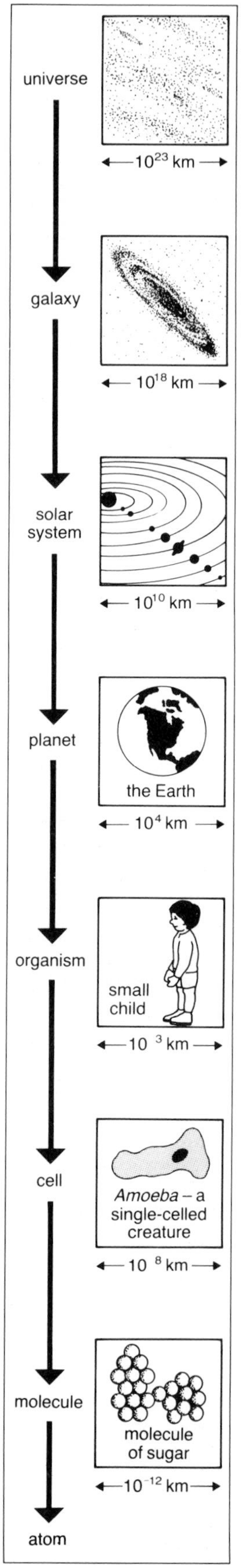

Figure 1.1 Building blocks.

Writing numbers using powers of ten

$10 \times 10 \times 10 = 1000 = 10^3$

One million $= 1000000 = 10^6$

One million million $= 10^{12}$

The diameter of the Earth $= 13000$ km
$= 1{\cdot}3 \times 10000$ km
$= 1{\cdot}3 \times 10^4$ km

$$\frac{1}{10} = 10^{-1}$$

$$\frac{1}{100} = \frac{1}{10} \times \frac{1}{10} = 10^{-2}$$

The height of a child $= 1$ m

$$= \frac{1}{1000}\text{ km}$$

$$= 10^{-3}\text{ km}$$

1.2 The solar system

The building blocks for solar systems are planets. Our own solar system contains nine planets which move around the Sun in roughly circular paths called **orbits**.

Figure 1.2 shows the relative sizes of the planets in our solar system and their distances from the Sun. The Earth, which is 150 million kilometres from the Sun, takes one year to complete its orbit. This is small compared to Pluto which is about thirty times further from the Sun and takes 250 years to complete one orbit.

Smaller bits of rock and dust also orbit the Sun. These include:

- **Comets** collections of gas and dust which reflect light from the Sun.
- **Meteors** tiny specks of rock which burn up on entering the Earth's atmosphere.
- **Meteorites** larger rocks which strike planets from time to time.

- As you read this book, you are moving in orbit around the Sun at about 30 kilometres each second. Why don't you notice this motion?

Our Sun is an average-sized star made mainly of hydrogen and helium. Its diameter is about a hundred times that of the Earth and it accounts for more than 99% of the mass of the solar system.

The temperature on the surface of the Sun is about 6000°C, but at its centre the temperature rises to about fourteen million de-

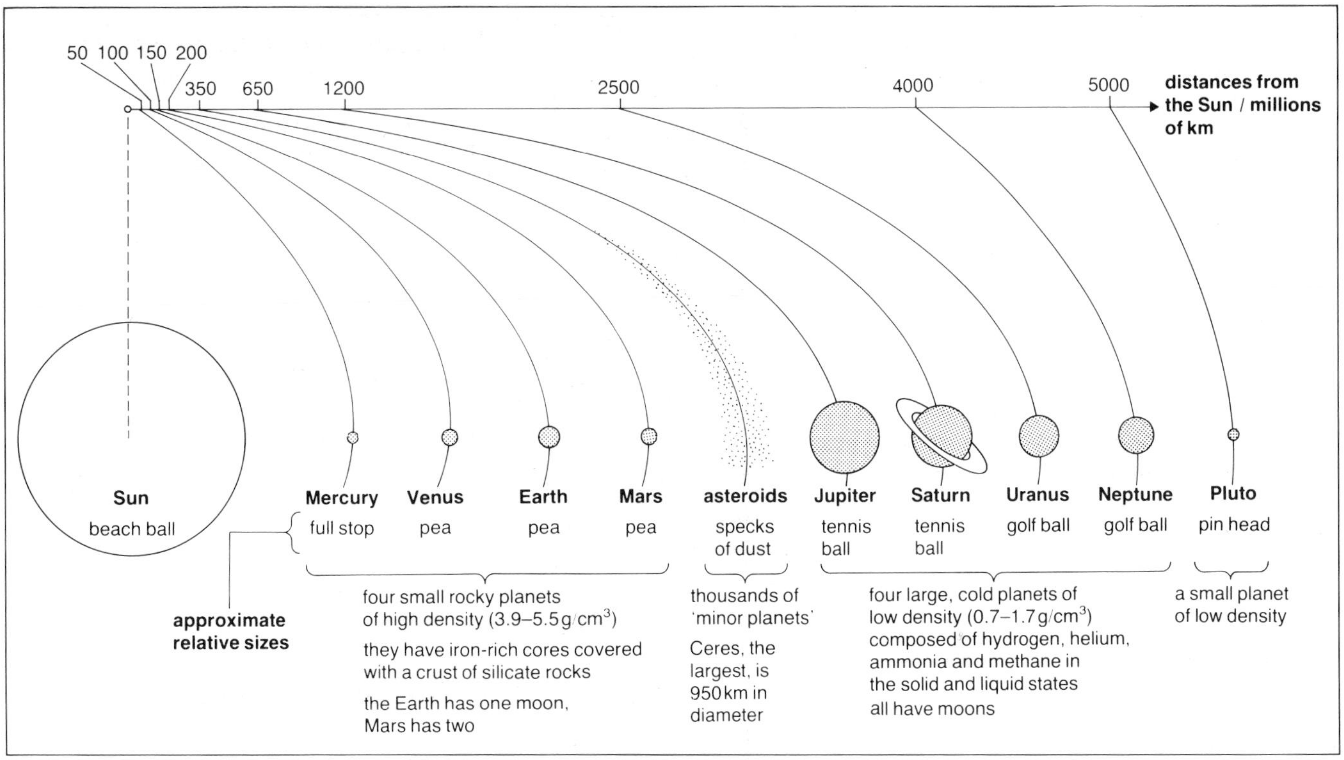

Figure 1.2 The solar system

grees celsius. These high temperatures result from continuous nuclear reactions. Within the Sun, hydrogen atoms are forced together (fused) at high temperatures and pressures forming helium. This gives out vast quantities of heat, which keeps the temperature high.

How did the solar system come into being?

All the planets in our solar system circle the Sun in the same direction and in the same plane. This has led to the suggestion that the solar system formed from a vast revolving cloud of gas which slowly contracted under its own gravity. As the material condensed, a large, hot central mass formed a new star (the Sun), while the surrounding cooler material condensed to form the planets.

1.3 Planet Earth

The Earth is probably the only planet in our solar system on which there is life. Why is this so?

We now know that the Earth was once a molten mass of rock which has cooled down over millions of years. During this period, heavier materials sunk to the centre of the Earth forming a **core** of dense molten rock surrounded by less dense, cooler material in the **mantle** (figure 1.3). Lighter materials remained on the surface forming a thin **crust** about fifty kilometres thick. Outside this crust, gaseous materials which have not condensed form the **atmosphere**. The Earth's atmosphere is composed mainly of nitrogen and oxygen, together with several other rarer gases. These gases remain close to the Earth's surface, forming a capsule around the planet. Heavier gases like oxygen and carbon dioxide tend to concentrate

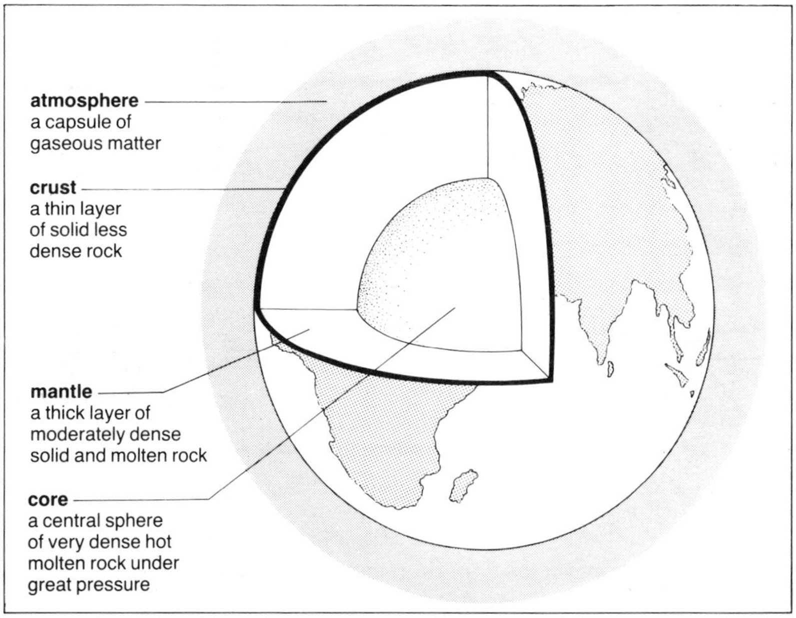

Figure 1.3 Layers of the Earth. Scientists have studied the layers inside the Earth using sound waves and the waves sent out by Earthquakes.

in the lower layers, while lighter gases like hydrogen and neon move into the upper atmosphere. The atmospheres on other planets in our solar system do not contain oxygen.

During the long cooling-down process, water vapour in the atmosphere condensed to form rivers, lakes and oceans on the Earth's surface. Scientists believe that the Earth is the only planet with oceans and lakes, although other planets, such as Mars, do have some water vapour and polar ice caps.

Although there may be living things elsewhere in the universe, it is unlikely that any of the other planets in our own solar system support life.

- What substances do the Earth's surface and atmosphere contain which are essential for living things?
- Why would the planet Mercury not support life even if it had the substances essential for living things? (Hint: look again at figure 1.2.)
- Why is it unlikely that there is any life on the planets Uranus, Neptune and Pluto?
- Why is Mars the one planet that might support life?

The Moon, a satellite of the Earth

For hundreds of years, people have observed the Moon and wondered what its surface would be like and whether it had any plants or animals, All the mystery and speculation ended in July 1969 when American astronauts landed on the Moon in order to carry out experiments and bring samples of dust and rocks back to Earth.

When we look at the Moon, we see dark, sunken areas and brightly reflecting rugged mountains. The whole landscape is pockmarked with craters. These craters are formed by the impact of meteorites, which do not burn up in the Moon's thin atmosphere as they would if they were approaching the Earth.

Tests on Moon rocks have shown that they are similar to those on Earth, but with different proportions of the elements. The high proportion of titanium has led some scientists to conclude that the Moon was never part of our own planet, as was once thought. They have suggested that the Moon formed separately and then became trapped in the Earth's gravitational field.

The surface of the Moon.

Experiments have also shown that the gases surrounding the Moon could not maintain the sort of life that has evolved on Earth. There is no evidence that any living thing, animal, plant or micro-organism, ever existed on the Moon.

The Moon takes 27.3 days to orbit the Earth. We can see the Moon at night because the Sun's rays are reflected from its surface. During the day, the sky is too bright for the Moon to be more than faintly visible.

Probably the most important influence that the Moon has on the Earth is in controlling the tides. The Moon's gravitational pull draws the oceans towards it and this causes the sea to rise at the point on the Earth closest to the Moon (figure 1.4). The Sun's gravitational pull also affects the tides.

Look closely at the photographs of the surfaces of the Earth and the Moon (page 1 and this page).

- What features can you recognise in the photograph of the Earth?
- (*Hard*) Which features may have resulted from the Earth's atmosphere and weather?
- (*Hard*) Which features suggest that there is life on Earth?
- How does the surface of the Moon differ from that of the Earth?

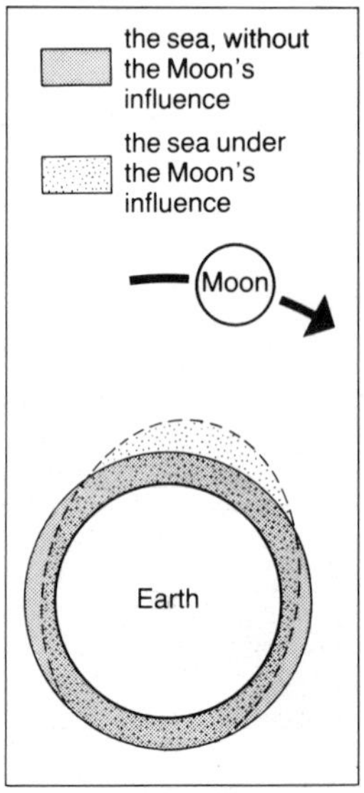

Figure 1.4 The influence of the Moon on the Earth's tides.

1.4 The Earth's crust: rocks and soil

The Earth's crust is composed of rocks and soils. Rocks provide us with many of the raw materials for industry. Crops grow and thrive on the soil and many animals and microbes live in it.

The Earth's crust is like the shell of a cracked egg. It consists of huge sections called **plates**. These vast plates move very, very slowly as a result of movements in the liquid mantle below the crust. When the plates rub against each other, various things can happen.

- Cracks may form in the Earth's surface and **faults** appear where the land slips away (figure 1.5).
- Stress can build up to such an extent that the plates bend. As they suddenly spring back into shape the ground shakes violently in an **earthquake**.
- As the plates are pushed together, the land is pushed upwards and downwards forming mountains and valleys. Many of the great mountain ranges of the world, such as the Alps, the Himalayas, the Rocky Mountains and the Scottish Highlands, formed in this way.

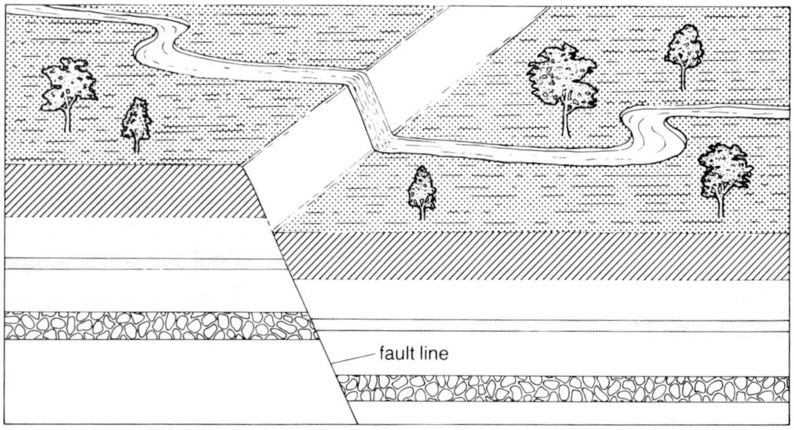

Figure 1.5 Formation of a fault in the Earth's crust.

(*Left*) The risk of earthquakes near the San Andreas Fault in California is very high. Here two major plates slip past each other several centimetres every year.
(*Above*) This house is five miles from the fault. It is built with an extremely strong geometrical shape.
(*Below*) At Palmdale in California, the motorway cuts right across the fault, which appears as a giant fold in the rocks.

Rocks in the Earth's crust

The Earth's crust contains three different kinds of rock.

Igneous rocks

When cracks appear in the Earth's crust, hot molten rock can force its way to the surface erupting as a **volcano** in a shower of dust, smoke and burning liquid. Eventually, the molten **lava** cools and solidifies. Rocks that have formed from molten material in the Earth's mantle are known as **igneous rocks**.

The most familiar igneous rocks are those produced by volcanoes forming rocks such as basalt. Igneous rocks also occur in the deepest layers of the Earth's crust next to the mantle. These rocks, such as granite, only appear on the Earth's surface when rocks above them are eroded in some way (figure 1.6).

When molten, igneous rock cools slowly, it can sometimes form hard attractive crystals, such as diamond, sapphire, emerald, opal and quartz.

Figure 1.6 (Below) Rocks in the Earth's crust.

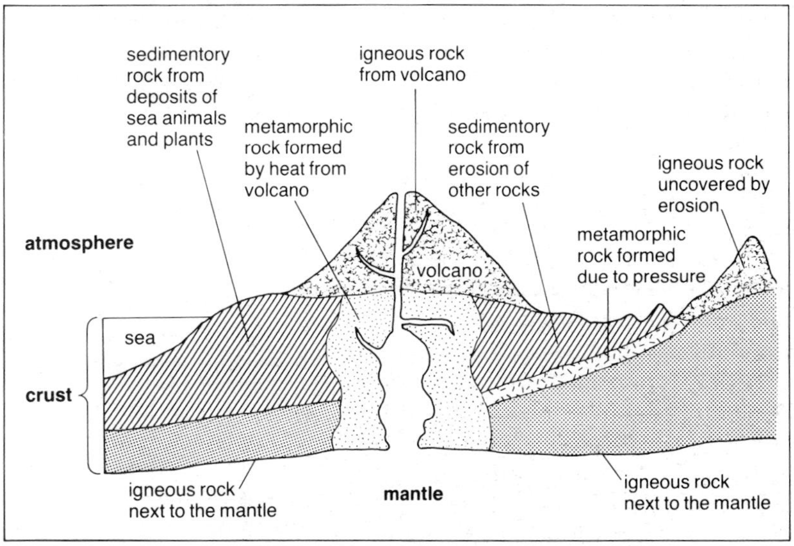

Sedimentary rocks

As the name suggests, **sedimentary rocks** are formed from sediments, which deposit in layers, such as sand and gravel in a river bed. As the layers (**strata**) build up, the material underneath is compressed together forming hard rock. Unlike igneous rocks, sedimentary rocks have formed extremely slowly over millions of years.

Some sedimentary rocks, such as sandstone, result from the **erosion** of other rocks by wind, rain, sea and frost. Other sedimentary rocks, such as limestone and coal, have formed from the remains of dead animals and plants.

Metamorphic rocks

Both igneous and sedimentary rocks can be changed into different, harder rocks at high temperature or by great pressure. The new rock has a different structure to the original rock. It is therefore known as **metamorphic rock** from a Greek word meaning *change of shape*.

Slate and marble are good examples of metamorphic rocks. Slate is formed when clay and mud are subjected to very high pressures, whilst marble is formed when limestone comes into contact with hot, igneous rock (figure 1.6).

- How are igneous, sedimentary and metamorphic rocks formed?
- What causes a) a volcano and b) an earthquake?
- Are the following igneous, sedimentary or metamorphic rocks?
  a) granite b) coal c) sandstone
  d) chalk e) quartz f) diamond
  g) marble

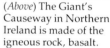

(*Above*) The Giant's Causeway in Northern Ireland is made of the igneous rock, basalt.

(*Left*) Mount St Helens in North America erupted in 1980. Volcanoes occur where hot molten rock forces its way through cracks in the Earth's crust.

Soil

How has soil formed?

Millions of years ago, the Earth's surface was nothing but bare rock. Slowly these rocks were broken up by wind, rain, sea and frost into smaller particles. When plants and animals appeared on the land, their decaying remains mixed with the particles of rock to form soil.

If you look at the edge of a cliff or pit you will see how the soil is composed of layers. The top layer is usually the darkest. This is called the **topsoil** where plants and other creatures live. Below the topsoil is a layer composed mainly of stones, clay and gravel, which contains very few living things except the deeper roots of trees. This is called the **subsoil** (figure 1.7). Below the subsoil is solid rock which is often non-porous, and so water tends to collect above it.

What does soil contain?

Soil contains four main constituents.

- **Rock particles** including sand, gravel, clay, lime and other mineral salts.
- **Water** – usually a thin film surrounding the solid particles in the soil.

- **Humus** is a black crumbly solid formed from the decay of dead plants and animals. Humus is rich in the nutrients and chemicals which plants need to grow. It is fibrous and holds water well, which stops soil from drying out too fast. Gardeners add compost to soil to increase its humus content.
- **Air** fills up the spaces between the solid particles. Oxygen in this air is needed for the respiration of living things in the soil and for the decay of humus.

The most fertile soils hold water well, but do not become waterlogged. They contain plenty of plant nutrients and chemicals. This requires a balance between clay (which holds water) and sand (which drains well) plus plenty of humus.

Finding the composition of soil

How much air is there in soil?

A student tapped down 50 cm^3 of soil into a large measuring cylinder. When he added 50 cm^3 of water from a second measuring cylinder and stirrred the soil to dislodge all the air bubbles, he found that the final volume was 90 cm^3.

- What volume of soil did the student take?
- What volume of air was dislodged from the soil?
- What is the percentage, by volume, of air in the original soil?

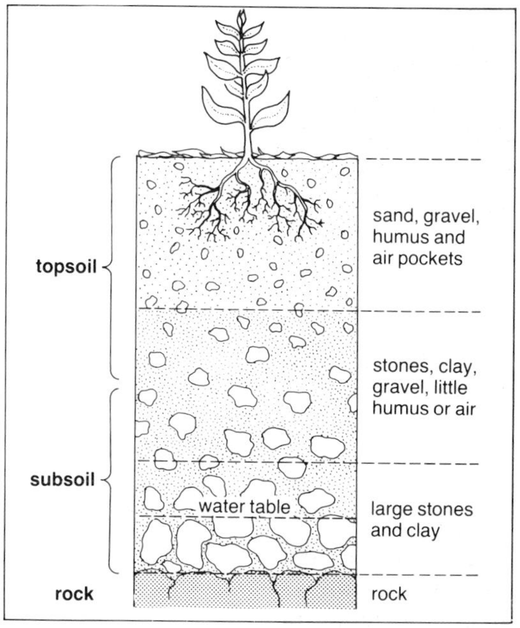

Figure 1.7 A worm's eye view of the soil.

(*Above*) At the Grand Canyon, USA, you can see the layers of different rocks deposited over millions of years.

How much water is there in the soil?

A student placed 10 g of soil in an oven at 100°C to evaporate any water in the soil. After one hour, she removed the sample from the oven and allowed it to cool. She found that it weighed 7.5 g.

- What is the mass of water in the 10 g of soil?
- What is the percentage, by mass, of water in the soil?
- (*Hard*) How could you check that all the water had evaporated from the soil?

How much humus is there in the soil?

5 g of the dried soil from the last experiment was heated strongly in a crucible for twenty minutes to burn the humus, forming carbon dioxide, water vapour and other gases. The final mass of the soil was 4.5 g.

- Why did the soil lose mass?
- What is the mass of humus in the 5 g of dried soil?
- What is the percentage, by mass, of humus in the soil?
- Why must the soil be dried before starting this experiment?

1.5 Raw materials from the Earth

The Earth provides a vast treasure store of minerals and materials for our use. Even before the Stone Age, men and women were interested in these raw materials. With time, they found ways to change useless things like iron ore into useful things like iron. Nowadays, large sections of the chemical and mining industries are geared to the production of valuable commodities like metals, fuels and plastics, from naturally occurring substances in the sea, in the atmosphere or in the Earth's crust.

The six most important sources of raw materials are: rocks, coal, oil, the sea, the air and plants.

- **Rocks and mineral ores** provide most of our metals and the materials we use in agriculture and the building industry. Some metals, like gold, occur naturally, but others must be extracted from minerals in the Earth's crust. Iron is extracted from iron ore (haematite) and aluminium from bauxite. Limestone is used to make lime for neutralising acid in the soil and for making cement.

> - Name a metal which occurs naturally, like gold.
> - (*Hard*) Which metals are obtained from a) rock salt, b) zinc blende and c) galena?
> - Which rock is used for making cement and mortar?

- **Coal, oil and natural gas** yield more than 80% of the fuel we require for our homes and industry. Coal and oil are also essential starting materials for making many other chemicals such as PVC, polystyrene, pesticides and perfumes.
- **The sea** contains 35 g of dissolved salts in every kilogram. A large part of the dissolved material is sodium chloride (common salt). In hot countries, salt is produced by evaporating sea water. Salt is used for preserving food and improving its flavour, for curing leather and for manufacturing sodium and chlorine.
- **Air** is a mixture of gases including nitrogen, oxygen and argon (section 14.2). Air can be separated into its constituents by fractional distillation of liquid air. Liquid air can be made by cooling and compressing the air. Nitrogen is used to make ammonia, nitric acid and fertilisers. Oxygen is used in hospitals, in oxyacetylene cutting and in the manufacture of steel. Argon is used to fill electric light bulbs.
- **Plants** provide most of our food, timber for the building industry and materials such as linen and cotton for clothing. Fruits, vegetables, flour and sugar all come from plants. Coconut, palm and olive trees give us oils for cooking, cosmetics and soap.

(*Above*) Using a small range of bricks, it is possible to build millions of different houses. In the same way, millions of different substances can be made from the 105 known elements

Elements, the building blocks for substances

Everything in the universe, whether it is alive or dead, a raw material or artificially made, is composed of elements. At present there are 105 known elements, including copper, iron, aluminium, nitrogen, sulphur and oxygen. In 1661, Robert Boyle suggested the name **element** for *a substance which cannot be broken down into a simpler substance*. This is still a fairly satisfactory definition for an element.

Anyone who has burnt toast has succeeded in making an element. When bread is toasted, the surface becomes covered with a black solid. This is carbon. Smoke rises from the toasted bread. This contains water vapour and carbon dioxide.

$$\text{bread} \xrightarrow{\text{heat}} \text{carbon} + \text{carbon dioxide} + \text{water} + \text{toast}$$

No matter how the black carbon is treated, it cannot be broken down into any simpler substance. Therefore, carbon is an element.

> - What elements does carbon dioxide contain?
> - Can carbon dioxide be broken down into simpler substances?
> - Is carbon dioxide an element?

Substances like water and carbon dioxide are not elements because they can be broken down into simpler substances.

When electricity is passed through water, the water breaks up forming hydrogen and oxygen, which are elements. Although there are millions of different substances in the universe, every substance which has been investigated can be split into one or more of the 105 known elements. Thus, *elements are the building blocks for all substances*, in the same way that bricks, tiles and timber are the building blocks for houses. Using a small range of different bricks, tiles and timbers (building blocks) it is possible to construct an infinite number of different houses.

What is the Earth made from?

Although there are 105 known elements, they occur in very different proportions in the Earth's crust. Figure 1.8 shows the abundance of the commonest eight elements in the Earth's crust. Notice that these eight elements account for more than 98% by mass of the Earth's crust. The remaining 97 elements account for only 1.5%.

What is more, the two most abundant elements, oxygen and silicon, make up almost three quarters of the mass of the Earth's crust. Oxygen forms 23% by mass of the air and 89% by mass of water. Most of the oxygen, however, is combined with other elements in rocks and soils. Sand, quartz and sandstone all contain roughly equal proportions of oxygen and silicon, which is the second most abundant element. Clays also contain silicon and oxygen, together with aluminium which is the third most abundant element. Chalk, limestone and marble (all of which are forms of calcium carbonate) contain 40% calcium, 12% carbon and 48% oxygen. These account for most of the calcium in the Earth's crust. Most of the iron is combined with oxygen in iron ore, which is rust-coloured iron oxide. Sodium, potassium and magnesium compounds are present in clays and in sea water.

The four main types of soil are sandy soil, clay soil, chalky soil and peaty soil.

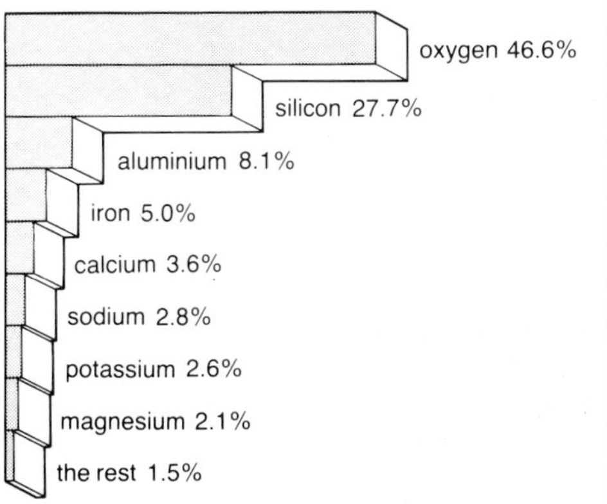

Figure 1.8 The abundance by mass of elements in the atmosphere and the Earth's crust.

(*Above*) The New Forest, Hampshire, is typical of an area with sandy soil.

(*Left*) The South Downs are a typical example of a chalky soil landscape.

- What are the most abundant elements in each soil type?
- What is the soil like where you live?
- Ideal garden soil contains about 50% sand, 30% clay, 10% chalk and 10% peat (humus). How does the soil in your area compare with this?

(*Below*) Lush grass and dairy farming are features of clay soil. The area near Leominster, in Hereford and Worcester, is typical of this.

(*Above*) At Spalding in Lincolnshire, peaty soil supports commerical tulip growing.

- What do the following scientists study?
  a) zoologist, b) metallurgist, c) surgeon.
- What are the special names for scientists who study
  a) the weather, b) plants, c) people's teeth?

1.6 What is science?

In this chapter we have studied the solar system, the Earth and the rocks and materials which are part of it. We have asked questions and suggested ideas (theories) to answer them. These ideas can be tested by doing experiments and obtaining more information. These activities illustrate very nicely what science is about and how scientists work.

Science is the study of things in the world about us. Science includes the study of stars, the Earth, the air, rocks, plants and animals. Science involves the study of so many different things that many scientists specialise in one particular area. Table 1.1 shows the special names for some scientists, and what they study.

Table 1.1

Scientist's name	*Subject name*	*What they study*
astronomer	astronomy	stars and planets
biologist	biology	living things
chemist	chemistry	substances and the changes they undergo
engineer	engineering	machines
geologist	geology	rocks and minerals
physicist	physics	the interaction of energy with matter

(*Below*) When doctors interview patients, they work as scientists. They ask questions and then suggest a reason (theory) for the illness. Sometimes they prescribe medicine (experiment) to see if this will cure the illness.

How do scientists work?

All these scientists seem to do very different jobs but there are some important links between all of them and the way they work.

- They study things in the world and ask questions.
- They put forward ideas (theories) to answer these questions.
- They check and test ideas by doing experiments and obtaining more information.

There is one more thing that links all scientists, something more important than their methods of work. *Their knowledge can be used to help others and benefit society, or it can work against the wellbeing of society.* It is easy to see how some scientists, like doctors and dentists, use their knowledge to help others. The benefits from other scientists are less obvious, but when you next visit your dentist, think of the engineers who designed the mirrors and drills in the surgery, the chemists who discovered the anaesthetics and the metallurgists who developed the amalgam for fillings.

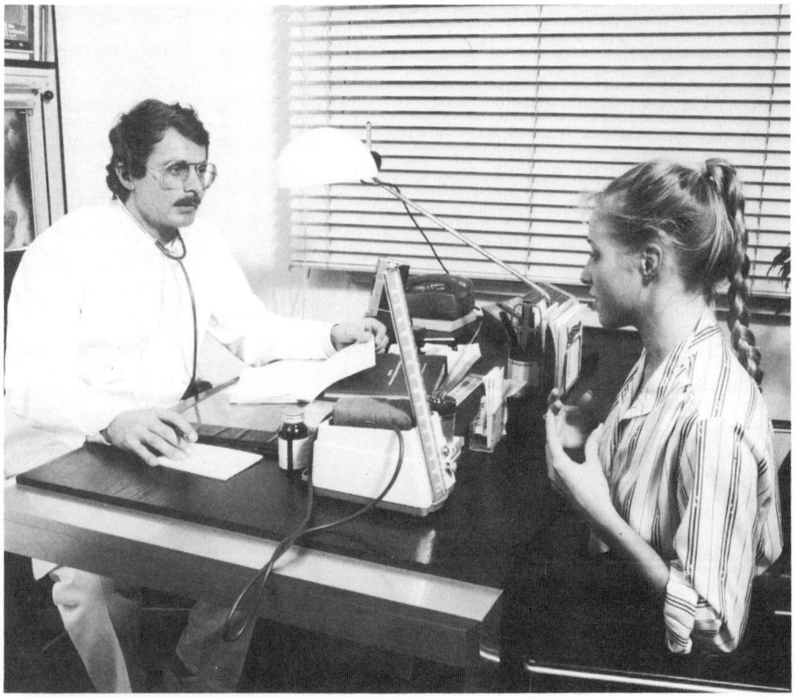

Summary

1 The Earth is only a tiny speck in the whole universe.

2 Building blocks are the units which make up larger units. Molecules are the building blocks for cells, planets are the building blocks for solar systems and galaxies are the building blocks for the universe.

3 Our solar system contains nine planets which move round the Sun in roughly circular orbits.

4 The Earth is probably the only planet in the solar system on which there is life.

5 The Earth has a core of dense molten rock surrounded by less dense cooler material in the mantle, which in turn is covered by a thin crust of lighter materials.

6 The Earth's crust contains three kinds of rock: igneous, sedimentary and metamorphic.

7 Soil contains four main constituents: rock particles, water, humus and air.

8 The six most important sources of raw materials are: rocks, coal, oil, the sea, the air and plants.

9 Elements are the building blocks for all substances. An element is a substance which cannot be broken down into a simpler substance.

10 Science is the study of things in the World about us.

11 Scientists study things in the World and ask questions. They put forward theories to answer questions and check their theories by doing experiments and obtaining more information.

Study questions

1 a) What do you understand by the terms (i) planet, (ii) satellite, (iii) light-year?
b) The speed of light is 300 000 $km\,s^{-1}$. How many seconds does it take light to travel the 375 000 km from the Moon to the Earth?
c) State three factors which have prevented life developing on the Moon.
d) Why is the Moon not always visible from the Earth?
e) What influence does the Moon have on the Earth?

2 Assume that you are in charge of the design of future US space capsules.
a) Will you use oxygen or air as the gas inside the capsules? Explain your choice.
b) How will you make sure that the gas the astronauts breathe remains fresh?
c) What other factors will you need to consider in order to keep the astronauts comfortable in their capsule during a long space flight?
d) (*Hard*) Why may corrosion become a problem during a long space flight? What steps can be taken to prevent it?

3 a) Give an example of (i) an igneous rock, (ii) a metamorphic rock and (iii) a sedimentary rock.
b) Explain how each of these rocks was formed.
c) What are the main factors which cause the erosion of rocks?

4 a) What two chemical elements are always present in carbonates?
b) Give one example of a carbonate occurring in large quantities in the Earth's crust.
c) Explain how this carbonate formed in the Earth's crust.

5 a) Name four normal constituents of soil.
b) Describe simple experiments to compare the amount of *two* of these constituents in different soils.
c) How is soil usually treated to reduce acidity?
d) (*Hard*) Name the *three* chemical elements essential for plant growth which are most frequently added to the soil in fertilisers.

6 Find out and write a paragraph about the work of *three* of the following scientists and the way in which they have helped us all. James Watt, Michael Faraday, Humphrey Davy, Alexander Fleming, Louis Pasteur, Isaac Newton, Marie Curie.

2 Introducing living things

What do we mean by life? What makes living things, like trees and humans, different from non-living things, like building and cars?

2.1 The variety of life

The Earth is a big place, so it is surprising how much you can learn about it in your own garden. Walk down your garden, or stroll through the park, and look out for living things. Birds, snails, cats, spiders, ants and flies are just a few of the animals you might see. Grass, trees, flowers, toadstools, mosses and water weeds are some of the plants. A wide variety, but what do a snail and a toadstool, or a spider and a tree have in common?

A garden is just one example of the many different **habitats** where living things may be found. In fact, within the garden itself, there are several different habitats. For example, underneath a stone the surrounding conditions (the **environment**) are very different from those up a tree. Because the conditions are different, the living things are different too. Living things are **adapted** to their chosen habitat. Woodlice like damp conditions, so they live under stones. Birds can fly, so they live in trees where they are safe from attack by predators.

The Earth provides many different habitats. The Amazon rain forest and the Arctic tundra are probably very unlike your garden. Yet in the garden live many members of the huge variety of living things on Earth.

What do we mean by 'living'?

Most people can judge instinctively whether a thing is living or not. It is obvious that horses and grasses are living, while cars and petrol are not. But in some cases it is harder to tell. Is a virus living? After reading section 16.1 you will realise that this is difficult to answer. And when does living stop? This is sometimes an important question for doctors to answer.

Most living things (**organisms**) have the following in common.

- **They reproduce** If a species of plant or animal is to survive, its members must produce young offspring. **Sexual** reproduction involves union between a male and a female of the same species. In **asexual** reproduction an organism reproduces on its own.
- **They grow** Young animals increase in size and weight until they become adults. Most plants grow continuously throughout their lives.
- **They feed** Organisms must feed to obtain the substances they need for growth. Even when an organism has stopped growing it must feed in order to replace worn-out parts. Food is also needed to provide organisms with energy.

  Plants and animals feed in very different ways. Animals take in complicated chemical substances by eating plants or other animals. They break these substances down into simpler chemicals, which they then use for energy or growth. Green plants make their own food from simple chemicals such as carbon dioxide and water, which they build up into more complex molecules. To do this, the plants need energy, which they get from sunlight. This way of making food is called **photosynthesis**. It requires a green chemical called **chlorophyll** which is present in the leaves of all green plants.
- **They use energy** Organisms need energy to grow and to move. They get energy by 'burning' food. This is called **respiration**. Respiration usually requires a supply of oxygen, which is obtained from the air.
- **They move** Most animals can move quite quickly from one place to another. Plants move much more slowly, and only a part of the plant moves – plants cannot move themselves to a new place.
- **They respond to stimuli** If you touch a hot dish, you quickly take your hand away. The heat of the dish is a **stimulus**; taking your hand away is the **response**. Human beings respond to light, sound, heat, touch and chemicals. Chemicals are detected by taste and smell, and you can probably work out how the other stimuli are detected. Organisms vary widely in their sensitivity to stimuli. Plants are generally less sensitive and respond more slowly than animals.
- **They get rid of waste products** Many complex chemical reactions go on in living things. These reactions produce waste products, which may be poisonous and must be removed by **excretion**. For example, animals excrete excess water and nitrogen-containing compounds as **urine**.

These seven characteristics apply to all living organisms, though in some cases they are difficult to see.

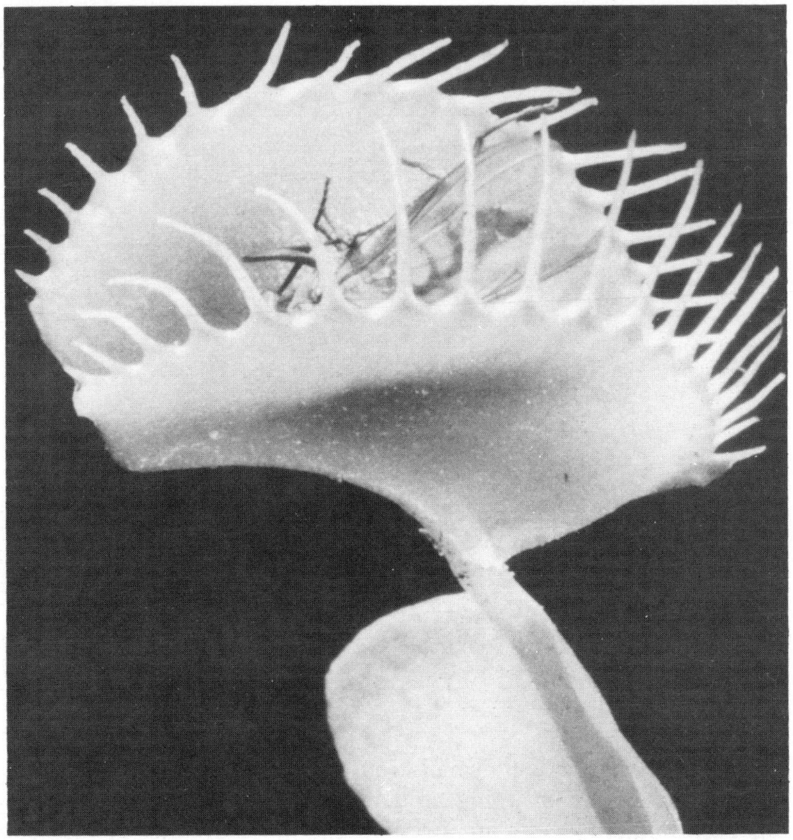

The Venus fly trap is an unusual plant. When an insect lands between the special hinged leaves, they snap shut before it can escape. The plant then digests the insect's body.

- For each of the following organisms, try to explain how each of the seven characteristics applies:
  a) an oak tree,
  b) a blackbird,
  c) (*Hard*) a barnacle.

2.2 How can we classify living things?

There is a vast variety of living things, and studying them would be impossible without sorting them into groups. Scientists sort living things into groups with similar characteristics. The smallest group is called a **species**. Members of a species are very like one another and can breed together. For example, all dogs are members of the same species and can breed together. Dogs cannot breed with cats, which are a different species.

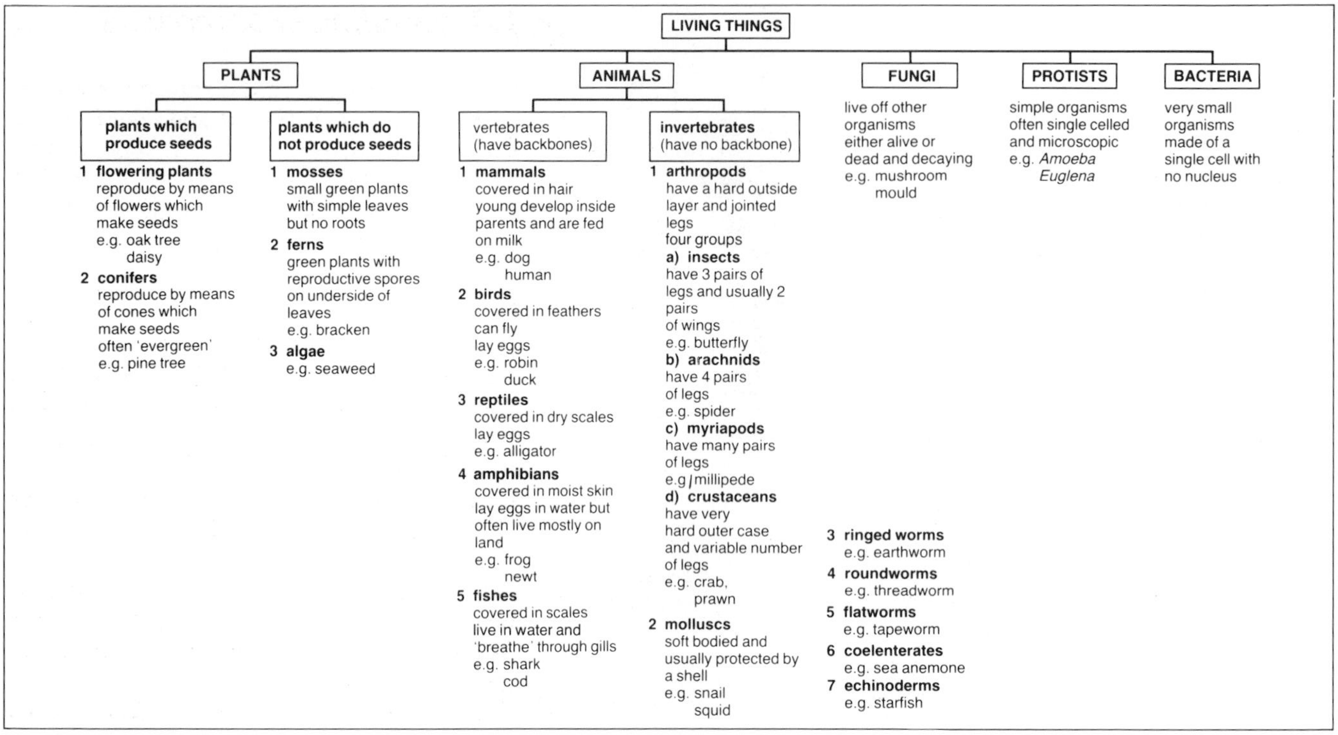

Figure 2.1 (*Above*) A simple way of classifying living things. Note that this classification only mentions the more important groups of organisms. However, all organisms (except viruses) belong in one of the five categories.

A species is a relatively small group, and ways are needed of grouping similar species together. Similar species are grouped into a **genus**. For example, all the cats, including lions and tigers as well as domestic cats, are in the same genus, called *Felis*. But there are still many, many different genuses, and further grouping together is needed.

Some broad classifications are fairly obvious, for example, plants and animals. Within the animals, it is easy to classify according to whether the animal has a backbone (**vertebrates**) or no backbone (**invertebrates**). Vertebrates themselves may be 'warm-blooded', like a human or a bird, or 'cold-blooded', like a frog or a lizard. Plants may be seed-producing or non-seed producing. A simple way of classifying plants and animals is shown in figure 2.1.

- Look at the plants illustrated in figure 2.2. Put each plant into its correct group.
- Look at the animals illustrated in figure 2.3. Put each animal into its correct group.

Naming living things

Each species of living things has a name. There are common names – tiger, buttercup, human. There are also systematic or proper names, often derived from Latin words. The proper name for a tiger is *Felis tigris*. *Felis* gives the genus of the animal, and *tigris* gives the species. Proper biological names always consist of two words, the first giving the genus, the second the species. Humans are *Homo sapiens*. There are several different species of buttercup, all grouped in the genus *Ranunculus*. One of the commonest species of buttercup is the meadow buttercup, whose proper name is *Ranunculus acris*.

- What genus do humans belong to?
- Are there any other members of this genus?

(*Below*) *Felis tigris*

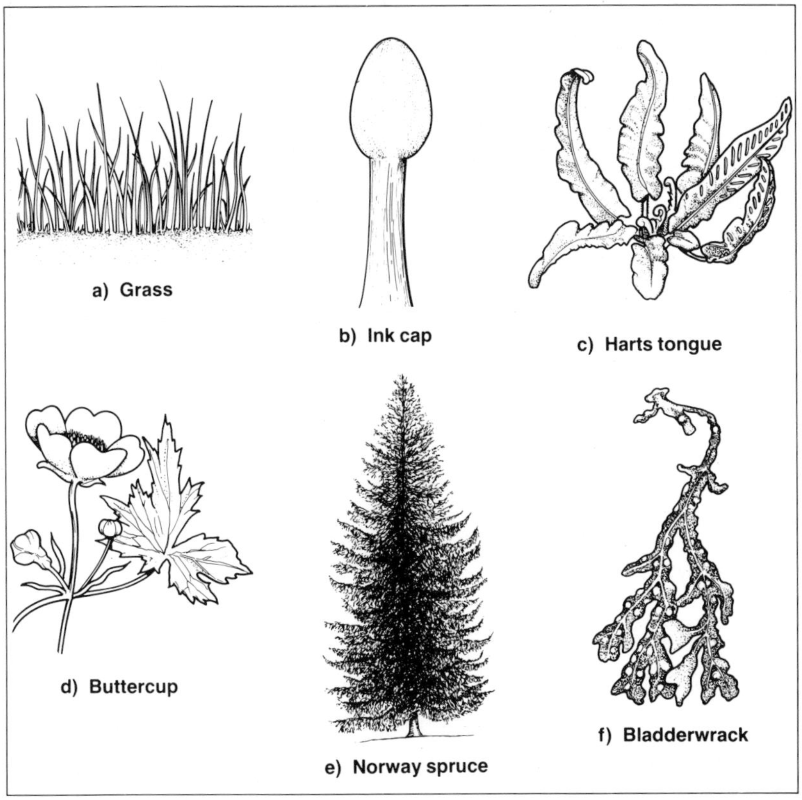

Figure 2.2 (Above)

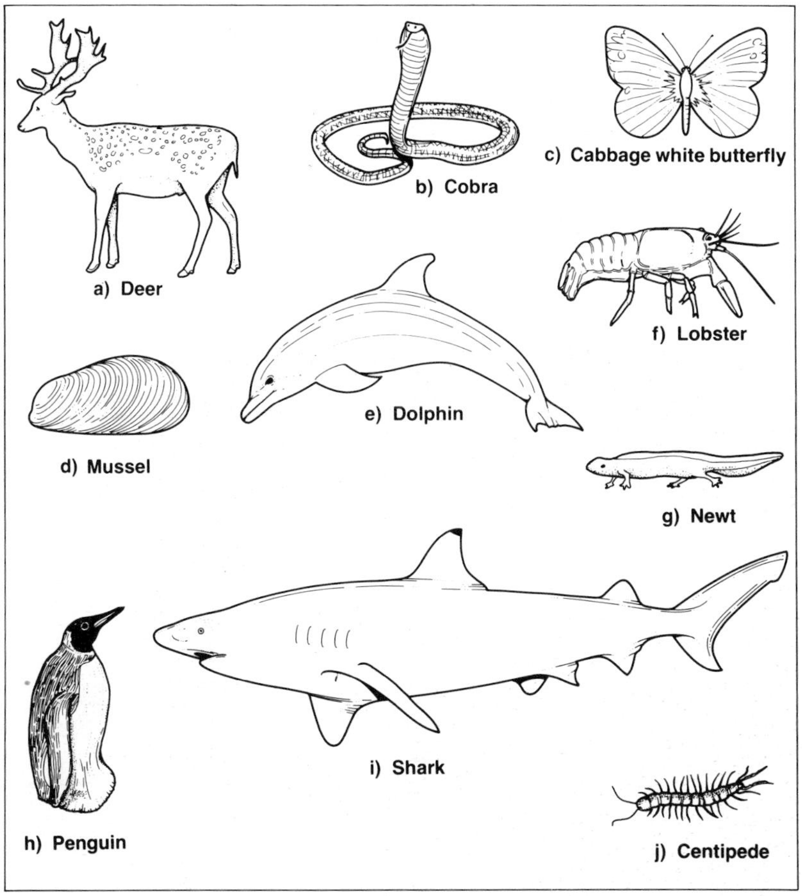

Figure 2.3

2.3 Variation in organisms

We have already seen the enormous variety of living things. Different species of organisms vary in many ways – in diet, in lifespan, in habitat, in size and in structure. Let us look more closely at some of these things.

Diet

All living things feed, but the variety of their diet is enormous. Many animals (lions and hawks for example) are **carnivores**, and eat nothing but meat. Many more (horses, grasshoppers, snails for example) are **herbivores**, and eat nothing but plants. Badgers and humans are examples of the many **omnivores** which eat both meat and plants. Another group are **parasites**, which live off other organisms. For example tapeworms feed of the contents of the human gut, and fleas feed on blood.

Most plants make their own food. Fungi lack the chlorophyll needed to do this. They are **saprophytes**, feeding off dead or decaying organisms.

Many of the characteristics of an organism are decided by its diet. Its food determines both where it lives, and the organs it needs to break down and use this food.

Lifespan

Living things vary greatly in the length of time they live. Generally, plants live longer than animals. Certain conifers in California are estimated to be over four thousand years old. Some insects, on the other hand, only live a few hours. *Homo sapiens* is one of the longest living animals; it is becoming quite common for humans to live for more than one hundred years.

Habitat

The variety of habitats occupied by living things is very wide. Plants and animals can be found in the frozen Arctic and Antarctic as well as in the burning desert. Between these extremes there is a wide range of temperatures, humidity and other factors important to life, and in every one of these habitats living things can be found. In general though, living things prefer moderate conditions – warm temperatures and plenty of moisture. That is why there are so many species in jungles, like the Amazon rain forest, and relatively few species in the desert.

Size

The smallest organisms are viruses, which are about 10^{-7}m across. Ten million fit on one metre. The largest are trees: Californian giant sequoias reach a height of over 100m (figure 2.4). Within this great range there are organisms of many different sizes. Humans are relatively large, with a height of about 1.7m.

Figure 2.4 (Top right) A virus (left) and a giant sequoia tree. The tree is 10^9 (one thousand million) times larger than the virus.

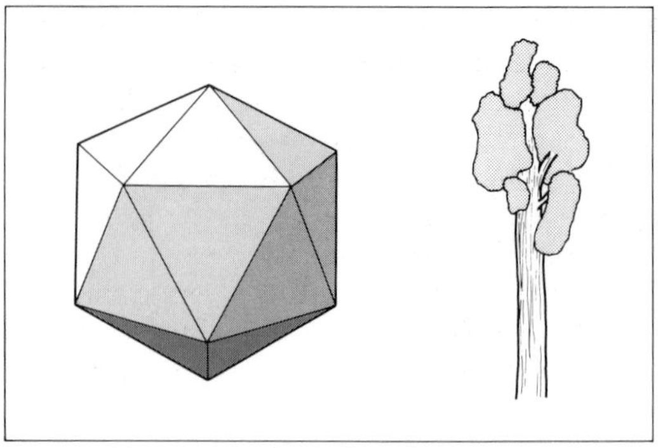

2.4 The building blocks of life

Organisms living together

Organisms rarely live alone. They usually depend on one another for food, shelter and other essentials.

A clear, newly dug piece of land does not stay clear for long. Plants such as grass and dandelions soon appear, and animals such as caterpillars quickly follow, using the plants for food and shelter. Soon a flourishing **community** of organisms is to be found on the once bare land. This community is made up of **populations** of different organisms – populations of dandelions, populations of caterpillars, and so on. Figure 2.5 shows the organisms and populations in a pond community. These populations depend on each other and on their non-living environment (soil in the example of the newly dug land) in many complex ways. The community of organisms and their environment together make up the **ecosystem**.

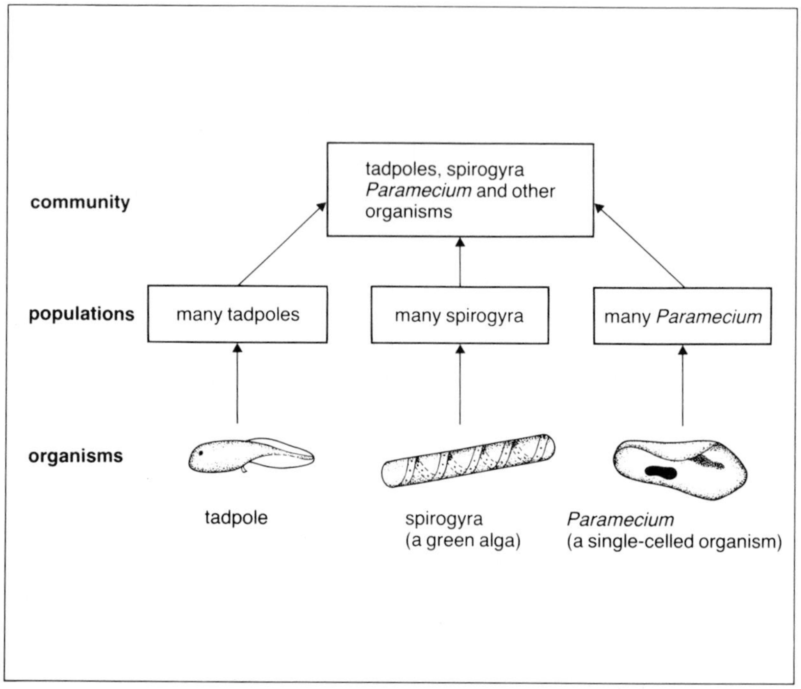

Figure 2.5 (Above) Organisms and populations within a pond community.

A garden inside glass – a miniature ecosystem.

Building blocks within an organism

We have already seen (section 1.1) that all matter is made up from building blocks. The smallest building blocks are atoms and molecules. Large molecules such as proteins and carbohydrates are the building blocks for **cells**, and cells are the building blocks for organisms. All organisms are made up from large numbers of cells. Your body contains about 100 000 000 cells. Cells are too small to see by eye, but can be quite easily observed under a microscope. You can scrape cells off the inside of your cheek and look at them under the microscope. A thin sheet of cells can be peeled off one of the inner layers of an onion and viewed microscopically.

It turns out that cells from animals (like the cheek cells) and cells from plants (like the onion cells) look rather different. Figure 2.6 shows a typical animal cell and a typical plant cell. Both types of cell have some parts in common. These are:

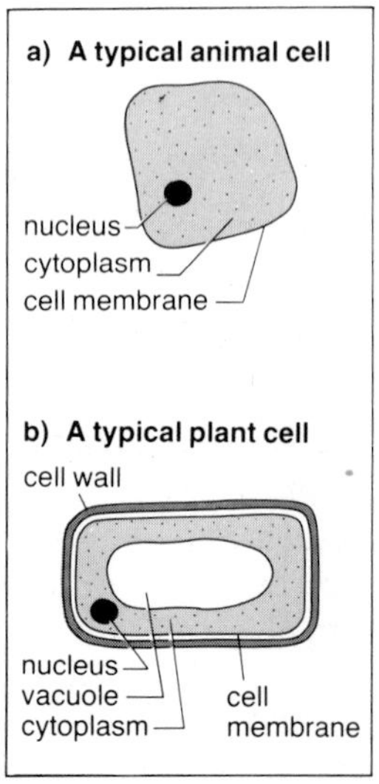

Figure 2.6

- **A nucleus** The nucleus controls everything going on in the cell. It contains chemicals needed to make the cell divide and form a new copy of itself.
- **Cytoplasm** The cell contains a substance called cytoplasm. All the living processes of the cell go on in the cytoplasm. It is the cell's workshop, producing energy, food and other chemicals needed by the cell.
- **The cell membrane** This thin layer forms the boundary of the cell, but it lets some substances (such as water) move in and out.

Plant cells have three other features which animal cells do not possess.

- **A cell wall** This wall is made of a tough material called **cellulose**. Just under the cell wall is the cell membrane. Because of the tough cell walls, groups of plant cells appear more regularly arranged than animal cells (see study question 4.) The tough regular cells help the plant to keep its shape.
- **A vacuole** A large part of the volume of a plant cell is occupied by a watery liquid. This part is the vacuole. The liquid in the vacuole creates a pressure on the cell wall which keeps the cell wall rigid. The vacuole is separated from the cytoplasm by a membrane.
- **Chloroplasts** The cytoplasm of cells from the leaves and stems of plants contains little green bodies called chloroplasts. These contain chlorophyll, and it is in these chloroplasts that photosynthesis goes on.

> - Why are animal cells unable to photosynthesise?
> - Why do you think animal cells have no cell wall?

2.5 Different cells and organs for different jobs

Different kinds of cells

We have already seen that plant and animal cells are different. There are many varieties of cells even within these two groups. Take the cells in our own bodies for example. There are many different jobs to do in the human body, and many of these jobs have cells specially designed to do them.

Muscle cells, for example (figure 2.7a) need to contract and relax rather like a rubber band. That is why they are long and thin. Nerve cells (figure 2.7b) are much rounder, but have long fibres leading from them. This is becase they need to carry messages from one part of the body to another.

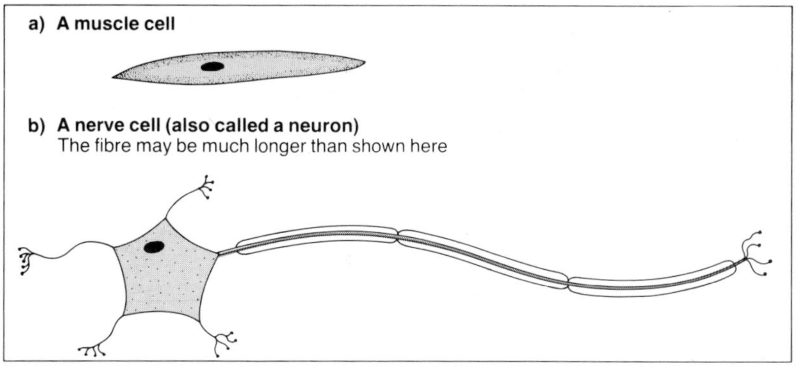

Figure 2.7

There are many other specialised cells, for example blood cells and skin (epithelial) cells. When lots of cells of a particular type are grouped together they form a **tissue**. Muscle is a tissue (figure 2.8), and so are skin and nerves. Blood is regarded as a tissue even though it is liquid.

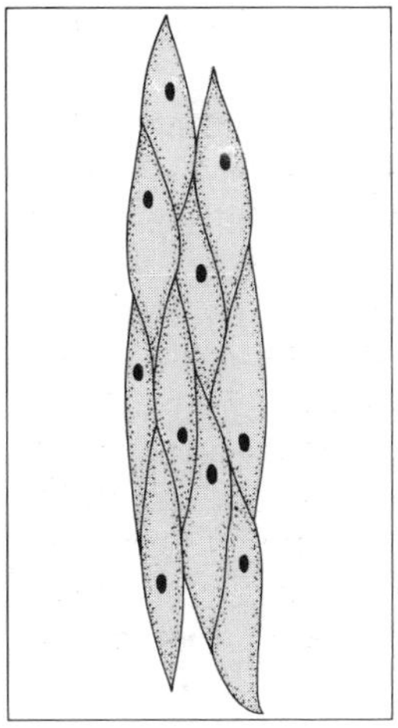

Figure 2.8 (Above) Muscle cells forming muscle tissue.

Some organisms such as *Amoeba* are **single-celled**. The one cell does all the jobs the organism requires. Most organisms though, are **multicellular**, with many different cells, tissues and organs.

Different kinds of organs

Cells of a particular type group together to form a tissue. Tissues are used to make **organs**. An organ is a complex part of a living thing that does a particular job.

Figure 2.9 shows the major organs of the human body. The structure of each organ is

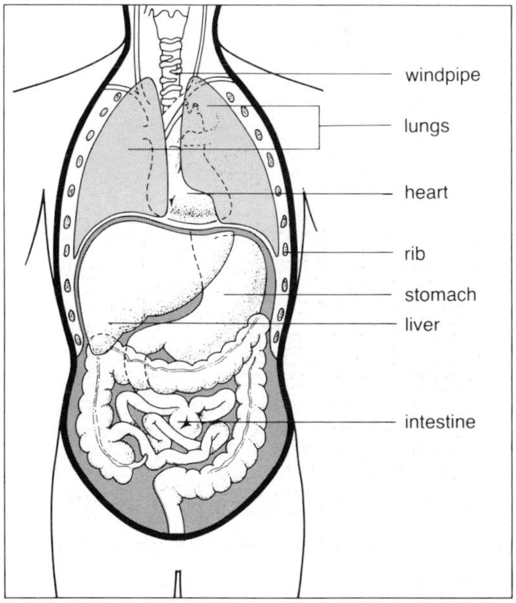

Figure 2.9 The major organs of the human body.

matched to the particular job it has to do. Here are some examples.

- **The lungs** pump air in and out so that oxygen can pass into the blood. They are in the form of two bags made from elastic skin tissue supplied with lots of tiny blood vessels (section 7.7).
- **The heart** pumps blood around the body. It is made of muscle tissue and contains four chambers. When the muscle contracts round a particular chamber, blood is squeezed out. The pumping and the opening and closing of the different valves is beautifully coordinated to make sure blood goes to the right place (section 5.2).

Some organs do more than one job.

- **The liver** has a very large number of jobs to do. Many of these involve processing food after it has been digested. For example, the liver controls the amount of sugar in our blood by storing glucose as a substance called glycogen. It also gets rid of excess nitrogen we obtain when we eat protein, and it removes poisons from the blood stream. It does many other jobs besides, most of them involving the blood in some way. For this reason the liver has a rich blood supply – about a litre of blood flows through it every minute. The liver is penetrated by a network of fine blood vessels. These make sure that every liver cell has a good supply of blood.

- What job do the intestines do? (Section 15.5.)
- One of the main blood vessels reaching the liver comes direct from the intestines. Why do you think this might be?
- Why do people who drink too much alcohol often damage their liver?

Organs in systems

Organs work together, and often several organs are grouped together in a **system** to do a particular job. For example, the heart and blood vessels (veins, arteries and capillaries) make up the circulatory system (section 5.2).

Atoms to ecosystems

We can now see how living things are made from building blocks of increasing size, from tiny atoms to large communities (figure 2.10).

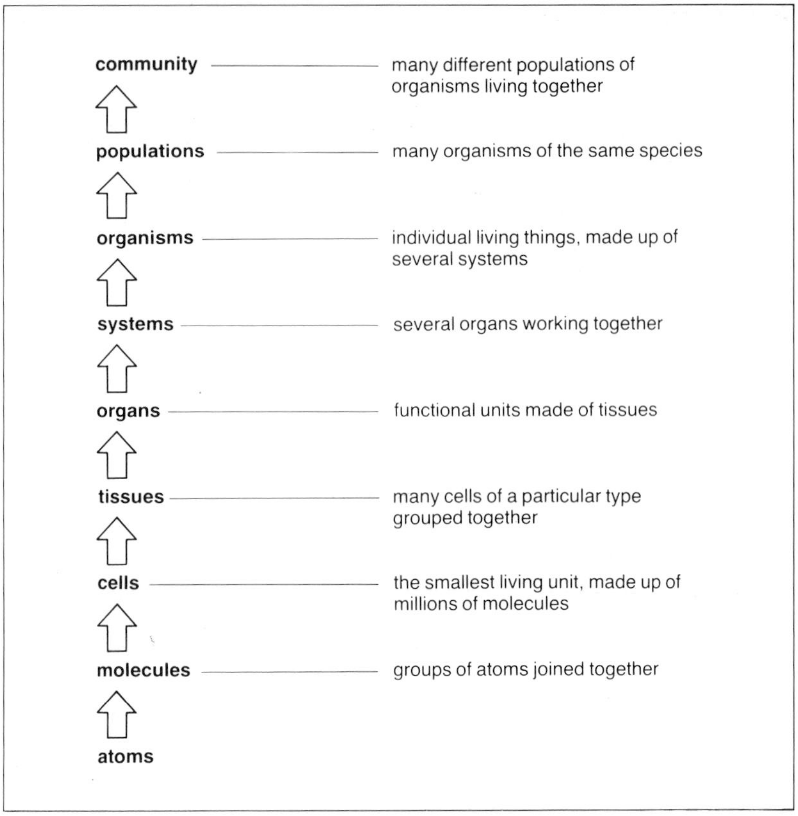

community
many different populations of organisms living together
populations
many organisms of the same species
organisms
individual living things, made up of several systems
systems
several organs working together
organs
functional units made of tissues
tissues
many cells of a particular type grouped together
cells
the smallest living unit, made up of millions of molecules
molecules
groups of atoms joined together
atoms

Figure 2.10 Atoms to ecosystems.

Summary

1. Living things are very varied, but they have seven characteristics in common. These are reproduction, growth, feeding, respiration, movement, response to stimuli and excretion.
2. Plants differ from animals in many ways, but particularly in being able to make their own food by photosynthesis.
3. Living things usually have a common name and a proper name. The proper name gives the genus and the species of the organism.
4. Living things vary in diet, lifespan, habitat and size.
5. A number of organisms of the same species living together is called a population. Different populations living together make a community and, with their surroundings, an ecosystem.
6. All living things are made from cells. Plant cells are different from animal cells in several ways.
7. Multicellular organisms usually contain a number of organs. Organs are made from tissues. Tissues are made up from large numbers of similar cells.

Study questions

1 An alien from another planet comes to Earth. It sees a motor car and decides the car is living because it feeds on petrol which it uses to produce energy. The car moves, responds and produces waste.
a) How would you explain to the alien that the car was not in fact living?
b) How would you investigate if the alien itself was living or a robot?

2 *Euglena* is a single-celled microsopic organism found in ponds. Figure 2.11 shows how it appears under a microscope. *Euglena* is a bright green because of its chlorophyll-containing chloroplasts. In sunlight it makes its own food by photosynthesis, but in the dark it feeds by absorbing soluble organic substances from the water. *Euglena* can move around by using its flagellum, which is rather like a whip. It uses this flagellum to swim towards the places where the light is bright. *Euglena* reproduces asexually: one individual splits, giving two smaller ones.
Use the information given above to answer these questions.
a) Look back to section 2.1. Which characteristics of *Euglena* show it is a living organism?
b) Why does *Euglena* swim towards the places where the light is bright?
c) Would you expect to find male and female *Euglena*? Explain.

3 Using figure 2.1, place each of the following organisms in its correct group:
a) a slug,
b) a scorpion,
c) *Pleurococcus* (a single-celled green organism that forms a green coating on tree trunks, walls, park benches, etc.),
d) a lobster,
e) a turtle (turtles lay eggs on land, but spend most of their time in the water),
f) a seal,
g) a toad (toads lay their eggs in water, but live mostly on land),
h) bread mould,
i) an apple tree.
j) an eel (eels have backbones).

4 Figure 2.12 shows a group of animal cells and a group of plant cells as they appeared under a microscope.
a) Name the parts of the cell shown in figure 2.12a.
b) Look at figure 2.6. What parts of the plant cell are not shown in figure 2.12b?
c) Why are the plant cells much more regularly arranged than the animal cells?
d) Suppose a plant cell appeared green under the microscope.
i) What causes the green colour?
ii) Would the cell be green all through? Explain.
e) It is often difficult to see the boundaries of animal cells under the microscope. Why is this?

5 Here is a list of the different ways living organisms can get food:
A by making their own food,
B by eating animals (carnivores),
C by eating plants (herbivores),
D by eating plants and animals (omnivores),
E by feeding off a living organism (parasites),
F by feeding off dead or decaying organisms (saprophytes).
Use one of the letters A to F above to describe the way each of the following gets its food:
a) pigs,
b) cows,
c) sharks,
d) toadstools,
e) head lice,
f) grass
The next questions are harder, and will test your knowledge of living things.
g) blackbirds,
h) blue whales,
i) earthworms,
j) ladybirds,
k) mistletoe,
l) oak trees,
m) bears.

6 A student put a spadeful of garden soil into a large glass tank. She covered the tank with a sheet of glass and left it outside for several weeks during the summer. When she came back to look at the tank she found many signs of life. She saw:
grass and small green plants,
earthworms,
springtails (a kind of insect),
ground beetles.
a) Where did all the living things come from?
b) Name some organisms not seen by the student, which might have been present in the tank.
c) What name is given to a group of living organisms like those in the tank?
d) What name is given to the tank and soil?
e) What name is given to the tank, soil and all the organisms?
f) Suppose the tank and its contents were left for a long time. How would you expect the numbers of the various organisms to change? Explain your answer.
g) Would the results of this experiment have been very different if the student had left the tank uncovered? Explain.

7 Choose one living thing. It can be any organism, from your pet dog to your favourite plant.
a) Classify the organism you have chosen, using figure 2.1.
b) Show that the organism has the characteristics of a living thing.
c) Name one tissue in the organism.
d) Name one organ in the organism.
e) What sort of habitat does the organism prefer?
f) How does the organism obtain food?
g) (*Hard*) What species does the organism belong to? (Give the common name *or* proper name.)

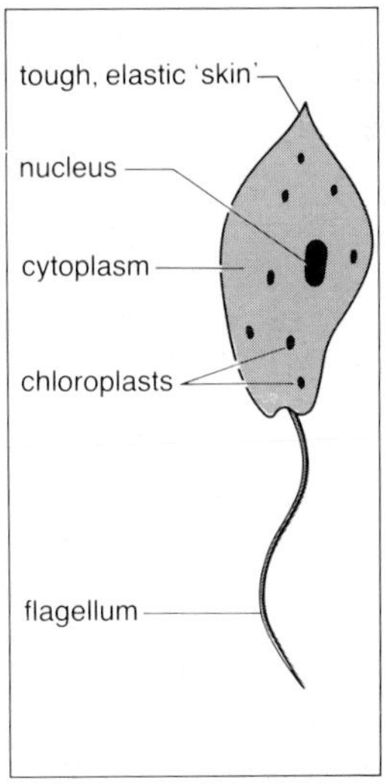

Figure 2.11 (Above) Euglena (actual size less than 0.1 mm).

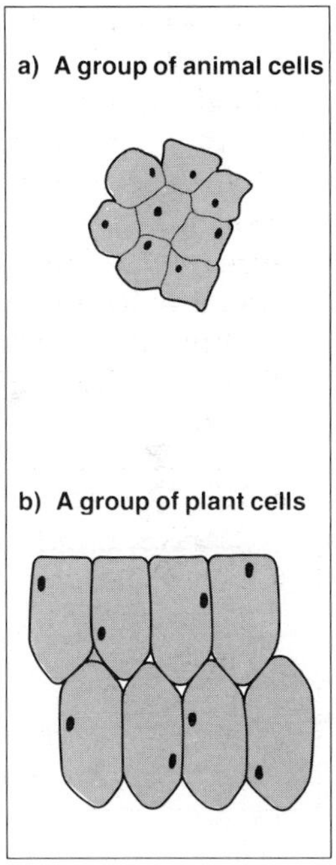

Figure 2.12

3 Particles on the move

What keeps a balloon blown up? Why do smells spread out? Why do plants without water droop? Why does water freeze when cooled? All these questions can be answered if we think of matter as being made up of moving particles.

3.1 Moving particles

Building blocks

The idea of building blocks is very useful in science. Building blocks come in many sizes, from huge planets to tiny living cells. Even smaller than cells are the building blocks from which all matter is made, atoms and molecules. For the moment we will simply call these tiny building blocks *particles*.

Why we believe matter is made of particles

Scientists now agree that matter is made of particles. You were probably familiar with this idea yourself even before you started studying science. There is plenty of evidence for particles. But seeing is believing, and perhaps the most striking evidence comes from electron microscope photographs of solids, like the one opposite, which plainly show regularly arranged particles.

Long before these powerful microscopes were built, scientists had evidence that matter consisted of particles, and that these particles were constantly moving. Some of the best evidence came from studies of Brownian motion and diffusion.

Brownian motion

In 1827 Robert Brown, a Scottish botanist, was using a microscope to study pollen grains suspended in water. To his surprise, he noticed that the tiny grains were constantly moving and darting around in a completely random way (figure 3.1). Similar random movements can be seen when smoke or dust particles are viewed under a microscope. This movement is called **Brownian motion**.

Smoke particles and pollen grains may be tiny, but they are much, much larger than the particles we have been talking about: atoms and molecules. When you see smoke particles darting and jittering about at random, you are seeing the effect of moving air molecules, not the molecules themselves. We can explain Brownian motion by proposing that air contains particles far too small to see. These air molecules move very fast, hitting the smoke particles at random, and knocking them first one way and then another (figure 3.2).

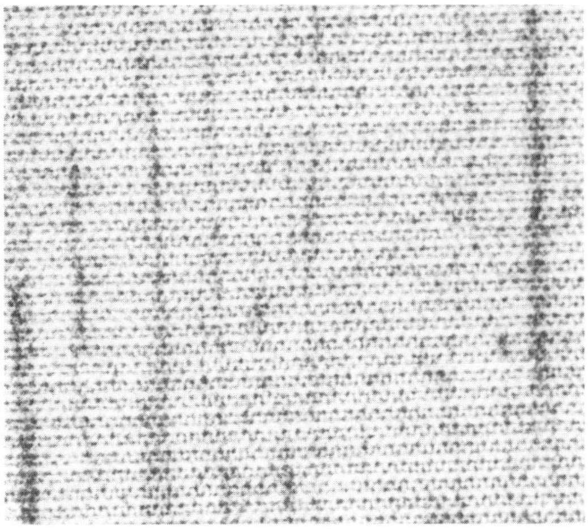

In an electron microscope, a beam of electrons passes through the object to give an enlarged image on a fluorescent screen. This can then be photographed. Electrons can resolve much finer detail than light. Here, a crystal of the enzyme catalase has been magnified 236000 times to show the individual molecules.

Diffusion

Baking bread has a delicious smell. If bread is being baked in the kitchen, you can often smell it all over the house. Particles of gas are released from the bread and these spread or **diffuse** throughout the house.

All gases diffuse to fill the space available to them, even heavy gases like bromine (figure 3.3). Why should gases diffuse? The explanation is easy if we accept that gases consist of tiny particles, and that these particles are constantly moving. If the movement is random, and the particles do not care where they go, sooner or later they are bound to fill all the space available. This will happen even if the gas is heavier than air, although gases like bromine and carbon dioxide diffuse more slowly than light gases such as hydrogen. This is because their heavier particles move more slowly.

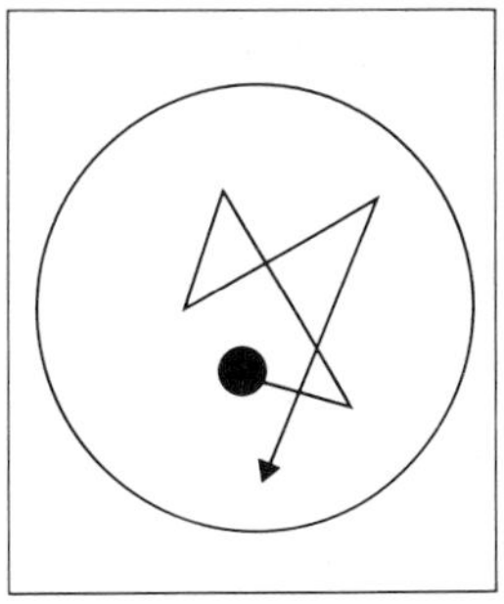

Figure 3.1 (Above left) Brownian motion of a pollen grain seen under a microscope.

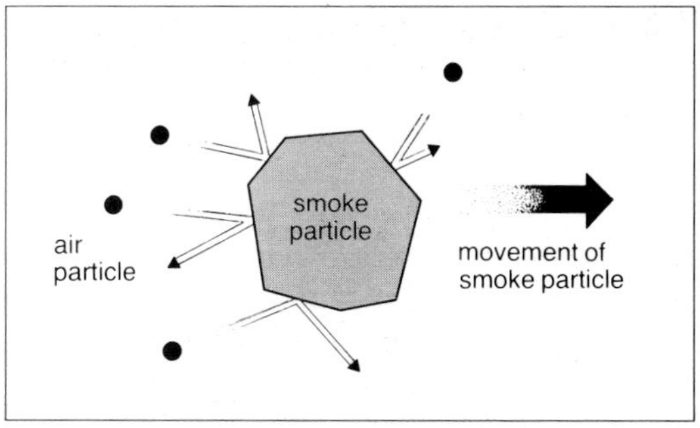

Figure 3.2 (Above right) Explaining Brownian motion.

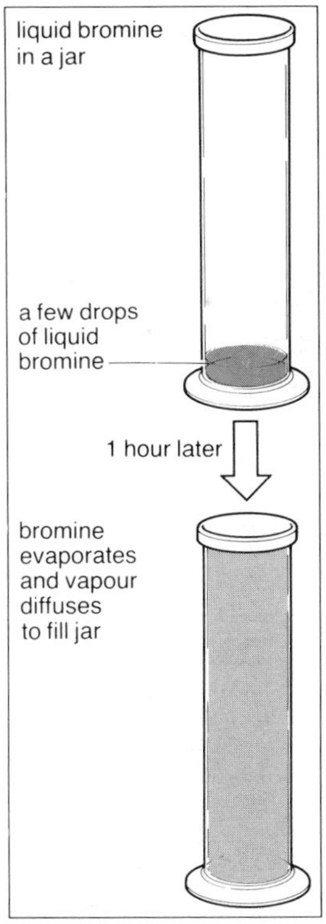

Figure 3.3 (Above) Diffusion of bromine.

Figure 3.4 (Below) Arrangement of particles in gases, solids and liquids.

3.2 The kinetic theory of matter

The idea that matter is made of small, constantly moving particles is called the **kinetic theory**. The main points of the theory are:

- All matter is made up of tiny, invisible, moving particles. Particles of different substances are of different sizes.
- The particles move continuously. The higher the temperature the faster they move.
- Heavy particles move more slowly than light ones, at a given temperature.
- In a gas, the distance between the particles is large and they are free to move anywhere. The particles exert virtually no forces on one another. They move very fast, colliding with each other and with the walls of their container (figure 3.4a).
- In a solid, the particles attract one another strongly. They are arranged regularly and are very close together. They have very little freedom of movement, and can only vibrate about fixed positions (figure 3.4b).
- In a liquid, the particles are quite close together, but the forces of attraction are weaker than in a solid. The particles have more freedom of movement than those in solids (figure 3.4c).

The kinetic theory can be used to explain many of the ways matter behaves, whether solid, liquid or gas.

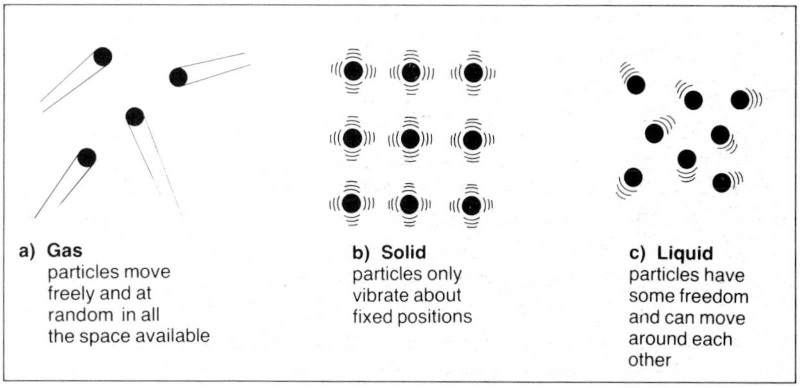

a) Gas
particles move freely and at random in all the space available
b) Solid
particles only vibrate about fixed positions
c) Liquid
particles have some freedom and can move around each other

Changes of state

The **state** of a substance (solid, liquid or gas) can be changed by heating or cooling it (figure 3.5).

Using the kinetic theory we can readily explain these changes. Look back at figure 3.4. In the solid, the particles are held in their regular positions by strong forces between each other. As the solid is heated, the particles vibrate faster and faster until they begin to break free from one another. The particles can now move around each other and the solid melts. A similar process occurs when a liquid turns to a gas.

- Use the kinetic theory to explain why gases condense to liquids when cooled.
- Why do gases remain gases, no matter how much they are heated?
- Use the kinetic theory to explain why some substances, like iron, are solid at room temperature, while others, like air, are gases.

Figure 3.5 (Right) Changes of state.

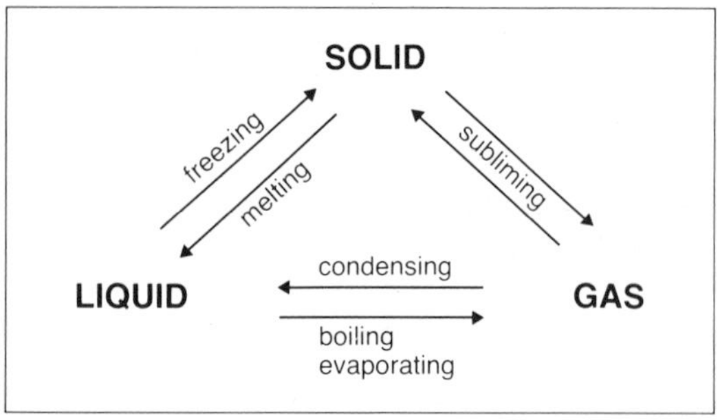

Figure 3.6 (Lower right) Gas pressure in a balloon.

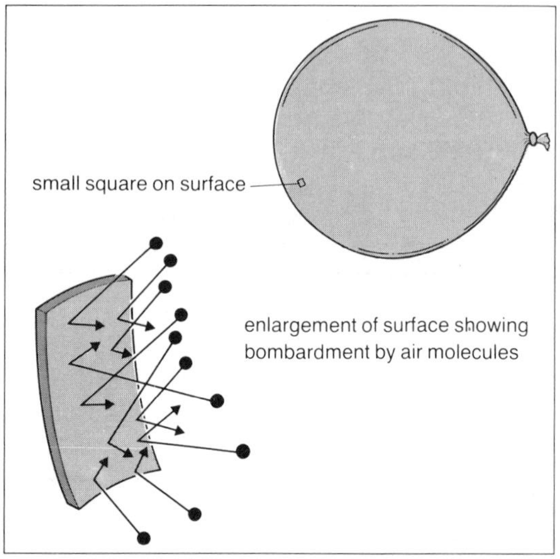

Figure 3.7 (Below) Diffusion of copper sulphate in water.

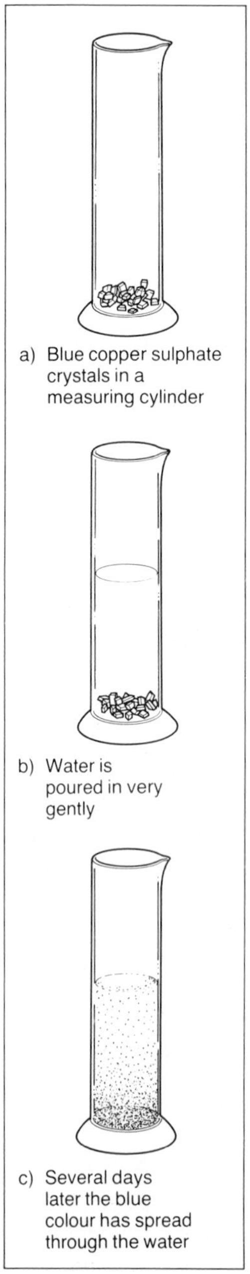

a) Blue copper sulphate crystals in a measuring cylinder
b) Water is poured in very gently
c) Several days later the blue colour has spread through the water

Gas pressure

Gases exert pressure on their surroundings. The air around us constantly exerts pressure on our bodies, on the earth, on everything. This is called **atmospheric pressure**. Normally we are not aware of atmospheric pressure because it is balanced by an equal pressure exerted by the liquids in our bodies. However, we soon notice gas pressure if it is not balanced by an equal and opposite pressure. For example, when a balloon is blown up, the gas pressure inside the balloon is greater than the atmospheric pressure outside. The pressure inside forces out the walls of the balloon until the rubber is so stretched that its elasticity balances the excess pressure.

Why do gases exert pressure? The kinetic theory provides a ready explanation. As the gas particles move around at random, they constantly collide with the walls of the balloon. Every square millimetre of the balloon is battered by millions and millions of tiny particles (figure 3.6). Each particle is too small to have much effect on the balloon wall by itself, so we cannot see the result of an individual collision. But the constant battering by millions of particles adds up to a steady force on each square millimetre, and this is what we call gas pressure. The average speed of the particles is always the same at a particular temperature, so the pressure is constant at that temperature. If the temperature is increased, the particles move faster, the pressure increases and the balloon expands.

Diffusion

An inflated balloon eventually goes down, because the thin rubber has tiny holes through which air particles slowly diffuse. All gases diffuse, but can diffusion occur in liquids too?

Look at figure 3.7. If water is poured gently onto blue copper sulphate crystals, the water remains colourless at first. Very slowly, the crystals dissolve and the blue colour spreads through the water. Even after a week, the colour is paler at the top of the water than at the bottom. The particles in the copper sulphate crystals are moving, and are attracted into solution by moving water molecules. The copper sulphate therefore dissolves. Its particles move around at random in the water and eventually diffuse throughout it. However, the rate of diffusion is slower in liquids than in gases, because the forces of attraction are greater, and the particles cannot move so freely.

- When copper sulphate diffuses, the blue colour spreads faster through the water at higher temperatures. Why is this?
- The blue colour spreads faster if the water is stirred. Why is this?
- Why is the blue colour darker at the bottom than the top, even after one week?

The copper sulphate experiment illustrates an important point. *Gases, liquids and dissolved substances (solutes) all diffuse from regions of high concentration to regions of lower concentration.* At first the copper sulphate particles were highly concentrated in the crystals. Slowly they diffused into the water where the concentration was low. Eventually, when all the water is the same blue colour, diffusion stops because the concentration is the same everywhere.

Diffusion in living organisms

Diffusion is very important in living organisms. It allows materials to get from one part of an organism to another. Consider a small organism like the *Amoeba* (figure 3.8). The *Amoeba* gets its oxygen by diffusion. Oxygen is used up inside the organism. As long as the concentration of oxygen in the surrounding water is higher than that inside the *Amoeba*, oxygen particles will always diffuse through the cell membrane into the organism. Of course, this assumes that the cell membrane will allow the oxygen particles through – it must be **permeable** to oxygen.

The *Amoeba* also gets rid of waste products, such as carbon dioxide by diffusion. Carbon dioxide at high concentration inside the *Amoeba* diffuses to the outside, where its concentration is low.

Larger organisms cannot get all the oxygen they need by diffusion through their surface, so they have a special respiratory surface, such as lungs (section 7.7). Even so, the oxygen still passes from the lungs to the bloodstream by diffusion.

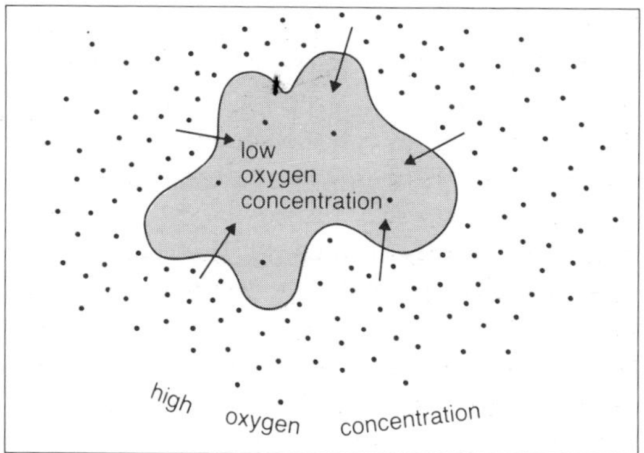

Figure 3.8 (Left) Diffusion of oxygen into *Amoeba*.

Have you ever wondered how the food you eat gets to the different parts of your body? Diffusion helps with this. After you have eaten a meal, the food passes down a long tube called the gut. In the gut, large food molecules are broken down into smaller ones. These smaller molecules diffuse through the gut wall into the bloodstream, and the blood carries them to the various parts of your body. Digestion and absorption of food are considered further in section 15.5.

Sometimes an organism needs to move dissolved substances from a region where they are in *low* concentration to a region of *higher* concentration. This, of course, is opposite to the direction the particles would naturally move by diffusion. For example, plants obtain mineral salts, such as nitrates, from the soil through their roots. In the soil, the mineral salts are at a lower concentrate than in the cells of the plant roots. Diffusion would therefore tend to make the mineral salts pass *out* of the roots and into the soil, instead of the other way. In this situation, the organism must transfer the dissolved substances in the opposite direction to normal diffusion. This requires energy, which must be supplied by the organism. We call this process **active transport**.

3.3 Osmosis, a special kind of diffusion

What is osmosis?

Look at the experiment illustrated in figure 3.9. A concentrated sugar solution is placed inside a sealed bag made of Visking tubing. Visking tubing consists of a thin membrane made from cellulose. This membrane has tiny invisible holes which let through particles of water but not the larger sugar particles. Such a membrane, which lets through small particles but not the larger ones, is said to be **partially permeable**. The bag of sugar solution is then placed in a beaker of water.

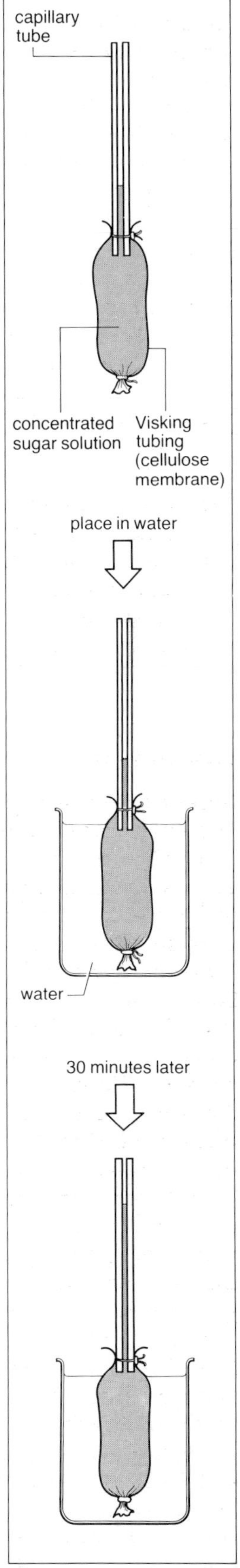

Figure 3.9 (Above) An experiment to illustrate osmosis.

- What evidence is there that water has passed from the beaker into the bag?
- If the Visking tubing is permeable to water, would you have expected water to pass
  a) From the beaker into the bag?
  b) From the bag into the beaker?
  c) In both directions?
- Suggest an explanation for what actually happens.

Whenever a concentrated solution is separated from a more dilute one (or water) by a partially permeable membrane, water passes into the concentrated solution. This process is called **osmosis**. The solute does not have to be sugar, and the solvent does not have to be water.

Osmosis is the flow of solvent through a partially permeable membrane from a dilute solution to a more concentrated one.

Osmosis may be readily explained using the kinetic theory. Look at figure 3.10. The molecules of sugar and water are constantly moving and constantly bombarding the partially permeable membrane on both sides. Sometimes a water molecule passes through one of the tiny holes. If there was pure water on both sides of the membrane, equal amounts of water would flow in each direction, and there would be no overall change. But in the sugar solution the presence of the larger sugar molecules hinders the movement of water molecules through the holes in the membrane, so the flow of water from the solution side is slower. The overall effect is that water flows through the membrane into the solution.

Osmosis is really only a special case of diffusion. In pure water, the concentration of water molecules is high. In a solution, the concentration of water is lower, because some water has been replaced by the solute. Therefore, water moves from a region of high water concentration (pure water) to lower concentration (the solution).

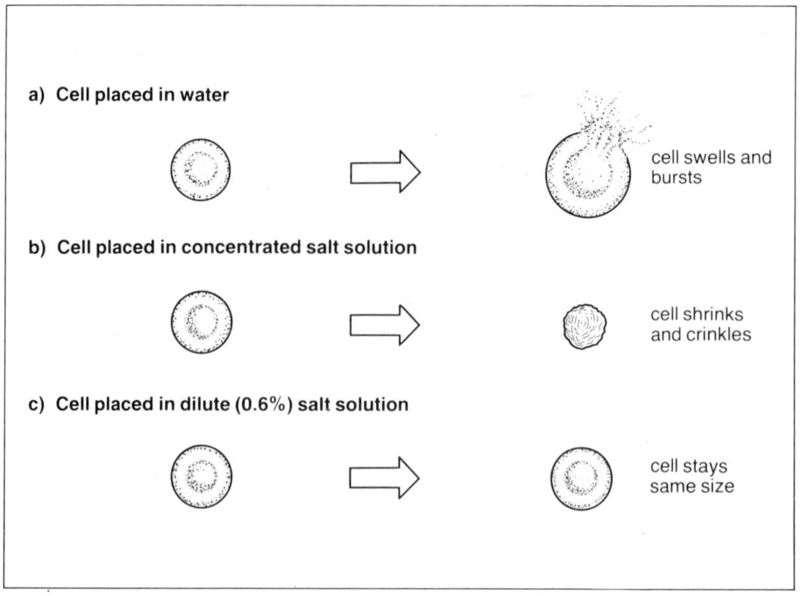

Figure 3.11 Behaviour of a red blood cell placed in various solutions.

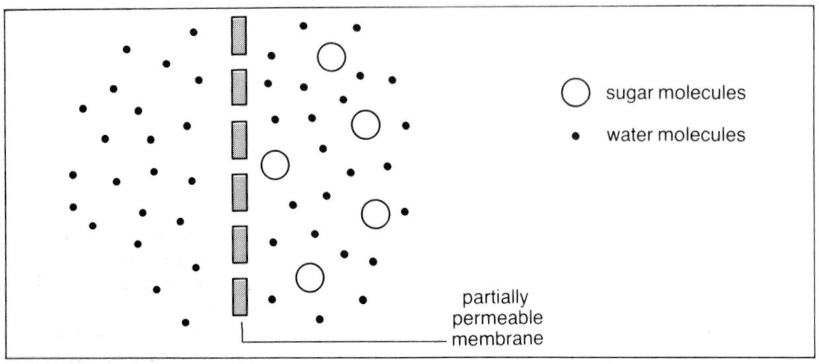

Figure 3.10 Explaining osmosis.

Osmosis in action

Osmosis is very important in living organisms, because the membranes of living cells are partially permeable. Suppose an animal cell, such as a red blood cell, is placed in various solutions (figure 3.11).

- Why does the cell swell and eventually burst in water?
- Why does the cell shrink in strong salt solution?
- Why does the cell stay the same size in 0.6% salt solution?

You can see from figure 3.11 that the concentration of the solution surrounding a cell is very important. The cell cytoplasm contains an aqueous solution of many different substances: salts, sugars, proteins etc. The cell membrane is partially permeable. Therefore, when the cell is placed in water or in a very dilute solution, water flows into the cell, making it swell and even burst. The opposite happens in a concentrated solution as in figure 3.11b, and the cell shrinks. It is therefore essential that the liquid surrounding the cells has the correct concentration to prevent too much osmosis. In the human body all sorts of mechanisms make sure that the body fluids are kept at exactly the right concentration. The kidneys (section 26.5) play an important part in this: we call it **osmo-regulation**. A 0.6% solution of salt in water, called saline, is just the right concentration to prevent osmosis with human cells. Such a solution is often used both in hospitals and in biological experiments.

- If you open your eyes under water it hurts a little, whether the water is fresh or salty. Suggest one reason for this.
- Why do the tears that bathe your eyes not make them hurt?

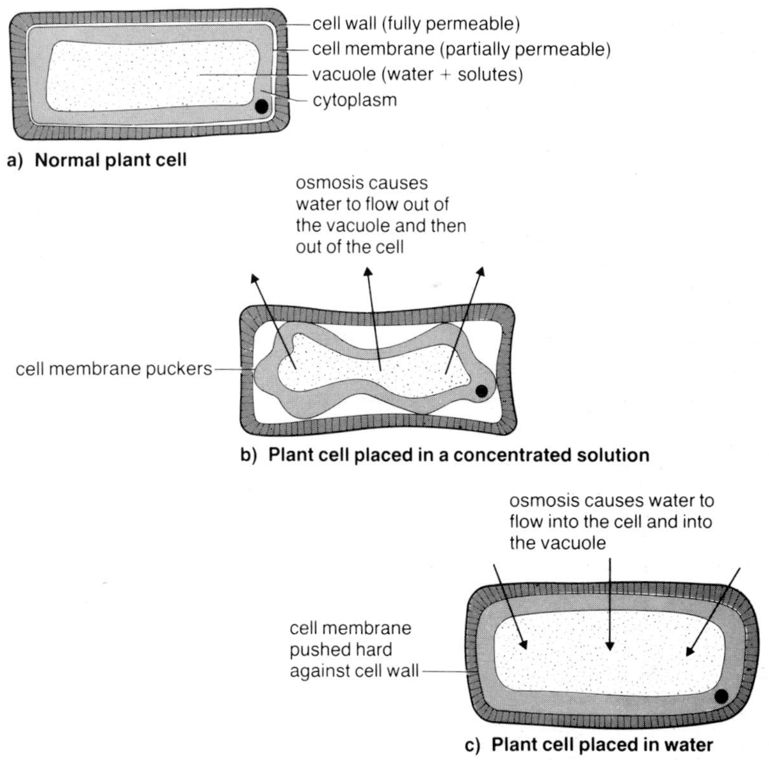

Figure 3.12 (Above) Effect of osmosis on plant cells.

Osmosis and plant cells

Plant cells differ from animal cells in having a strong, relatively rigid cell wall (section 2.4). This cell wall is completely permeable to water and solutes, but inside this wall are the cell membrane and cytoplasm, and these are partially permeable.

Figure 3.12 shows how plant cells, such as onion skin cells, are affected by osmosis. When the cell is in a concentrated solution (of salt, sugar or whatever) the vacuole and the cytoplasm lose water by osmosis, and shrink. This causes the surrounding cell membrane to shrink inwards (figure 3.12b). The cell wall however, keeps its shape, though it is less stiff than when the cytoplasm is pressing against it.

When the cell is placed in water, osmosis allows water to flow into the vacuole. The vacuole swells, pressing the cytoplasm and its enclosing cell membrane against the cell wall. This makes the cell walls even more stiff and rigid. The cell wall is stiffened in the same way that a bicycle tyre is stiffened by the pressure of an inflated inner tube.

When a plant cell is swollen in this way, it is said to be **turgid**. **Turgor** stiffens plant cells and this is one of the major ways in which plants support themselves and keep themselves upright. A non-woody annual plant, like a dandelion, relies on turgor to keep its stem and leaves erect. When such a plant loses its water supply, for example by cutting or drought, the cells are no longer stiffened by turgor. The plant droops or wilts. Plants that continue from year to year (perennials) usually produce wood to stiffen their stems, and do not rely completely on turgor for stiffness.

(*Left*) Onion skin cells seen under the microscope. In one of the two pictures, the cells were in a concentrated solution. Which picture?

How do plants obtain their water supply?

Plants get water from the soil by osmosis. Plant roots are covered in tiny hairs called **root hairs**. These hairs greatly increase the surface area of the roots in contact with the water in the soil.

Imagine a root hair (figure 3.13), surrounded by damp soil. Osmosis causes water to pass from the soil into the root hair. The water then flows towards the centre of the root, eventually joining a system of distribution vessels called xylem (section 5.3). As long as water is being used up elsewhere in the plant (by evaporation from the leaves, for example), the flow of water into the root continues.

(*Above*) The root hairs of a wheat plant are revealed by the scanning electron microscope (magnification 300 times).

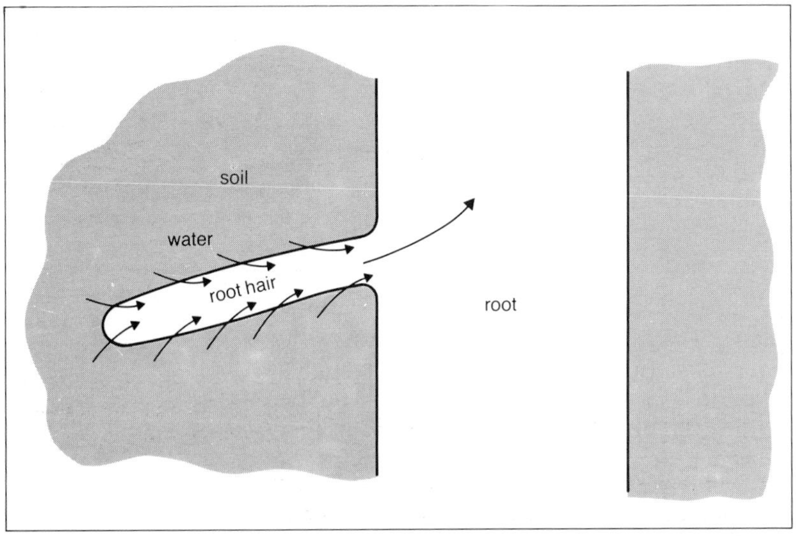

Figure 3.13 How water enters plant roots (note that only one root hair is shown; there would in fact be very many).

3.4 How small are the particles of matter?

If all matter is made up of particles, how small are they? They must be very small indeed, because the largest particles can only just be seen under the most powerful electron microscopes. Here are some simple calculations and experiments which will give us a rough idea of the size of particles.

The evidence of your nose

If a person wearing strong perfume walks into a room, the perfume spreads to all parts.

- To smell the perfume you must have at least one 'perfume particle' in your nose. Suppose the volume of your nasal cavity is 10 cm^3. This means there must be at least one perfume particle per 10 cm^3 of air, and probably far more.
- Suppose the room is 10 m long, 5 m wide and 3 m high. Its total volume is therefore 150 m^3, or 150 000 000 cm^3. Dividing this by 10 cm^3, we find there are 15 000 000 'nosefuls' of air in the room!
- Every 'noseful' must contain at least one perfume particle, and probably far more. Therefore the *minimum* number of perfume particles in the room must be 15 000 000 (15 million). Remember, these came from only a few drops of perfume, not all of which will have evaporated to fill the room.

Clearly, the particles are very small. We can actually measure them in the school laboratory using the oil drop experiment.

The oil drop experiment

The evidence of your eyes

If oil is poured onto water, it spreads out to give a very thin layer. You have probably noticed the rainbow effect due to a film of oil on puddles on the road. If we can measure the thickness of an oil layer, we can get some idea of the size of oil particles, because the layer cannot be less than one particle thick. Here are the details of such an experiment.

- A solution of olive oil is made by dissolving 1 cm^3 of oil in 1000 cm^3 of alcohol.
- Some water is put in a clean tray and its surface is sprinkled with a fine powder.
- One drop of the oil solution is dropped onto the dusty surface. The solution spreads out and the alcohol dissolves in the water, leaving a thin layer of oil. This layer pushes aside the dust leaving a clear patch (figure 3.14).

- The oil patch is measured and its area is found to be $250\,cm^2$.
- If we assume that fifty drops make up $1\,cm^3$, the volume of one drop of oil solution must be

$$1/50 = 0.02\,cm^3$$

- The solution contained only $1\,cm^3$ of oil in $1000\,cm^3$, so the volume of actual oil in one drop of solution is

$$0.02/1000 = 0.00002\,cm^3$$

- If we assume the layer has uniform thickness, and we call this t cm, then

$$\text{volume of oil in the layer} = \text{area} \times \text{thickness} = 250 \times t\,cm^3.$$

- We now have two expressions for the volume of the layer. Putting them equal to one another:

$$250 \times t = 0.00002$$
$$\Rightarrow t = 0.00002/250$$
$$= 0.00000008\,cm$$
$$= 8 \times 10^{-8}\,cm$$

- The thickness of the layer is therefore estimated to be 8×10^{-8} cm, or 0.0000000008 m. If the layer is one particle thick, this must be the size of the particles.

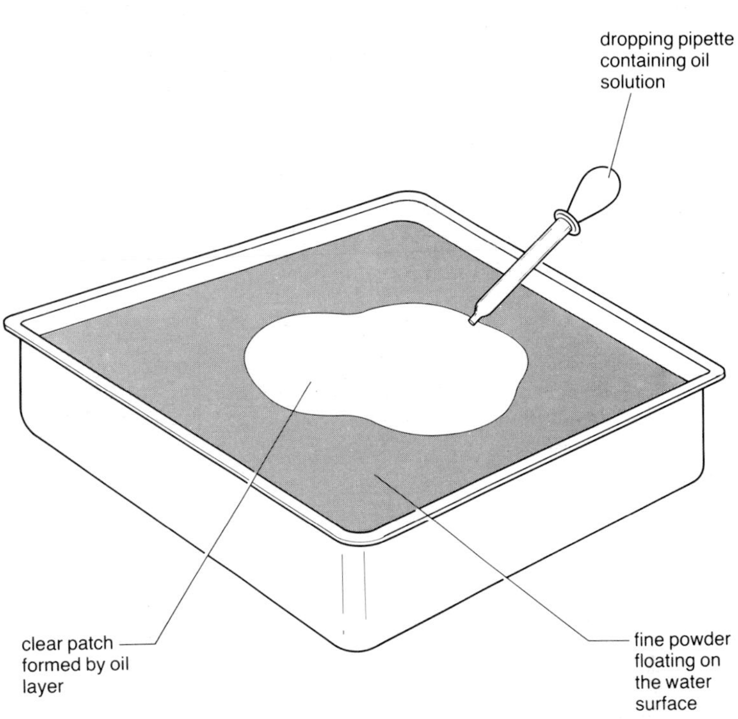

Figure 3.14 The oil drop experiment.

- Is this answer likely to be too big or too small? Explain your answer.
- Why does the oil patch spread out, but stop spreading when it has reached a certain size?
- Why is a solution of oil in alcohol used, instead of pure oil?

This simple experiment gives a rough idea of the size of the particles of matter. To get accurate measurements a different method, called X-ray diffraction is used. Scientists have obtained very accurate values for the sizes of the particles that make up matter using X-ray diffraction.

Getting an idea of the size of particles

Particles vary a lot in size, but they are all very, very small.

- The smallest atom (the hydrogen atom) is about 10^{-10} m (i.e. 0.0000000001 m) across.

In order to measure and describe these very small particles, scientists use a unit called the **nanometre** (nm).

$$1 \text{ nanometre} = 10^{-9}\,m = 1/1000000000\,m$$

Therefore a hydrogen atom measures about 0.1 nm

- Compared to hydrogen atoms, sugar molecules are moderately large at about 1 nm. But there are still about 10^{19} molecules or

  10000000000000000000 molecules

  in one grain of sugar!

The following facts should give you some idea of how small the particles of matter are.

- A glass of water contains about 10^{25} molecules of water.
  How big is 10^{25}? If you could count five particles a second it would take you 10^{17} years to count 10^{25} particles. 10^{25} grains of sand would cover the entire Earth with sand 5 cm deep.
- A glass of water contains on average, seven water molecules that were drunk by William Shakespeare.
- A thimble full of air contains more molecules than there are grains of sand on a large beach.
- If a drop of water were magnified to the size of the Earth, the water particles in it would only be as big as golf balls.

Summary

1 All matter is made of constantly moving particles. Evidence for this includes electron microscope photographs, Brownian motion and diffusion.

2 The theory of constantly moving particles is called the kinetic theory. This theory explains much of the behaviour of matter, for example gas pressure, changes of state and diffusion.

3 Diffusion can occur in liquids and solutions as well as in gases. Substances always diffuse from regions of high concentration to low concentration.

4 Diffusion is one of the major ways living organisms move materials around.

5 Sometimes organisms must move materials in the opposite direction to the way they move by diffusion. This requires energy and is called active transport.

6 Osmosis is the flow of solvent through a partially permeable membrane from a dilute solution to a more concentrated one.

7 Osmosis has important effects on living cells. Cells surrounded by water or dilute solutions tend to swell up. Cells surrounded by concentrated solutions tend to shrink.

8 When plant cells are swollen with water they are stiffened and turgid. Turgor helps plants to support themselves.

9 Plants obtain water through their root hairs by osmosis.

10 The particles making up matter are very, very small. The smallest atoms are about 0.1 nm (i.e. 10^{-10} m) across.

11 The size of particles can be measured approximately using the oil drop experiment, and accurately using X-ray diffraction.

Study questions

1 a) State the main points in the kinetic theory of matter.
  b) Use the kinetic theory to explain each of the following.
    i) Gases diffuse to fill all the space available.
    ii) Liquids turn to gases when heated.
    iii) If smoke is examined under a microscope, the tiny smoke particles are seen to be in constant random motion.
    iv) A car tyre can be made hard and rigid by pumping air into it.
    v) Gases can easily be compressed, but solids and liquids are very difficult to compress.

2 a) A flask containing 300 cm^3 of a very smelly gas was accidentally opened in a school chemistry laboratory. The gas could soon be smelled throughout the laboratory and the two laboratories next to it. Each laboratory measured 15 m by 15 m by 3 m high. Assuming the volume of a 'noseful' of air is 10 cm^3, estimate the minimum number of gas particles there must have been in the flask.
  b) A molecule of olive oil measures about 1 nm (10^{-9} m) across. One drop of pure olive oil is dropped onto the surface of a large swimming pool and spreads out until the layer is one molecule thick. What is the total area of the layer? (Assume fifty drops of olive oil make up 1 cm^3.)
  c) Saccharin is a very sweet substance. 0.001 g in a cup of tea can easily be tasted.
    i) What is the minimum number of saccharin particles in a sip of tea if the saccharin is to be tasted?
    ii) Assuming the volume of a sip is 5 cm^3 and the volume of a cup of tea is 300 cm^3, how many sips are there in a cup of tea?
    iii) What is the minimum number of particles in 1 g of saccharin?
    iv) Why is this likely to be a very low estimate?

3 Suggest an explanation for each of the following.
  a) An air-filled balloon slowly goes down over the course of a week or two, even if the neck is securely tied.
  b) A hydrogen-filled balloon goes down much faster than an air-filled one.
  c) A balloon goes down faster on a warm day than on a cold one.
  d) 1 g of water occupies a volume of 1 cm^3. But 1 g of steam, which contains the same number of particles, occupies about 1700 cm^3.
  e) If a piece of gold and a piece of silver are pressed together for several years, a few atoms of silver pass into the gold, and a few atoms of gold pass into the silver.

4 a) What is osmosis?
b) A 10% sugar solution and a 20% sugar solution are separated from one another by a partially permeable membrane. Water is found to flow from the 10% solution into the 20% solution. Use the kinetic theory to explain why this happens.

5 a) Use your knowledge of osmosis to explain each of the following observations.
i) Lettuce leaves go limp and floppy a few hours after the lettuce plant has been cut.
ii) Limp lettuce can be made crisper by placing the leaves in fresh, cold water for a while.
iii) Cooks who put lettuce leaves in salty water to get rid of insects and slugs find that the leaves become very limp.
b) Underneath the shell of a hen's egg there is a thin membrane. The shell can be carefully dissolved away with acid, and the egg left intact, enclosed only by the membrane. If this shell-less egg is placed in fesh water, it soon swells in size. If it is placed in salty water it shrinks. Explain both these observations.

6 a) Ether has a strong smell. If some ether is spilled, it can be smelled all over the room in a few minutes. It has been estimated that at room temperature, ether molecules move at the speed of a jet plane. Why, then, does it take some minutes for the smell to spread across the room?
b) Why don't the gases in the Earth's atmosphere diffuse away into space?

7 Many substances move into and out of living organisms by diffusion. For each of the following cases, name an organism and say in which part of the organism the diffusion process happens.
a) Oxygen moves into an organism.
b) Carbon dioxide moves out of an organism.
c) Food moves into an organism's bloodstream.
d) Water moves into an organism.
e) Water moves out of an organism.

8 a) Crystals of sodium chloride (salt) are always cubic in shape. What does this suggest to you about the arrangement of particles in sodium chloride?
b) Sodium chloride dissolves easily in water. What happens to the sodium chloride particles when it dissolves?
c) Why does sodium chloride dissolve faster in hot water than in cold water?

4 Atoms and molecules

Atoms and molecules are the building blocks from which elements are made. By studying atoms and the way they are joined together, we can learn more about the properties of elements.

4.1 Different kinds of particles

Look at the photograph of a man breaking concrete with a sledgehammer. Simple enough, but look more closely and ask a few questions. Why does the concrete break but not the sledgehammer? Why is the head of the hammer made of iron, not plastic? Why is the shaft made from wood, not rubber?

The answers to all these questions are related to the properties of the materials being used. Concrete is hard and brittle, but iron is hard and resilient. Wood is tough and rigid whereas rubber is flexible. Why do different materials have different properties? We can answer this question by looking at the particles from which they are made and how these particles are joined together.

The world contains an amazing number of different materials; iron, concrete, wood and rubber are just a few. Fortunately, although there are millions of different materials to study, they are all made from the same building blocks – elements – and there are only about a hundred of these.

Elements and compounds, atoms and molecules

Elements cannot be broken down into anything simpler. Iron is an element, and whatever you do you can never break it down into anything else. You can, however, make iron join together with other elements to form **compounds**. For example, iron and oxygen combine to form iron oxide. It is possible (though not always easy) to break down compounds, like iron oxide, and re-form the elements.

All matter is made of particles, and the simplest particles are **atoms**. Elements are

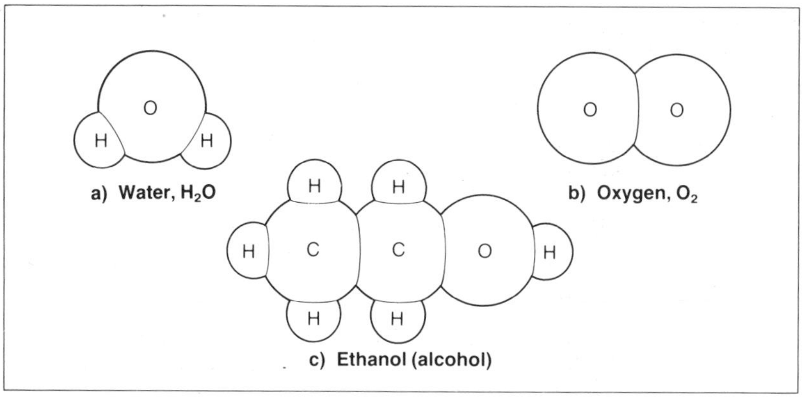

Figure 4.1 Some molecules.

composed of only one type of atom: iron contains only iron atoms and oxygen contains only oxygen atoms. There are 105 different types of atom, since there are 105 different elements, though only 92 elements occur naturally. Each element has a name and a symbol, which is normally a shortened form of its name. Table 4.1 (p. 32) gives some common elements and their symbols.

Atoms can join together in groups. These groups, which may be large or small, are called **molecules**. One of the commonest molecules on earth contains two hydrogen atoms and one oxygen atom (figure 4.1a). We represent this as a **formula**, H_2O. It is of course a molecule of water. The number following each symbols shows how many atoms of that element are present in the molecule. For example, the formula of glucose is $C_6H_{12}O_6$, and this indicates there are six carbon atoms, twelve hydrogen atoms and six oxygen atoms in one glucose molecule.

Figure 4.1c shows a molecule of ethanol.
- How many atoms of carbon, oxygen and hydrogen does a molecule of ethanol contain?
- What is the formula of ethanol?

Molecules of compounds contain two or more different kinds of atoms. Sometimes, however, identical atoms join together to form a molecule, like the oxygen molecule O_2 in figure 4.1b. So, it is possible for elements as well as compounds to be made of molecules. The molecules of elements are usually very simple, but many molecules, particularly those found in living organisms, are large and complex and contain several different types of atom. For example, chlorophyll, the pigment that gives leaves their green colour, has the formula $C_{51}H_{72}O_4N_4Mg$.

4.2 How heavy are atoms?

We have already discussed the size of atoms (section 3.4) and found they are very small indeed. How much do atoms weigh? Finding this out is very tricky, because it is impossible to weigh such tiny things directly.

Fortunately, there is a method for finding the mass of atoms. This is called **mass spectrometry**. Using this method, it is found that the smallest atom, hydrogen, weighs

0.000 000 000 000 000 000 000 0017 g

or 1.7×10^{-24} g. Even the heaviest atoms weigh only

0.000 000 000 000 000 000 0005 g

or 5×10^{-22} g. These numbers are so tiny that a new scale is used for measuring atomic masses. Instead of working in grams, we measure the masses of atoms *relative to one another*. This gives numbers that are much easier to handle.

The basis of this **relative atomic mass scale** is the carbon atom, which is given a mass of exactly 12.

Relative atomic mass of C = 12.000.

The mass spectrometer shows us that magnesium atoms are twice as heavy as carbon atoms, so the relative atomic mass of magnesium is twice that of carbon, $2 \times 12 = 24$ (figure 4.2). In this way we find the relative atomic masses of all the elements. Some relative atomic masses of elements are given in table 4.1 (p. 32).

Figure 4.2 Magnesium atoms are twice as heavy as carbon atoms, therefore the relative atomic mass of magnesium is 24.

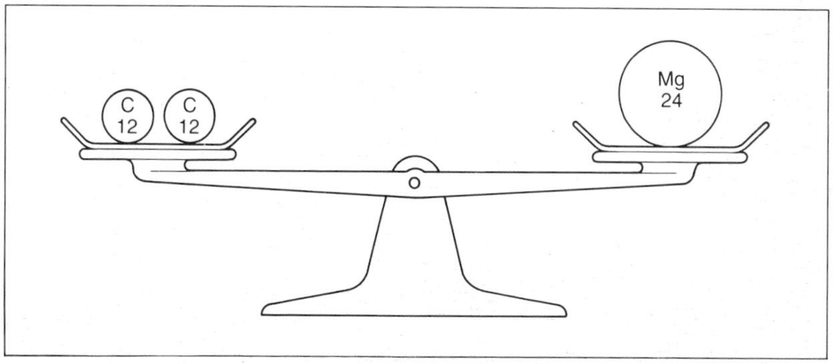

- How many times is one sulphur atom heavier than one oxygen atom?
- How many hydrogen atoms make up the same mass as one sodium atom?
- How many hydrogen atoms make up the same mass as one hundred sodium atoms?

Table 4.1
Relative atomic masses of some elements

Element	*Symbol*	*Relative atomic mass*
aluminium	Al	27
bromine	Br	80
calcium	Ca	40
carbon	C	12
chlorine	Cl	35.5
copper	Cu	63.5
fluorine	F	19
gold	Au	197
helium	He	4
hydrogen	H	1
iodine	I	127
iron	Fe	56
lead	Pb	207
magnesium	Mg	24
nitrogen	N	14
oxygen	O	16
phosphorus	P	31
potassium	K	39
silicon	Si	28
silver	Ag	108
sodium	Na	23
sulphur	S	32
uranium	U	238
zinc	Zu	65

How heavy are molecules?

We can measure the mass of molecules in the same way as atoms, using a mass spectrometer. However, if the formula of the molecule is known, its relative molecular mass can be worked out from the relative atomic masses of the elements it contains. For example, what is the relative molecular mass of water?

The formula of water is H_2O. This means one water molecule contains two hydrogen atoms and one oxygen atom.

relative mass of two hydrogen atoms $= 2 \times 1$
$= 2$
relative mass of one oxygen atom $= 16$
$\Rightarrow$ relative molecular mass of water $= 18$

- Calculate the relative molecular mass of each of the following, using table 4.1:
  a) carbon dioxide, CO_2
  b) hydrogen chloride, HCl,
  c) sulphuric acid, H_2SO_4.

4.3 Counting atoms

Scientists often need to count out atoms. Suppose, for example, you wanted to make some iron sulphide, FeS. This is easily done by heating together iron and sulphur. One atom of iron combines with one atom of sulphur to give iron sulphide:

$$Fe + S \rightarrow FeS$$

If you were manufacturing FeS, you would want to do it as cheaply as possible. This would mean using exactly the right quantities of iron and sulphur, so none was left over and wasted. You need an atom of sulphur for every atom of iron, but to get a reasonable amount of FeS you would need very large numbers of atoms. If you took a million atoms of iron, you would need a million atoms of sulphur, but how could the atoms be counted out? They are so small that counting them out one by one is clearly out of the question.

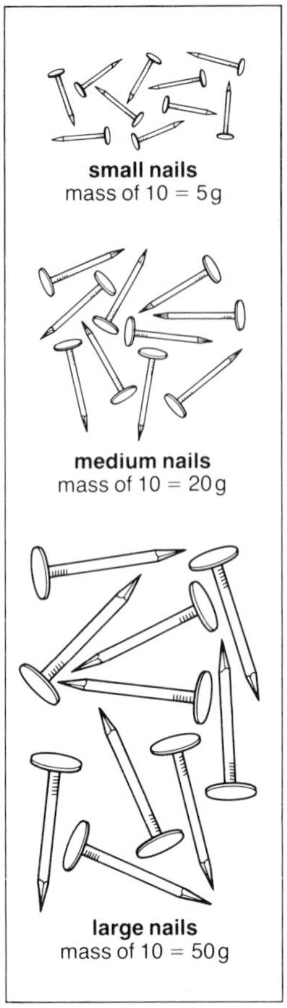

Figure 4.3 Counting nails.

The mole, a counting unit

When people count out large numbers of very small things, they often use a counting unit. If you go into a hardware shop to buy nails, the shopkeeper will not sell nails singly. He might sell them in units of ten, twenty, thirty etc. Rather than waste time counting individual nails, he might *weigh* them out. If he knows the mass of ten nails, he can work out the mass of say, fifty, and weigh them out.

Look at figure 4.3.
- How would you measure out fifty large nails without counting?
- How would you measure out one hundred medium nails without counting?
- How much heavier is a large nail than a small nail?

Ten nails is the shopkeeper's counting unit. Because he knows the mass of ten nails, he can measure out nails by mass to save counting them.

The same method is used to measure out large numbers of coins in banks. Knowing the mass of say, £1 worth of 10p pieces, a clerk can work out the value of a bag of 10p coins by weighing it.

Chemists can count atoms by weighing in the same way that bank clerks count money by weighing and shopkeepers count nails. Atoms are much too small to count out one by one, so a counting unit is used. Atoms are far, far smaller than nails, so the counting unit is much, much larger. It is in fact

600 000 000 000 000 000 000 000 (6×10^{23}) atoms

This number is used because it turns out that

6 ×10^{23} atoms of any element have a mass equal to the relative atomic mass of the element in grams.

Some examples will make this clearer. Look at table 4.1 again.

6 × 10^{23} atoms of carbon weigh 12 g
6 × 10^{23} atoms of hydrogen weigh 1 g

The number 6 × 10^{23} is called the **Avogadro constant**. This is in honour of the Italian scientist Amadeo Avogadro. The counting unit 6 × 10^{23} is known as one **mole**.

One mole of atoms of an element = 6 × 10^{23} atoms.

This has a mass equal to the relative atomic mass in grams.

Look at table 4.1.
- What is the mass of one mole of iron, Fe?
- What is the mass of one mole of sulphur, S?
- How many atoms are there in 20 g of hydrogen?
- What is the mass of 0.5 mole of magnesium, Mg?
- How many moles of oxygen atoms are there in 64 g of oxygen?
- How many moles of magnesium are there in 0.24 g of Mg?
- What mass of iron contains the same number of atoms as 16 g of sulphur?

A mole of anything

A mole is just a counting unit. It simply means 6 ×10^{23} of anything. Theoretically you could have a mole of paper clips or a mole of shoes. In practice there are not nearly enough shoes or paper clips in the world to make anything like 6 × 10^{23} of them. The mole is much too big as a counting unit for use with anything but very tiny things like atoms and molecules.

Molecules are counted out in just the same way as atoms. For example, the relative molecular mass of water, H_2O, is 18.

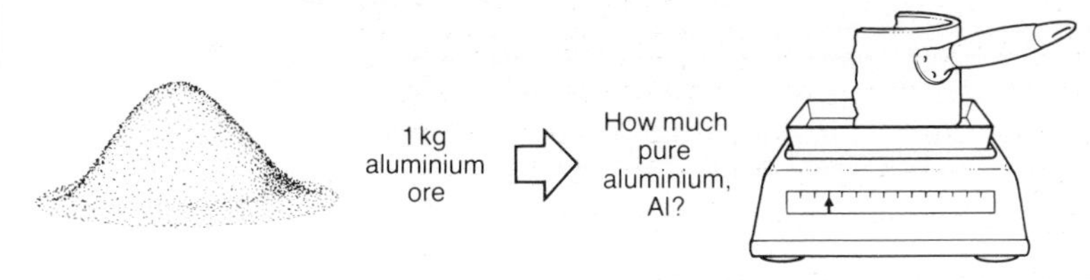

Figure 4.4 How much aluminium can be made from 1 kg of its ore?

Therefore one mole of H_2O molecules, containing 6 × 10^{23} molecules, weighs 18 g.

Look at table 4.1.
- What is the mass of one mole of carbon dioxide, CO_2?
- How many H_2O molecules are there in 36 g of water?
- How many moles of CO_2 are there in 0.44 g of CO_2?
- What is the mass of 1 × 10^{23} molecules of glucose, $C_6H_{12}O_6$?

Using the mole idea

The mole is a very useful quantity. Using it, we can measure out known numbers of atoms simply by weighing – we do not have to count them.

We have already considered the reaction between iron and sulphur to form iron sulphide.

$$Fe + S \rightarrow FeS$$

Using the mole idea, we know that
56 g iron contains 6 × 10^{23} Fe atoms.
32 g sulphur contains 6 × 10^{23} S atoms.
So, to make the iron sulphide, we would heat together 56 g of iron and 32 g of sulphur. This would provide equal numbers of iron and sulphur atoms. We would get 56 g + 32 g = 88 g of iron sulphide. If we wanted more or less than 88 g, we could scale the quantities up or down. But we must always keep the mass of iron and the mass of sulphur in the ratio 56:32.

Here is another example. Aluminium is an important metal, used to make saucepans, bicycles, aeroplanes and many other things. Aluminium is extracted from an ore called bauxite. The formula of purified aluminium ore is Al_2O_3. What mass of aluminium could be made from, say, 1 kg of aluminium ore (figure 4.4)? This is an important question if you are an aluminium manufacturer.

The formula Al_2O_3 tells us that each Al_2O_3 can give two Al atoms.

⇒ one mole of Al_2O_3 gives two moles of Al

Now one mole of Al_2O_3 weighs 102 g, and two moles of Al weigh 54 g

⇒ 102 g Al_2O_3 gives 54 g Al

⇒ 1 g Al_2O_3 gives $\frac{54}{102}$ = 0.53 g Al

⇒ 1 kg Al_2O_3 gives 0.53 kg Al

So 1 kg of aluminium ore gives 0.53 kg of aluminium.

4.4 Using the mole to find the formula of compounds

We have used formulas quite a lot already. But how are formulas found out? How do we *know* that the formula of water is H_2O?

All formulas are calculated from the results of experiments, using the mole idea. When we write the formula H_2O, this means that

one molecule of H_2O contains two H atoms and one O atom

or that

one mole of H_2O molecules contains two moles of H atoms and one mole of O atoms

Numbers of moles can be measured experimentally by weighing. If water is split up into hydrogen and oxygen, it is always found there are twice as many moles of H atoms as moles of O atoms. Therefore, the formula must be H_2O.

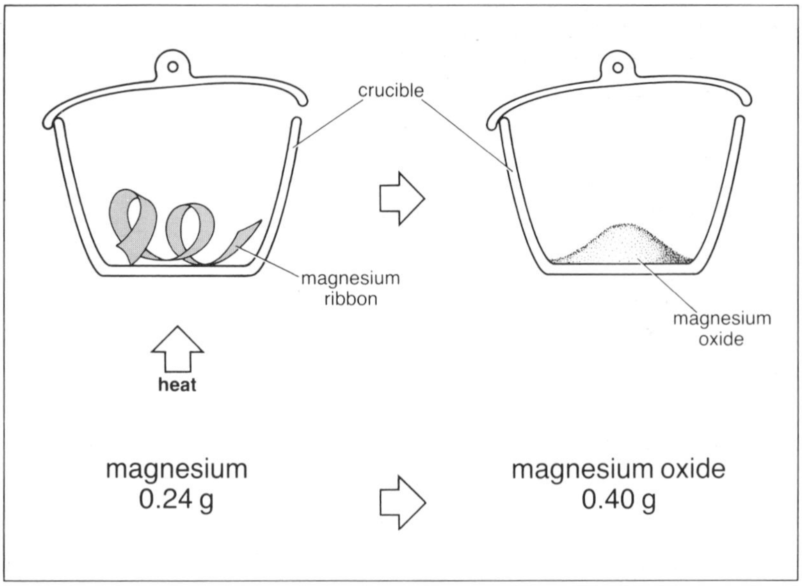

Figure 4.5 Finding the formula of magnesium oxide.

Finding the formula of magnesium oxide

When a piece of magnesium ribbon is ignited, it burns with a brilliant white flame, forming a white powder, which is magnesium oxide.

magnesium + oxygen → magnesium oxide

The formula of magnesium oxide can be found out by a simple experiment (figure 4.5).

Take a piece of magnesium ribbon of mass 0.24 g and heat it strongly in a porcelain crucible. The magnesium ignites and burns forming magnesium oxide. (Keep a lid on the crucible to prevent magnesium oxide escaping, but leave a small gap to let air enter the crucible so the magnesium can burn.) You will find that 0.40 g of magnesium oxide has formed.

0.24 g magnesium + oxygen
→ 0.40 g magnesium oxide

So the mass of oxygen that combined with 0.24 g of magnesium is

0.40 g − 0.24 g = 0.16 g

Our magnesium oxide contains 0.24 g of magnesium and 0.16 g of oxygen.

To find the formula of magnesium oxide we need to know the numbers of atoms of magnesium and oxygen present. This is impossible to count directly, but if we can find the *numbers of moles* of atoms present, that will do just as well.

1 mole Mg weighs 24 g
⇒ 0.24 g Mg is 0.01 mole Mg
1 mole O weighs 16 g ⇒ 0.16 g O is 0.01 mole O

Thus the magnesium oxide contains 0.01 mole of magnesium for every 0.01 mole of oxygen. So the ratio of Mg to O is 1:1, and the formula of the oxide is **MgO**. This calculation is set out in table 4.2.

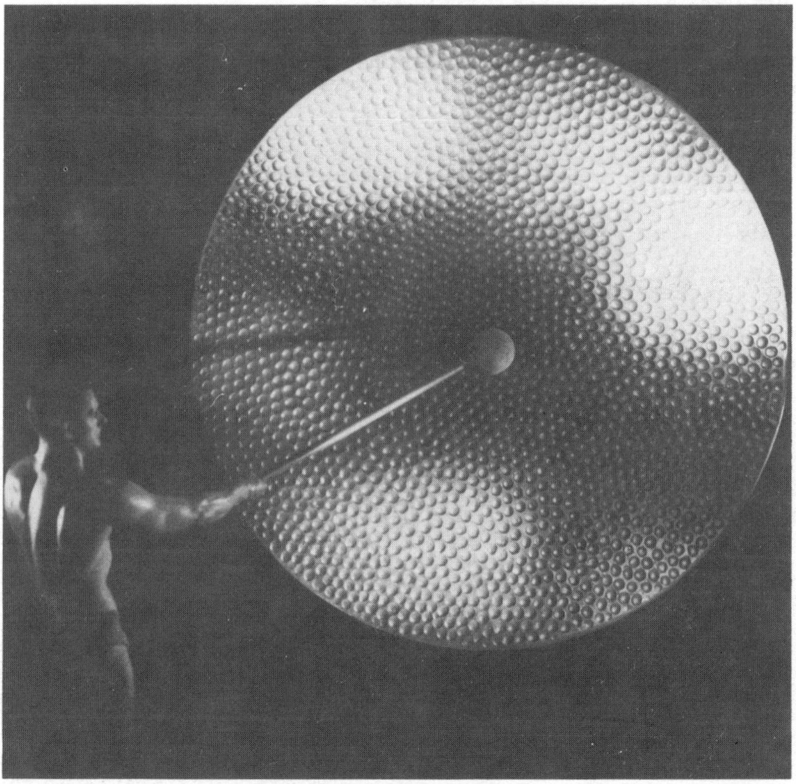

The gong that introduces Rank films uses the properties of metals. It was made by beating metal into shape (malleability). Its shiny surface reflects light (lustre). When it is struck, it vibrates with a ringing sound (sonority).

- Calculate the formulas of the following compounds from the data given. Set out your calculations as in table 4.2.
  a) Methane is a compound of carbon and hydrogen. A sample of methane contained 0.12 g of C combined with 0.04 g of H.
  b) 4.0 g of black copper oxide contains 3.2 g of copper.

4.5 Classifying elements

There are millions of different compounds known to scientists. Fortunately they are all made from different combinations of the same hundred or so elements. We have already seen how scientists classify living things into groups possessing similarities. The same approach is used with elements and compounds. Once we know a compound's formula we can classify it according to the elements it contains. But how can the elements themselves be classified?

As we have seen, ninety-two different elements make up our planet. Some elements, like oxygen, are very common. Others, like gold, are rare. In addition to the 92 naturally occurring elements, scientists have succeeded in producing a further thirteen elements, using advanced experiments involving nuclear reactors. Plutonium is an example.

Metals and non-metals

Table 4.3 lists some of the elements you are likely to meet every day.

- From your knowledge of the elements in table 4.3, classify each element as a metal or non-metal.
- What differences are there between the properties of metals and non-metals?

Table 4.4 summarises the typical physical properties of metals.

Study table 4.4.
- Think of iron as a typical metal. Does iron have all the metallic properties listed in the table?

Table 4.2
Calculating the formula of magnesium oxide

	Mg	O
Masses combined:	0.24 g	0.16 g
Mass of 1 mole:	24 g	16 g
Number of moles present:	0.01	0.01
Simplest ratio of number of moles:	1	1
Formula:	MgO	

Table 4.3
Some common and useful elements

Element	*Where we come across it*
iron	hammers, nails, cars, bridges, dustbins, etc.
copper	electrical wires, pans, ornaments, etc.
oxygen	makes up 1/5 of the air
aluminium	aeroplanes, cooking foil, bicycles, saucepans etc.
nitrogen	makes up 4/5 of the air
carbon	charcoal, soot, burnt toast, etc.

Table 4.4
Typical properties of metals

Metals are usually solid
Metals usually have high melting and boiling points
Metals conduct heat and electricity well
Metals usually have high density
Metals are hard and strong
Metals can be readily formed into new shapes, for example by hammering (they are **malleable**)
Metals can be polished to a high shine (they are **lustrous**)
Metals give a ringing sound when hit (they are **sonorous**)

Prototype of British Railways' Advanced Passenger Train. Why are the rails, wheels and overhead wires all made from metal? Which parts could be replaced by a suitable non-metallic material?

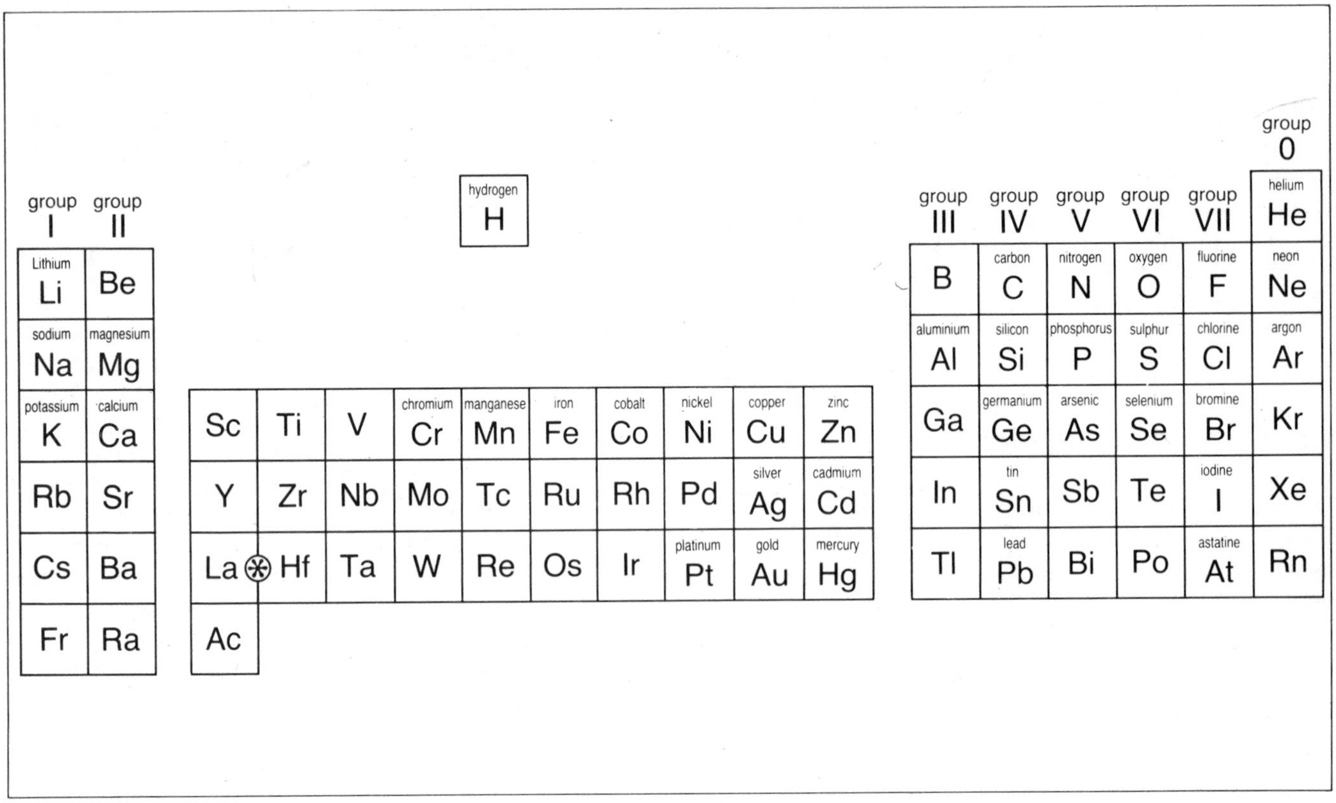

group 0
hydrogen H
group I group II
group III group IV group V group VI group VII
helium He
Lithium Li Be
B carbon C nitrogen N oxygen O fluorine F neon Ne
sodium Na magnesium Mg
aluminium Al silicon Si phosphorus P sulphur S chlorine Cl argon Ar
potassium K calcium Ca
Sc Ti V chromium Cr manganese Mn iron Fe cobalt Co nickel Ni copper Cu zinc Zn
Ga germanium Ge arsenic As selenium Se bromine Br Kr
Rb Sr
Y Zr Nb Mo Tc Ru Rh Pd silver Ag cadmium Cd
In tin Sn Sb Te iodine I Xe
Cs Ba
La ⊛ Hf Ta W Re Os Ir platinum Pt gold Au mercury Hg
Tl lead Pb Bi Po astatine At Rn
Fr Ra
Ac

Figure 4.6 The modern form of the periodic table. Twenty-nine of the rarest elements have been omitted from this table. Fourteen of them (the rare earth elements) come between La and Hf in the position marked by an asterisk. The other fifteen (all radioactive and mostly artificially made) come after Ac.

The periodic table

Over three-quarters of the elements are metals, so we need to make further classifications beyond the simple metal/non-metal distinction.

In 1869, the Russian chemist, Dimitri Mendeléev, arranged the elements in a table, in order of increasing relative atomic mass. Mendeléev put elements with similar properties into vertical columns called **groups**. His **periodic classification** has been updated a little since Mendeléev's time, but it is still the most important way we have of classifying elements. A modern form of the table is shown in figure 4.6.

> *Look at the table in figure 4.6.*
> - Find the positions in the table of all the metallic elements you know.
> - Find the positions of all the non-metallic elements you know.
> - Which general regions of the table are occupied by (a) metals and (b) non-metals?

Important features of the periodic table

- Metals are found on the left of the table, non-metals on the right.
- Elements in the same group (in a vertical column) have similar properties. For example, group I (lithium, sodium, potassium, rubidium, caesium and francium) are all reactive non-metals.
- Although the properties of the elements in a group are similar, they also show a **gradation**. This means the properties gradually change, in a steady, regular way as you move down the group. The gradation of properties among the halogens is described in section 4.10, at the end of this chapter.
- The horizontal rows in the table are called **periods**. Moving from left to right across a period, the elements change from reactive metals on the left to reactive non-metals on the right. Finally, in group 0, are the very unreactive gases called the noble gases. In the middle of the period, the elements are rather unreactive, and sometimes show both metallic and non-metallic properties.
- Reading from left to right and from top to bottom, the elements are in order of increasing relative atomic mass. (Strictly speaking they are in order of increasing atomic *number*, section 27.3, but this is closely related to atomic mass.)

The periodic table is often divided into blocks of similar elements (figure 4.7). Moving from left to right, the blocks are:

- **The reactive metals** This is the left-hand block, made up of groups I and II.

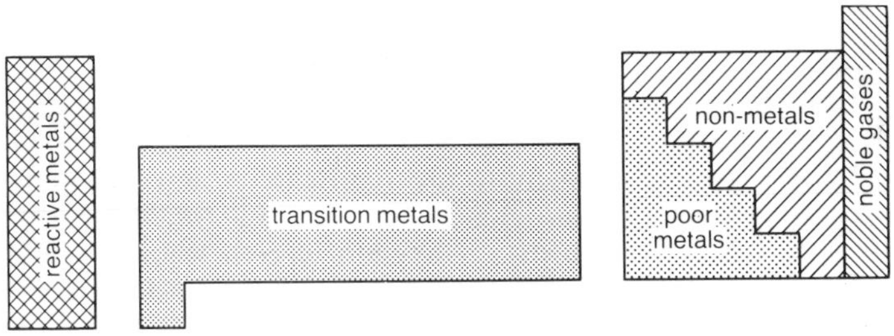

Figure 4.7 Blocks of the periodic table.

- **The transition metals** This is the large central block, between group II and group III. The transition metals are all hard, strong and dense, and they are not very reactive. These properties make them very useful metals for construction. Most of the metals used in cars, bridges and buildings, for tools and for electrical equipment are transition metals.
- **The 'poor' metals** This is the triangular block with Al, Po and Tl at its corners, lying between the metals and non-metals. The elements in this block are like metals in some ways, but like non-metals in others. Because they do not have all the properties of typical metals, these elements are sometimes called 'poor' metals.
- **The non-metals** This is the triangular block above the 'poor' metals.
- **The noble gases** These are the elements in group 0. They are very unreactive.

Look at figures 4.6 and 4.7.

- To which block does each of the following elements belong? Chromium, Cr; argon, Ar; calcium, Ca; germanium, Ge; sulphur, S.
- Which of the following elements will be most like selenium, Se? Bromine, Br; arsenic, As; iodine, I; sulphur, S; aluminium, Al.
- Why is argon, Ar, used to fill light bulbs?
- Would you expect iodine, I, to conduct electricity?
- Which is the more reactive metal, sodium, Na, or aluminium, Al?

4.6 Joining atoms to form structures

How are the atoms of elements joined together? This is an important question, because the way the atoms are joined determines the properties of the element, such as its melting point and its density.

The atoms of an element join together to form a **structure**. The structure of an element can be investigated using a method called X-ray diffraction. Using this method a kind of map can be built up, showing how the atoms are arranged. It is often found that the atoms in a solid are arranged in a very regular way. This regular arrangement of atoms on a small scale builds up to give a solid with a regular shape, called a **crystal**. Sometimes, as in most metals, the crystals are very small and cannot be seen without a microscope. In other cases, such as a diamond, the crystals are large and can easily be seen.

Two general types of structure are found: giant structures and simple molecular structures.

(*Above*) The regular arrangement of the atoms gives rise to the regular shape of these quartz crystal.

Giant structures

In this type of structure, every atom is joined to several others, forming a continuous giant network. The atoms are held together by forces called **chemical bonds**. There are several types of bonds, and these are described more fully in section 9.4.

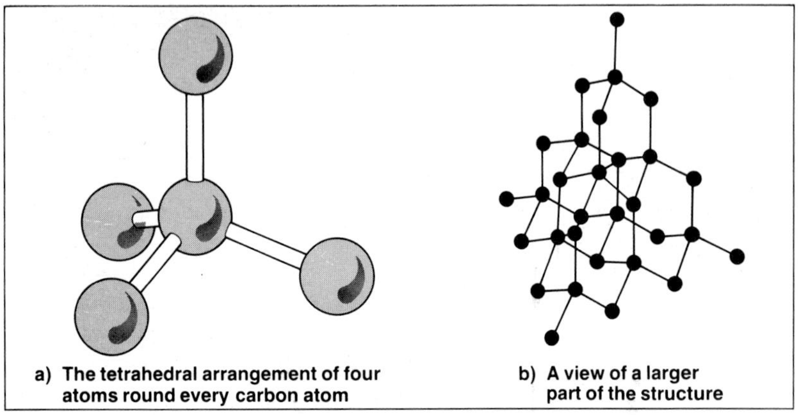

a) The tetrahedral arrangement of four atoms round every carbon atom
b) A view of a larger part of the structure

Figure 4.8 (Above) The arrangement of carbon atoms in diamond.

Diamond has a giant structure. Diamond is a form of carbon, in which every carbon atom is joined to four other atoms arranged *tetrahedrally* round it, as shown in figure 4.8. The lines joining the atoms in figure 4.8 represent strong chemical bonds. Because these bonds are strong, the structure is itself strong and rigid – that is why diamond is so hard.

More examples of giant structures are given later on in this chapter. In general, elements with giant structures are hard and have high melting points and boiling points. All metals have giant structures (section 4.9).

Compounds, as well as elements, can have giant structures. Most rocks contain silicon, oxygen and a few other elements bonded together in a giant structure. That is why rock is so hard and difficult to melt. This type of giant structure, like that of diamond, extends in three dimensions, but some giant structures are two dimensional, for example graphite (section 4.8). One-dimensional giant molecules are also possible. They have chains of atoms linked together and are called **polymers**. Living organisms contain many polymers, including proteins, cellulose and starch. Without the strength of these giant polymers, muscles could not pull and trees would collapse.

Simple molecular structures

In most non-metals the atoms join together in small groups forming simple molecules. Instead of a continuous network of atoms, the element contains large numbers of small, simple molecules. Within these molecules the atoms are held together by strong bonds, but between the individual molecules, the forces are very weak. The molecules can easily break away from each other, so elements with simple molecular structures are easily turned into gas. They have low melting and boiling points, and many of them are gases at room temperature.

Oxygen is an example of an element with a simple molecular structure (figure 4.9). Each oxygen atom is strongly bonded to another, forming O_2 molecules. We say oxygen is **diatomic**. But between these simple molecules the bonds are very weak, so the molecules drift apart, and oxygen is a gas. This is just as well for living things, because if oxygen were a solid it would be difficult to get into their bodies!

Compounds as well as elements can have simple molecular structures. Carbon dioxide (CO_2) and water (H_2O) are examples. The fact that they are a gas and a liquid, respectively, shows that, although the bonds within their molecules are strong, there is little to hold these molecules to one another.

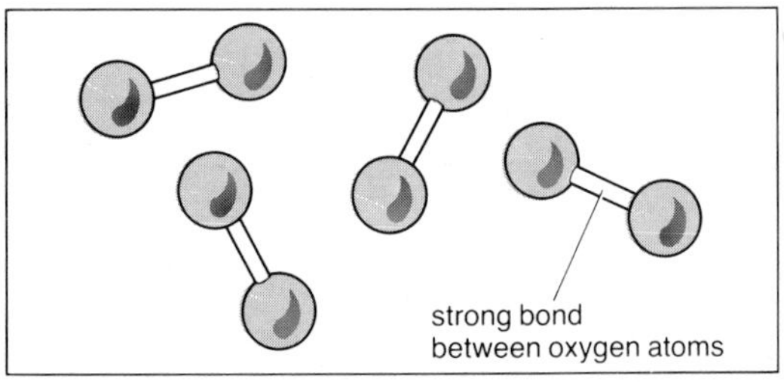

Figure 4.9 (Right) Oxygen – a simple molecular structure.

- Both CO_2 and H_2O are important to living things. Why is it vital that they have simple molecular structures?

Figure 4.10 summarises the difference between giant and simple molecular structures. (The bonding and properties of simple molecular structures are discussed further in section 9.4.)

Figure 4.10 (Below) Giant and simple molecular structures.

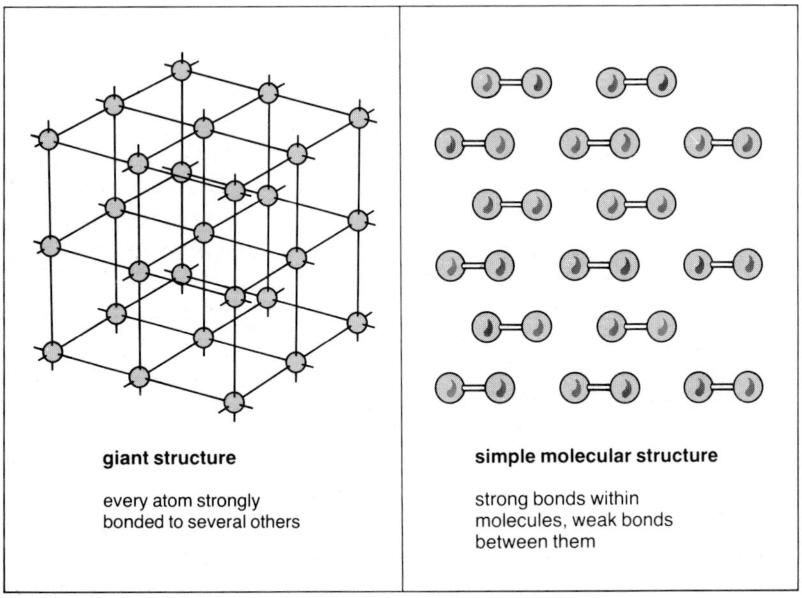

giant structure
every atom strongly bonded to several others
simple molecular structure
strong bonds within molecules, weak bonds between them

4.7 Elements with simple molecular structures

Hydrogen

You have probably heard of hydrogen-filled balloons. These are balloons which rise in the air, and are sometimes big enough to carry loads and even people.

Hydrogen has a simple molecular structure. The gas contains molecules which consist of pairs of hydrogen atoms, formula H_2. These molecules exert little force on one another, so hydrogen is a gas. Hydrogen is the lightest of all the elements. Its relative atomic mass is 1, so the relative molecular mass of H_2 molecules is 2. Hydrogen gas therefore has a very low density – its molecules are light, and widely spaced. Because hydrogen has a lower density than air, it rises in air, and this is the principle behind hydrogen balloons.

Unfortunately, hydrogen is highly flammable. You will probably have heard the popping sound when a test tube of hydrogen is ignited and the hydrogen burns in air, forming water. Because of this flammability, hydrogen balloons are dangerous. Since the Hindenburg disaster it has not been used in balloons where there is any danger of fire. Helium, a safer but more expensive gas, is used instead.

(*Above*) When the Hindenburg exploded in 1947, 35 of the 97 passengers were killed. Hydrogen is no longer used in air ships.

Sulphur

Sulphur is a yellow non-metal. It is brittle, it melts at 120°C and it does not conduct electricity. You may have seen powdered sulphur or cylinders of roll sulphur.

Sulphur is used to make some important industrial chemicals, in particular sulphuric acid (section 25.2). Sulphuric acid is used in almost every major industry, and over 2.5 million tonnes of H_2SO_4 are used in Britain each year. A lot of sulphur is needed to make this amount of sulphuric acid.

There are two major sources of sulphur. Fossil fuels, such as coal and oil contain a good deal of sulphur, which can cause acid rain pollution when the fuel is burned (section 25.2). Most of the sulphur in crude oil is removed (recovered) when the oil is refined. About half of the sulphur used in Britain is obtained in this way. The other major source is the large underground deposits of sulphur in such places as Texas, USA. These deposits are easily extracted, because sulphur has a simple molecular structure.

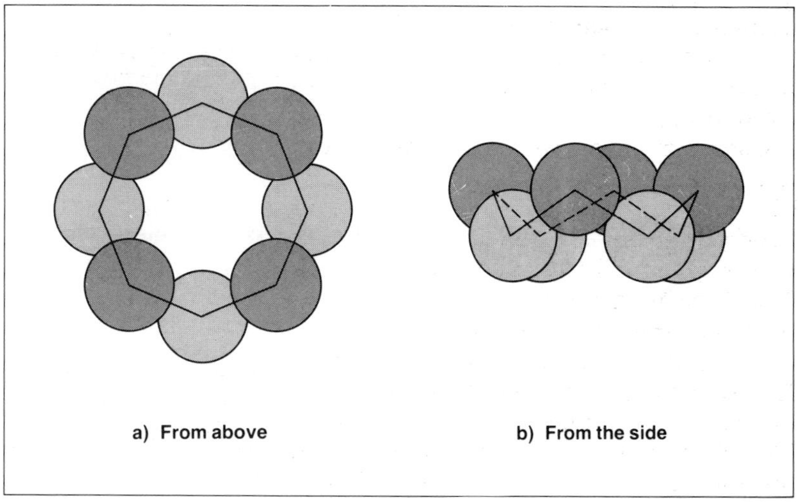

Figure 4.11 A molecule of sulphur.

Sulphur molecules contain rings of eight atoms, S_8 (figure 4.11). Although the forces between these molecules are relatively weak, they are strong enough to make sulphur a solid at room temperature. However, it can be melted easily, and this is how the underground sulphur deposits are brought to the surface.

Hot pressurised water is pumped down to the sulphur bed. This melts the sulphur, which is then forced to the surface by hot compressed air. The sulphur produced in this way is more than 99% pure. Impurities such as rock are left behind because they have giant structures and do not melt easily.

4.8 Forms of carbon with giant structures

Diamond and graphite

Most non-metal elements have simple molecular structures. Because of this non-metals are usually liquids or gases. Carbon is an exception though. We have already seen how one form of carbon, **diamond**, has a giant structure. This gives diamond a very high melting point and makes it very hard. Indeed, diamonds are often used as the cutting edge in tools and in the tips of drills.

Diamonds are rare and expensive, unlike the second, much commoner form of carbon, called **graphite**. Table 4.5 compares the properties of diamond and graphite.

- What evidence is there that graphite has a giant structure?
- Which property of graphite is not typical of non-metals?

Table 4.5
The properties of diamond and graphite

Property	*Diamond*	*Graphite*
appearance	transparent	shiny and dark grey
melting point	3500 °C (sublimes, turns straight to a gas, at this temperature)	3730 °C
hardness	very hard	soft and slippery
electrical conductivity	does not conduct electricity	conducts electricity

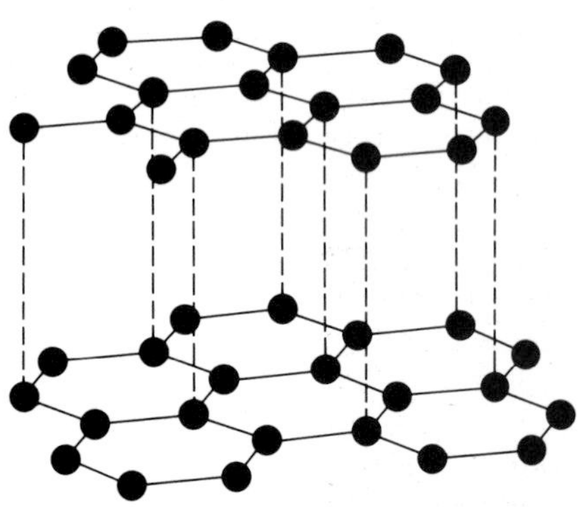

Figure 4.12 The structure of graphite. The distance between carbon atoms in the same layer is only 0.14 nm, but the distance between carbon atoms in successive layers is 0.34 nm.

Slate has a giant layer structure, which means it is easily split into thin sheets. This makes it an ideal natural material for roofing.

The high melting point of graphite indicates a giant structure. But graphite must have a different structure from that of diamond, because it is soft and slippery and conducts electricity. In fact, graphite has a **giant layer structure** (figure 4.12). Within each layer, every graphite atom is bonded strongly to three others, forming a pattern of interlocking hexagonal rings. The graphite atoms are difficult to separate from one another, which is why its melting point is so high. However, the forces *between* the different layers are weak and the layers are able to slide over one another easily, rather like a pack of cards. This makes graphite soft and slippery.

Some rocks have a giant layer structure like graphite. Slate is an example, and the layer structure makes slate easy to split into flat sheets.

Uses of graphite

As a result of its unusual properties, graphite is a very useful material. Because of its slippery nature, it is a good lubricant, and powdered graphite is often mixed with lubricating oil.

When a piece of graphite is rubbed on paper, layers flake off and stick to the paper. Nowadays, pencil 'leads' no longer contain the metal lead, but a mixture of graphite and clay. When you write with a pencil, a trail of graphite sticks to the paper. In fact, the name *graphite* comes from a Greek word meaning *to write*.

Graphite has some important electrical uses. The conducting rod in the centre of a torch battery is graphite. The carbon brushes is an electric motor (section 11.5) are made from graphite, because of the smooth, self lubricating contact it makes with the revolving metal shaft.

Other forms of carbon

Other forms of carbon, such as soot, coke and charcoal, are all grey or black. Close examination of their structure shows that they contain microscopic graphite crystals. Thus, as far as structure is concerned, there are only two forms of carbon, diamond and graphite.

Different forms of the same element in the same state are called **allotropes**. Diamond and graphite are allotropes of carbon. Sometimes, as with diamond and graphite, allotropes have very different properties. Sometimes though, their properties are similar. For example, sulphur has two crystalline allotropes (called rhombic and monoclinic sulphur) which are quite similar. Whatever the differences between allotropes, they can always be related to differences in structure: the way the atoms and molecules are arranged.

4.9 Giant metallic structures

Without metals our modern civilisation would collapse. The hardness, resilience, strength and malleability of metals long ago gave people weapons and tools. Today we rely on the same properties of metals not only for weapons and tools, but also to support our buildings, make our vehicles and most of the things we build. In addition, the electrical conductivity of metals is the basis of the electronic and electrical devices we use.

Why do metals have these valuable properties? Metals have giant structures in which the metal atoms are packed together as closely as possible, like tightly packed billiard balls. Every atom touches twelve others, in a **close-packed** structure. This close packing is one of the reasons for the high density of metals. Figure 4.13 shows the arrangement of metal atoms in one layer.

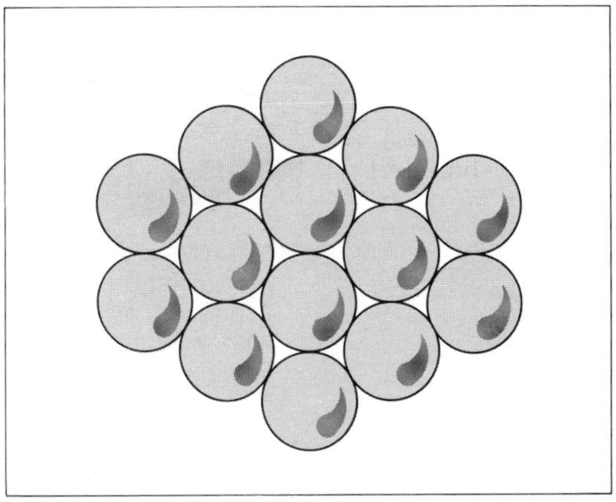

Figure 4.13 (Top left) The close-packed metallic structure, a single layer.

(*Lower left*) The malleability of metals means that complicated shapes can be stamped from a sheet of metal. Hardness and strength are important for the finished car.

The bonds between the metal atoms are strong, yet flexible. The rows of atoms can be moved to new positions without breaking apart (figure 4.14). This is one reason why metals are malleable.

Two or more different metals can be melted together to form **alloys**. The liquid metals mix, and solidify to give an alloy with different properties from either of the original metals. Often the alloy is stronger. For example, brass is an alloy of copper and zinc. It is stronger than either of the separate metals. Steel is iron alloyed with small amounts of other metals and carbon. For example, stainless steel contains iron with chromium or nickel. It is stronger than iron and does not rust.

Table 4.6 gives information about some of the most important metals in use today.

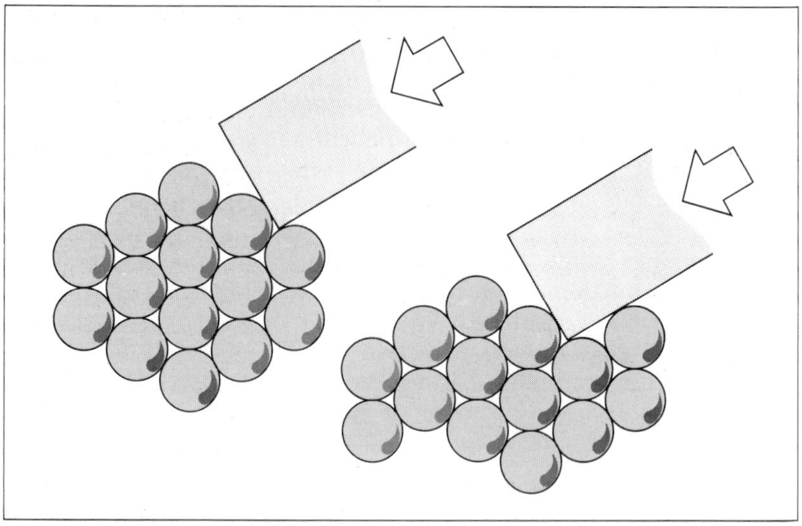

Figure 4.14 Why are metals malleable? Whole rows of atoms can move to new positions without breaking them apart. This movement is called *slip*.

Table 4.6
Important metals

Metal	*Important properties*	*Price (1984) per tonne*	*Annual World production (1983) / thousands of tonnes*	*Main uses*
aluminium	light, does not corrode	£900	1400	kitchen utensils, foil, structural alloys in vehicles aircraft etc.
copper	tough, good electrical and thermal conductivity, corrodes slowly	£1100	9500	electrical wires and components piping making alloys, e.g. brass, bronze
iron	strong, cheap	£130	450000	many structural uses (as steel), e.g. tools, buildings, bridges, vehicles, engines etc.
tin	resists corrosion	£10000	160	coating iron to make tin plate for food cans making alloys, e.g. bronze, solder, pewter
zinc	corrodes slowly	£700	4500	protecting iron from corrosion (galvanising) making brass

- Which metal is produced in the largest quantity?
- Which two metals are alloyed to make bronze?
- Which is the main metal used to make 'tin' cans?
- Which metal is normally used to coat a steel dustbin to stop it rusting?
- Which metal is normally used to make a tent frame?

Table 4.7
Some properties of fluorine, chlorine and bromine

Halogen	*Relative atomic mass*	*Formula of molecule*	*State at room temperature*	*Boiling point / °C*	*Colour*
fluorine	19	F_2	gas	−188	pale yellow
chlorine	35.5	Cl_2	gas	−34	green
iodine	127	I_2	solid	183	very dark purple

4.10 The halogens

A group of simple molecules

The family of non-metal elements called the halogens forms group VII of the periodic table. They are fluorine, F; chlorine, Cl; bromine, Br; and iodine, I. The fifth halogen, astatine, is radioactive and unstable.

Table 4.7 shows some information about fluorine, chlorine and iodine. Using this information, and remembering that elements in the same group have similar properties, you should be able to predict some of the properties of bromine. Remember that the halogens are a typical family or group of elements in the periodic table. They show many similarities to one another. But like all groups of elements, there is a gradation of properties. Thus their properties change gradually as you move down the group.

- Study table 4.7 and then predict the following properties of bromine:
  a) the formula of its molecule,
  b) its boiling point,
  c) its state at room temperature.

The halogens all have simple molecular structures, with diatomic molecules. Thus bromine is Br_2. As with all simple molecular structures, the molecules are easily separated, so the halogens are readily turned to gas. Moving down the group the relative atomic masses of the halogens increase, the molecules get larger and the forces between them increase. Therefore, from fluorine to iodine, the halogens get gradually more difficult to vaporise. The boiling points increase down the group. Fluorine and chlorine are gases at room temperature. Bromine is a liquid, boiling at 58 °C. Iodine is a solid.

There are gradations of this sort in all the properties of the halogens. Their colours become deeper and more intense moving down the group. Fluorine is very pale yellow, chlorine is green, bromine is dark red and iodine is such a deep purple that the solid looks dark grey. The chemical reactions of the halogens also show gradation. Fluorine is the most reactive of all non-metals; there are very few substances that do not react with fluorine. On the other hand, iodine is only moderately reactive. Table 4.8 shows how the halogens react with the two elements, hydrogen and iron. Look at the table and notice the trend in reactivity.

Table 4.8
The reaction of the halogens with hydrogen and iron

Halogen	*Reaction with hydrogen*	*Reaction with iron*
fluorine	explodes, even in the dark, forming HF	iron bursts into flames, forming FeF_3
chlorine	explodes in sunlight, forming HCl	iron reacts vigorously, forming $FeCl_3$
bromine	reacts rapidly if heated, forming HBr	iron reacts forming $FeBr_3$
iodine	reacts only slightly when heated, forming HI	no reaction

Uses of the halogens

The halogens are reactive elements. They all react with a wide variety of elements and compounds. In particular they react with the chemical compounds from which living things are made. The halogens are therefore dangerous: they react with proteins and other compounds in our lungs, skin etc. In fact, chlorine was used as a poison gas in the First World War.

Halogens can kill bacteria and viruses as well as human tissue. This makes them useful as antiseptics and disinfectants. Chlorine is added to drinking water and swimming pools to prevent infection by bacteria. A solution of iodine is sometimes used as an antiseptic. Chlorine also reacts with many coloured compounds, turning them colourless, so it is often used as a bleach.

Because of their reactivity, the halogens form many compounds. These compounds are usually unreactive and stable. For example, sodium chloride (salt) is an essential part of the human diet, and small amounts of iodine are also vital to our health.

Many of the things we use each day are manufactured from halogens, particularly chlorine. PVC (polyvinyl chloride), pesticides, photographic film, aerosol propellants and dry cleaning liquids are all made from halogens (table 4.9).

Table 4.9
Some uses of the halogens and their compounds

Halogen	*Uses*
fluorine	non-stick coatings for pans etc. (PTFE) aerosol propellants anaesthetics
chlorine	aerosol propellants anaesthetics polyvinyl chloride (PVC) dry cleaning fluids bleach disinfectants, water purifiers pesticides
bromine	petrol additives
iodine	photographic film antiseptics

Summary

1 Elements contain one type of atom only, and cannot be broken down to anything simpler. Compounds contain more than one type of atom and can be broken down to their elements.

2 Molecules are groups of atoms joined together by chemical bonds.

3 The atomic mass of an element is the mass of its atoms relative to the mass of a carbon atom. The mass of a carbon atom on this scale is 12.0000.

4 The relative molecular mass of a compound can be calculated from its formula, knowing the relative atomic masses of the atoms it contains.

5 The mole is a counting unit used to count out atoms and molecules. One mole of an element contains 6×10^{23} atoms, and its mass is equal to the relative atomic mass of the element in grams.

6 The formula of a compound can be found by measuring the masses of the elements combined in the compound.

7 Elements can be usefully classified as metals and non-metals, but the periodic table is a more detailed classification.

8 A vertical column of the periodic table is called a group. Elements in the same group show similar properties, but with a gradation down the group.

9 A horizontal row of the periodic table is called a period. Elements change from metal to non-metal from left to right across a period.

10 The way the atoms of an element are joined together is called its structure. Giant structures form a continuous network. Simple molecular structures have small, separate molecules.

11 Hydrogen, H_2, and sulphur, S_8, have simple molecular structures. Sulphur is important for the manufacture of sulphuric acid.

12 Diamond and graphite are allotropes of carbon. Their different properties and uses are due to their different giant structures.

13 Metals have giant structures consisting of close-packed atoms. Their special properties make them very useful structural materials.

14 The halogens are a group of non-metals showing similar but graded properties. Their chemical reactivity gives them many important uses.

Study questions

1 Vitamin C is an essential part of the human diet. Shortage of it causes a skin disease called scurvy. The structure of a molecule of vitamin C is shown in figure 4.15.
  a) Which elements does vitamin C contain?
  b) Write down the formula of vitamin C.
  c) Using table 4.1, calculate the relative molecular mass of vitamin C.
  d) How many moles of vitamin C molecules are there in 17.6 g of vitamin C?
  e) Find out, if you do not already know, which foods are good sources of vitamin C.

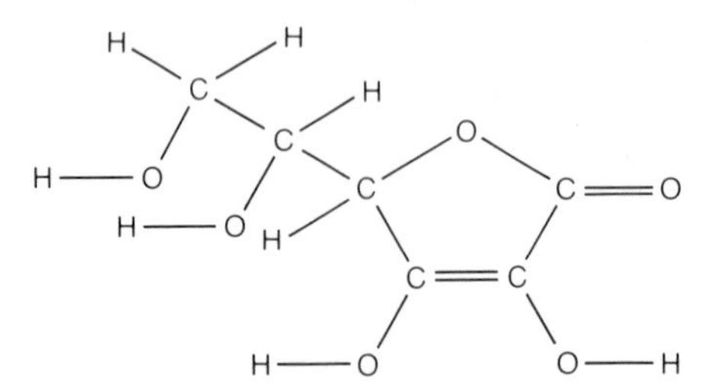

Figure 4.15 Vitamin C.

2 Use table 4.1 to help you when you answer this question.
  a) Calculate the number of moles of
     i) iron, Fe, in 5.6 g of iron,
     ii) aluminium, Al, in 540 g of aluminium,
     iii) helium, He, in 1 g of helium,
     iv) chlorine, Cl_2 in 3.55 g of chlorine
     v) carbon dioxide, CO_2 in 88 g of carbon dioxide.
  b) Calculate the mass of
     i) 0.01 mole of silver, Ag,
     ii) 20 moles of uranium, U,
     iii) 0.5 mole carbon dioxide, CO_2,
     iv) 6 moles of hydrogen, H_2,
     v) 3 moles of methane, CH_4.
  c) i) How many iron atoms are there in 5.6 g of iron?
     ii) How many helium atoms are there in 1 g of helium?
     iii) How many H_2O molecules are there in 36 g of water?
     iv) How many hydrogen atoms are there in 0.000001 g of hydrogen?
  d) i) What mass of silver contains the same number of atoms as 1.97 g of gold?
     ii) What mass of magnesium contains the same number of atoms as 1 g of carbon?

3 Use table 4.1 to find the relative atomic masses you need to answer this question. Set out your answers as in table 4.2.
  a) Lead and oxygen form a brown compound. In an experiment it was found that 2.39 g of brown lead oxide contains 2.07 g of lead.
    i) What mass of oxygen is there in 2.39 g of the oxide?
    ii) What is the formula of brown lead oxide?
  b) Sulphur burns in air to form a choking gas, sulphur oxide. 1 g of sulphur gives 2 g of sulphur oxide when it burns.
    i) Find the formula of sulphur oxide.
    ii) Does sulphur oxide have a simple molecular structure or a giant structure? Give a reason for your answer.
  c) There are two kinds of copper oxide. One is black copper oxide, CuO. The other is a red solid with a high melting point. 3.2 g of copper combines with 0.16 g of oxygen to give red copper oxide.
    i) Find the formula of red copper oxide.
    ii) Does red copper oxide have a simple molecular structure or a giant structure? Give a reason for your answer.

4 This question is about the element sulphur.
  a) What properties of sulphur are typical of non-metals?
  b) What is the formula of a sulphur molecule?
  c) What is the relative atomic mass of sulphur?
  d) What is the relative molecular mass of sulphur?
  e) How is sulphur extracted from underground deposits?

5 a) List the typical properties of metals.
  b) In each of the following examples, which typical metal property is being used? (Note: more than one property may be involved.)
    i) Metals are used for electrical wiring.
    ii) Saucepans are made from metal.
    iii) Car engines are made from metal.
    iv) Bells are made from metal.
    v) Metals are used to make bridges.
    vi) The 'element' of an electric fire is made from metal.
  c) When metals are hit with a hammer they bend, but do not break. When diamond is hit, it shatters, and when graphite is hit it breaks into flakes. Explain these differences.

6 Copy or trace the periodic table in figure 4.6.
  i) Shade blue all the elements with giant metallic structures.
  ii) Shade red all the elements with simple molecular structures.
  iii) Shade green all the elements with giant structures linked by covalent bonds (like diamond).
  (You will have to leave blank the elements whose structures you do not know or can not decide. Alternatively you could look these up in an advanced chemistry book.)

Table 4.10

Property	*Silicon, Si*	*Germanium, Ge*	*Tin, Sn*
relative atomic mass	28		119
melting point/°C	1410		232
density/g cm^{-3}	2.33		7.31
appearance	grey solid		silvery metal
formula of oxide	SiO_2		SnO_2

7 Germanium, Ge, is an element in group IV of the periodic table. Mendeléev predicted the properties of germanium before it was discovered, from the properties of silicon and tin which are above and below it in group IV. Copy out table 4.10, and fill in your predictions for germanium. Check your answers using a data book.

8 Diamond and graphite are allotropes of carbon.
  a) Explain what is meant by *allotropes*.
  b) i) Why is graphite flaky and slippery whilst diamond is hard?
    ii) Why does graphite conduct electricity whilst diamond does not?
  c) Diamond and graphite can both be burned in oxygen to give carbon dioxide, CO_2. A wealthy student did some experiments to show that diamond and graphite both contain carbon alone. In separate experiments she burned 3 g of diamond and 3 g of graphite. She collected the carbon dioxide formed and weighed it. In both cases 11 g of CO_2 was formed.
    i) How many moles of carbon, C, are there in 3 g of carbon?
    ii) How many moles of CO_2 can be formed using this number of moles of carbon?
    iii) What is the mass of this number of moles of CO_2?
    iv) Why do these results prove that diamond and graphite both contain carbon alone?

9 Astatine, At, is the last element in group VII. Very little is known about its properties because it is radioactive and unstable. Predict the following properties of astatine using the information given in section 4.10:
  a) the formula of astatine molecules,
  b) the appearance of astatine,
  c) the boiling point of astatine
  d) the reaction, if any, of astatine with hydrogen,
  e) the reaction, if any, of astatine with iron.

5 Motion and movement

Movement is all around us. The atoms and molecules which make up matter are in constant motion. Even as you sit quite still reading this page, you are hurtling around the Sun at about 30 km per second.

The rate of movement (speed) of different things varies enormously, as table 5.1 shows.

Look at the figures in table 5.1.
- How long would it take an air molecule to cross a room 5 m wide, assuming there are no other molecules in its path?
- How long would it take a snail to cross the same room?
- Estimate your normal walking speed.

What makes things move?

Suppose you have a wheeled trolley standing on a flat road. What do you do to get it moving? You give it a push, or a pull. If you want to keep it moving, you still need to push, but not as hard as you needed to start it. If the road is very smooth and the wheels are very well oiled, you will hardly need to push at all. These pushes and pulls are examples of **forces**. You will see in chapter 6 that a force is needed to get a thing moving.

5.1 How do animals move?

Animals must move around to find food, to escape predators (hunters), to seek a mate and to carry out the other activities necessary for survival. Animals move in different ways, and each animal is adapted to its particular type of movement. But for all animals the basic principle of movement is the same. The animal pushes and exerts a force against something. Whatever is pushed against, pushes back with a force in the opposite direction, which makes the animal move.

(*Left*) The cheetah is the fastest land animal with a top speed of 27 m/s.

Table 5.1
The speed of different things

	Speed	
	metres per second (m/s)	*kilometres per hour (km/h)*
light	300 000 000	10 800 000 000
rocket escaping from Earth's gravitational field	11 000	39 600
air molecules at room temperature	500	1800
fastest land vehicle (Budweiser rocket car)	330	1190
fastest bird (spine-tailed swift)	47	169
fastest fish (sailfish)	30	110
fastest land animal (cheetah)	27	97
fastest human sprinter	13	47
tortoise	0.08	0.3
snail	0.014	0.05

(*Above*) What force gives this sprinter her flying start?

Flight

Birds and insects fly, and so do a few other animals such as bats and flying fish. All flying animals have wings of some sort. To move themselves along they use their wings to exert a force against the air.

Flight is very useful to animals: it is fast, and provides a good way of escaping from predators. Section 6.6 tells you more about flight.

Swimming

Most water animals swim. There are several different ways of swimming.

A fish swims by pushing against the water with its tail and the rear part of its body (figure 5.1). Fish have large muscles all along either side of their bodies to provide this push. The water pushes back on the fish's tail and body and this moves the fish forward.

- Watch a fish swimming and then identify its different parts using figure 5.2.
- How is the shape of the fish adapted to reduce water resistance?
- In what way do the different fins move?
- What part do the fins play in swimming?

Some very simple organisms swim by beating against the water with a whip-like 'tail' called a **flagellum**. A good example is *Euglena*, which is illustrated in figure 2.11.

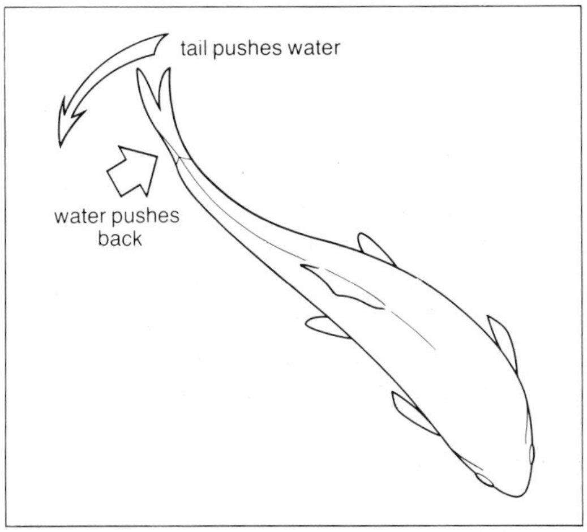

Figure 5.1 How a fish swims.

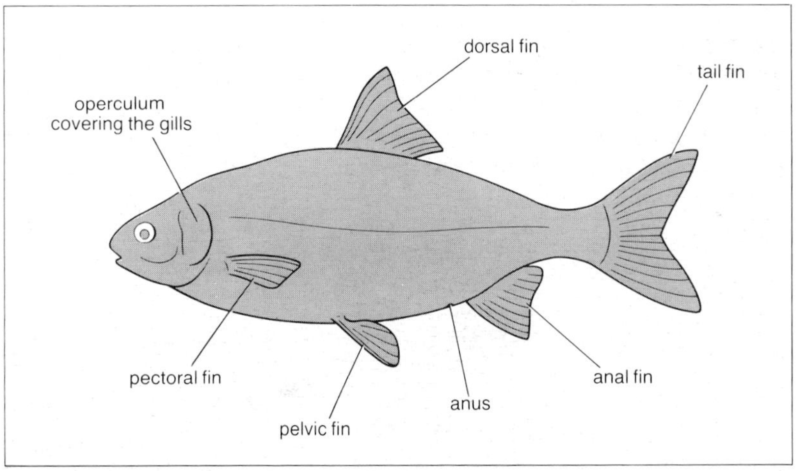

Figure 5.2 The structure of a typical fish.

A few animals move through water by jet propulsion. Squids normally swim forwards using their lateral fins. When they are in danger, though, they move rapidly backwards by shooting out a jet of water from a funnel at the front. This jet exerts a force on the surrounding water, and the water pushes back. This is very similar to jet propulsion in an aeroplane (figure 5.3).

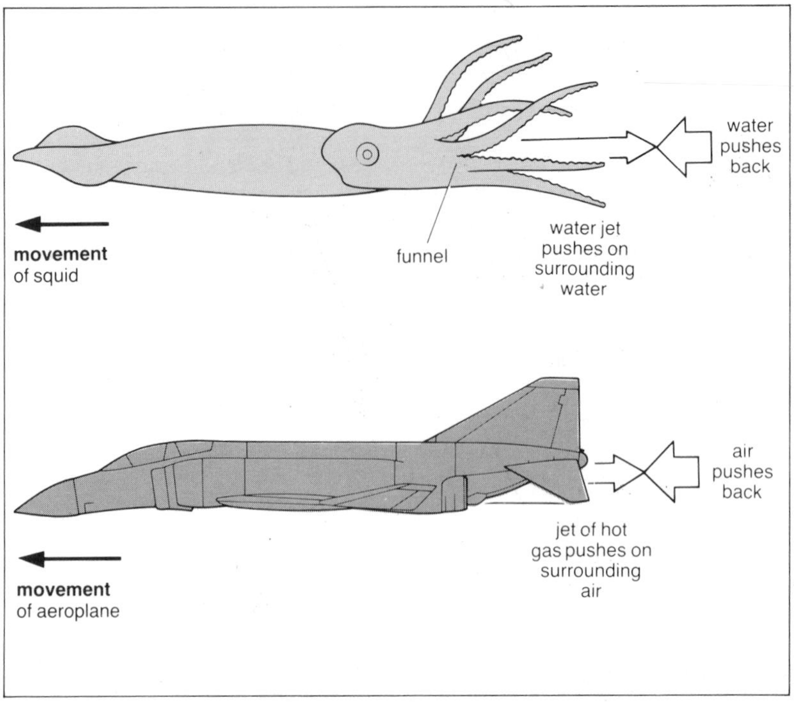

Figure 5.3 (Above) Jet propulsion of a squid and an aeroplane.

Movement on land

There are several different ways of moving across land, but they all rely on the same general principle. The animal pushes against the ground, usually with feet. Because of friction the ground pushes back, and this moves the animal forward.

- Give examples of animals that move in each of the following ways:
  a) crawling
  b) jumping
  c) running in bounds
  d) running on four legs

How are animals adapted for movement?

A bird needs wings to fly. A fish needs a tail and fins to swim. A horse needs legs to run. Each of these animals is specially designed or **adapted** to its particular type of movement.

- Look at the photograph of a seal. Unlike most mammals, it swims, instead of walking on land. How is the seal adapted for swimming?

(Above) How is the seal adapted for swimming?

Some animals are versatile and can move in more than one way. They are **adaptable** in their types of movement.

- How are (a) kangaroos, (b) bats, and (c) ducks adapted to their particular type of movement?
- How adaptable are (a) ostriches, (b) squirrels and (c) humans in the way they move?

Adaptation and adaptability are important in living organisms, and they apply to other things as well as movement. For example, animals are adapted to their habitat and to the way they feed (section 24.3).

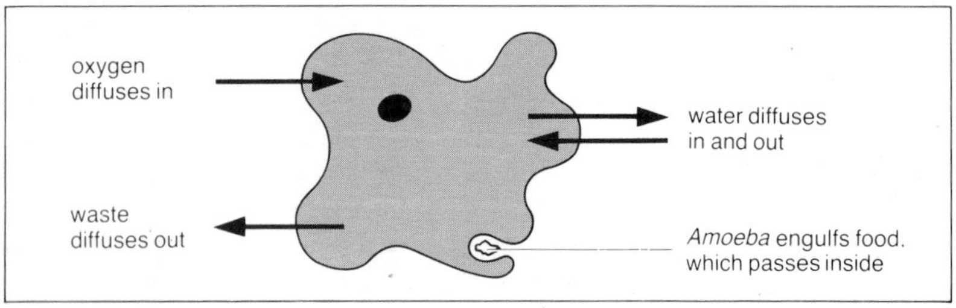

Figure 5.4 Transport in *Amoeba*.

5.2 Transport systems in animals

Many organisms can move about from place to place, but all organisms must be able to move substances around inside themselves. They need to get food from one place to another – from the leaf of a plant to its growing tip, for example. Organisms also need to move oxygen and water around and to remove waste products.

This movement of materials inside an organism is called **biological transport**. For very small organisms, such as the *Amoeba* in figure 5.4, this is not much of a problem.

The organism is so small that its surface area is very large compared with its volume. No part of the animal is far from its surface, so it is easy for materials to pass in and out, often by simple diffusion.

For larger organisms transport is not so easy. Most of the interior of the organism is too far from its surface for materials to move in and out in this simple way. A transport system or **mass–flow system** is needed to carry materials around the organism. In mammals, including humans, the most important mass–flow system is the circulation of blood.

Circulation of blood

Blood has many important jobs to do (see p. 51). Its major function is to act as a transport system, carrying oxygen and food to all parts of the body, and carrying away waste products. To do this it **circulates** around the body through a system of blood vessels.

The main parts of the human body through which the blood circulates are shown in figure 5.5.

- **The heart**, which pumps the blood around the system.
- **The lungs**, where the blood collects oxygen and gets rid of carbon dioxide.
- **The stomach and intestine**, where the blood collects digested food.
- **The liver**, which processes and stores some of this food.
- **The kidneys**, which remove waste products from the blood.
- **The rest of the body** (muscles, brain etc.), which the blood supplies with food and oxygen and which produce wastes that are carried away by the blood.

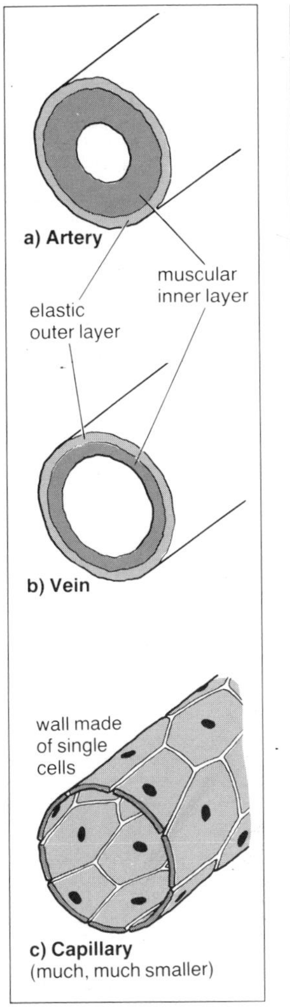

Figure 5.6 Blood vessels (not to scale).

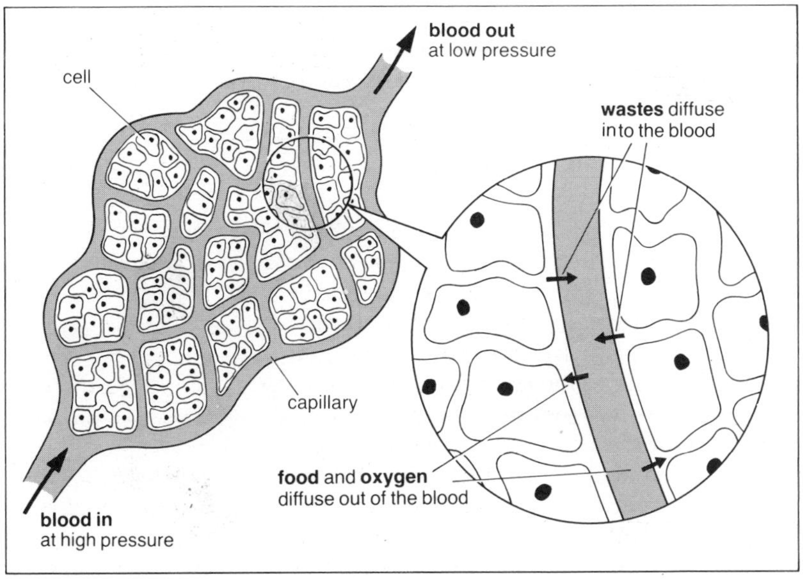

Figure 5.7 How capillaries supply the surrounding cells.

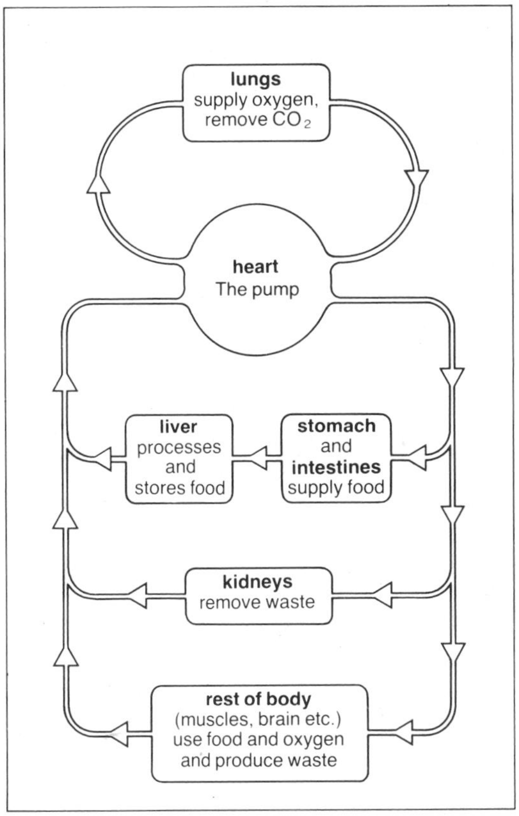

Figure 5.5 Circulation of blood round the human body.

You will see from figure 5.5 there are really two circuits, one to the lungs and one to the rest of the body.

Blood vessels

The heart is a 'blood pump'. When blood leaves the heart, it is under high pressure. The vessels carrying the blood away from the heart have to withstand this pressure, so they have thick, muscular walls. Vessels carrying blood away from the heart are called **arteries** (figure 5.6a). When an artery comes near the surface, it is sometimes possible to feel the surging pressure caused by the heart beating. This is called a **pulse**. You can feel a pulse in your wrist.

Arteries branch into smaller vessels called arterioles. These in turn branch into a huge network of tiny vessels spreading throughout the body. These are called **capillaries** (figure 5.6c). They are very small and are so numerous that no living cell is far from a capillary. Capillaries are permeable, so the watery part of the blood leaks out. The cells are bathed in this watery fluid, called **tissue fluid**. Food and oxygen diffuse from the blood to the cells via this tissue fluid. Waste products diffuse through it in the opposite direction (figure 5.7).

Blood flows through the capillaries back towards the heart. The capillaries join together into larger vessels called venules, and these join to form **veins** (figure 5.6b). Veins carry blood back to the heart. By now the pressure of the blood is lower, so veins have thinner, less muscular walls than arteries. To prevent the blood flowing the wrong way, veins contain one-way valves.

Eventually the veins all join together and return the blood to the heart, where it starts its journey again. Blood circulates surprisingly fast. On average a blood cell takes about 45 seconds to circulate around the body and get back to the heart.

- Blood in the arteries contains more oxygen and more food molecules than blood in veins. Why is this?
- Why is it more dangerous to cut an artery open than to cut a vein?
- Arteries are usually deep in the body, while veins are nearer the surface. Why might this be?
- Why is it important for capillaries to have very thin walls?
- Why do veins need one-way valves, while arteries do not?

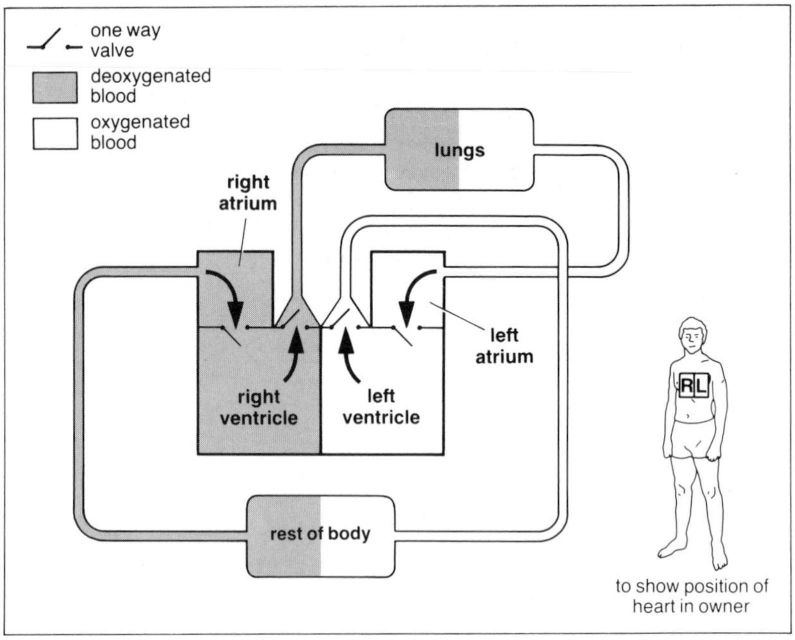

Figure 5.8 (Above) Simplified diagram of the heart, seen from the owner's front.

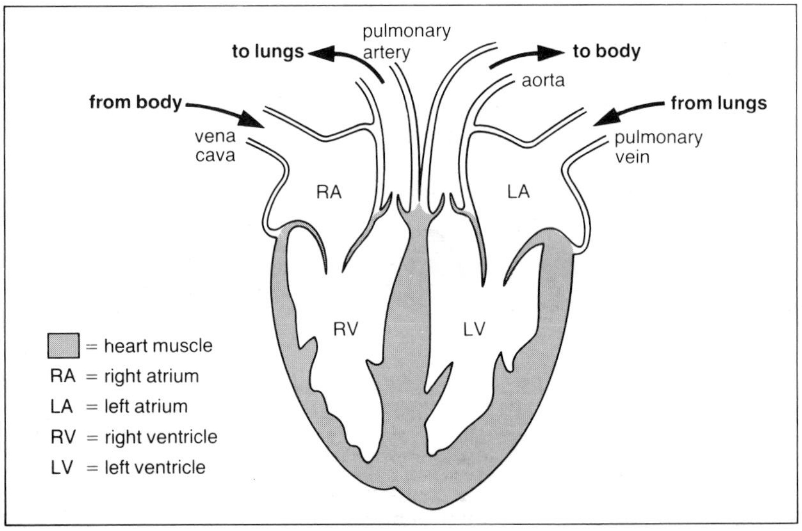

Figure 5.9 Structure of the heart.

Circulation diseases

The pumping of the heart causes pressure in the arterial blood. This is called **blood pressure**. If the blood pressure becomes low, blood will not flow properly around the body. If the blood pressure is too high, on the other hand, there is an extra strain on the heart, and a danger that the arteries may be stretched or even burst. If an artery bursts in the brain, brain cells are killed, and this may cause paralysis of part of the body, or even death. This is called a **stroke**.

In many older people the arteries become hardened because a layer of fat is laid down inside them. The artery may then get blocked by a blood clot, causing a **thrombosis**. If thrombosis happens in one of the blood vessels supplying the heart, the heart may not be able to work properly. This is a **heart attack**.

The heart

Put your hand in the middle of your chest and you will feel a rhythmic beating as your heart pumps blood around your body. The most important job of the blood is to carry oxygen from the lungs to all parts of the body. The heart is specially designed for this purpose, and also to prevent oxygenated (oxygen-containing) blood mixing with deoxygenated blood.

The heart is really two pumps arranged side by side (figure 5.8). The pump on the left of the owner of the heart sends oxygenated blood from the lungs to the rest of the body. The pump on the right sends deoxygenated blood from the body to the lungs, where it collects a fresh supply of oxygen before returning to the left pump.

Each pump has two chambers: a collecting chamber called an atrium and a pumping chamber called a ventricle. There is a one-way valve between each atrium and ventricle to stop blood being pumped back the wrong way. There is also a one-way valve between each ventricle and the vessel leading from it. Figure 5.9 shows the actual structure of the heart.

The ventricles have muscular walls, and when these contract, the pressure inside increases and blood is forced out (figure 5.10a). When the muscles relax, the ventricles expand, the pressure inside them falls, and blood flows in from the atria (figure 5.10b).

The heart beats about seventy times a minute. This happens continuously, day and night. To do this endless job the heart needs its own blood supply, which arrives via the **coronary artery**. Heart muscle is different from other muscular tissue. Unlike muscles in say, your arms and legs, heart muscle never gets tired.

- How does the design of the heart prevent oxygenated blood and deoxygenated blood mixing?
- The left ventricle is larger and more muscular than the right ventricle. Why do you think this is?
- What is a coronary thrombosis?
- Oxygenated blood is bright red, while deoxygenated blood is a darker colour. Yet when you cut a vein (which contains deoxygenated blood) the blood flowing out is bright red. Why do you think this is?
- Why does your heart beat faster when you take exercise?

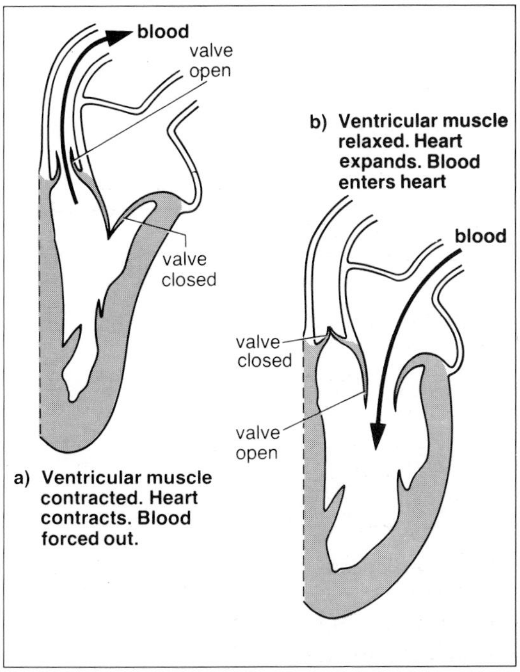

Figure 5.10 Pumping action of the heart (left side only shown).

Functions of the blood

The blood does many important jobs. Most of these come into the two categories transport and defence.

Transport

- Transport of oxygen from the lungs to the body tissues.
- Transport of carbon dioxide from the body tissues to the lungs.
- Transport of digested food from the digestive system to other parts of the body.
- Transport of water around the body.
- Transport of waste products from the body tissues to the kidneys, which get rid of the waste.
- Transport of hormones. Hormones are chemical messengers. They are released into the blood and carried to parts of the body where they cause organs to behave in a particular way (section 21.3).
- Transport of heat. Some parts of the body (for example the liver and active muscles) produce more heat then others. The blood distributes this heat around the body (section 17.6).

Defence

The blood plays a major role in defending the body against infection.

- Attacking bacteria (see below).
- Clotting. When you cut yourself, you may bleed for a while. Provided that the cut is fairly small, the bleeding soon stops. This is because your blood solidifies or **clots** when it meets air. Clotting is a complicated chemical reaction in the blood. Not only does clotting stop you losing blood from a wound, it also prevents bacteria getting in.

Composition of the blood

Blood is a liquid tissue. It contains living cells suspended in a liquid called **plasma**. Plasma contains important dissolved chemicals such as glucose, salts and hormones. There are several types cells in blood.

Red cells

Red cells (figure 5.11a) are by far the most common. One drop of blood contains millions of them. Their job is to carry oxygen from the lungs to the cells. They contain a red compound called **haemoglobin**. In the presence of oxygen (in the lungs), haemoglobin changes to unstable **oxyhaemoglobin**.

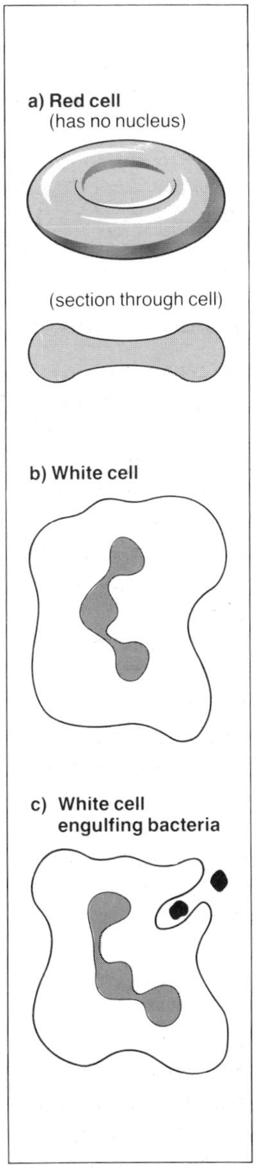

Figure 5.11 Blood cells.

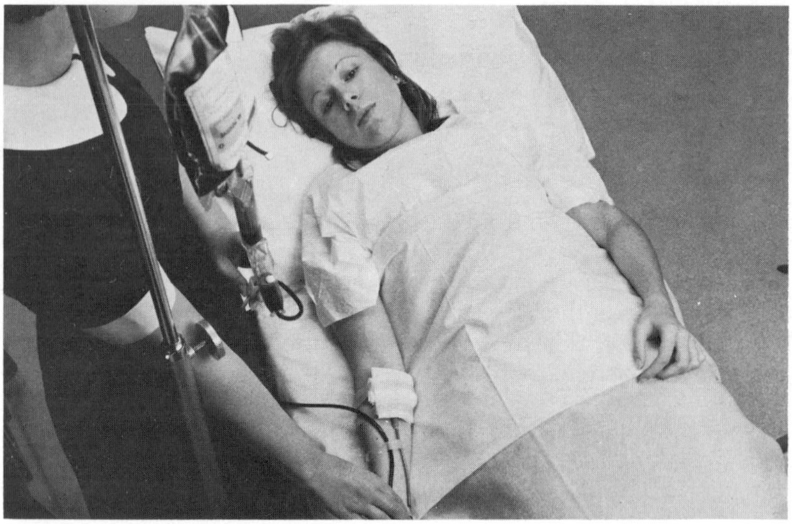

When a person has a blood transfusion to replace lost blood, the blood must be from someone with a compatible blood group.

Where oxygen is in short supply (in the body tissues), oxyhaemoglobin gives up oxygen and turns back to haemoglobin.

$$\text{haemoglobin} + \text{oxygen} \underset{\text{in body tissues}}{\overset{\text{in lungs}}{\rightleftharpoons}} \text{oxyhaemoglobin}$$

The concave disc shape of red cells gives them a high surface area so oxygen can pass in and out quickly.

If a person is short of haemoglobin, their blood cannot carry oxygen as well as it should. This condition is called **anaemia**. Haemoglobin contains iron, and anaemia is sometimes caused by too little iron in the diet. Anaemia is often treated by taking iron tablets.

Red blood cells only live for four months on average. New red blood cells are constantly being made in the red bone marrow, which is soft tissue in the hollow interior of certain bones.

White cells

There are several types of white blood cell. Figure 5.11b (p. 51) shows one kind. All white cells help defend the body against invading bacteria. Some white cells can engulf bacteria and digest them (figure 5.11c). Others produce chemicals called **antibodies** which attack and destroy harmful bacteria. White cells are very flexible and can squeeze between the cells making up the walls of blood capillaries. In this way they can move into the body tissues and hunt down invading bacteria.

There are about seven hundred red cells to every white blood cell.

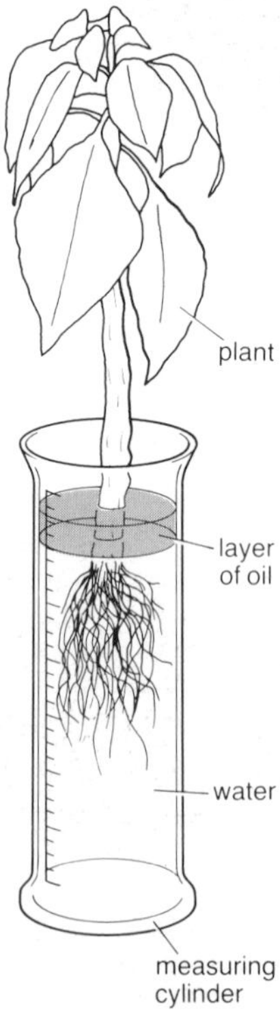

Figure 5.12 An experiment to investigate transpiration.

Blood transfusions

If someone loses a lot of blood, for example in a road accident, a **blood transfusion** is given to replace the lost blood. It is important to give the right kind of blood in a transfusion. The body will only accept certain types of blood, depending on its **blood group**. Before a blood transfusion is given, a doctor must know the patient's blood group and give blood from another person with a compatible (similar) blood group.

5.3 Transport systems in plants

Plants also need to transport materials to different parts of themselves. They must transport water, which enters their roots from the soil, to their leaves and other parts. Plants make food in their leaves, and this food (mostly sugars) has to be transported from the leaves to other parts of the plant. Although they can make their own food, plants need a supply of mineral salts, such as nitrates and potassium salts, which they obtain from the soil.

All but the simplest plants, therefore, need a transport system connecting together roots, stem and leaves. This is called the plant's **vascular system**. If you cut a plant stem and look closely at the cut end, you will see a liquid oozing out. This liquid, which is escaping from the cut vascular system, is called **sap**.

Transpiration

Figure 5.12 shows an experiment with a small plant. The level of water in the cylinder was read at the start of the experiment and on each of the next four days. Table 5.2 gives the results.

- Why did the level of the water in the cylinder fall?
- Could the water evaporate directly from the cylinder? Explain.
- Did all the water that left the cylinder end up in the plant? Explain.
- If your answer to the last question is 'no', where did the water go?

The movement of water through a plant, as demonstrated in this experiment, is called **transpiration**. Look at the diagram of the plant leaf in section 20.10. Notice that the leaves contain tiny holes called air pores or **stomata**. Water vapour, evaporating from

Table 5.2
Results of an experiment to investigate transpiration

Time	*Volume of water in cylinder/cm^3*
start	100
day 1	97
day 2	95
day 3	92
day 4	90

cells in the leaves, escapes from these stomata. To replace this water, more flows into the leaf from the stem through the vascular system. This in turn draws more water up the plant's stem from the roots (figure 5.13). This **transpiration stream** keeps water flowing continuously from roots to leaves. Only a very small proportion of this water stays in the plant. The majority goes in at the roots and evaporates away at the leaves.

- What kind of weather conditions would cause a rapid rate of transpiration?
- Why do plants wilt in hot, dry weather?

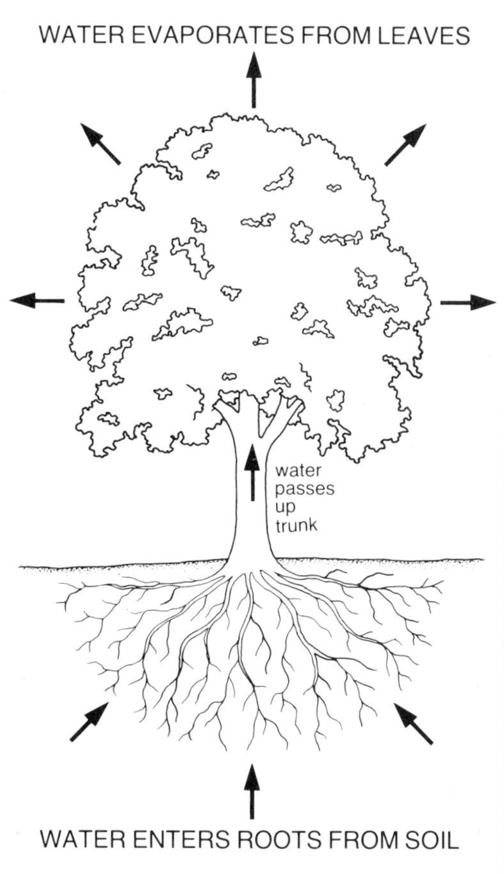

Figure 5.13 The transpiration stream in a plant.

Where in the plant is the vascular system?

The photograph below shows a section cut through a plant stem. This shows the **vascular bundles**, which are illustrated diagrammatically in figure 5.14.

The vascular bundles are bundles of tubes. They contain two types of tissue. The inner tissue is called **xylem** and is made up of long, hollow dead cells, joined together. This gives a system of tubes reaching from the roots to the leaves. Along these tubes flow water and dissolved salts, swept along by the transpiration stream. (The way in which water enters the roots in the first place is explained in section 3.3). *Xylem makes up the plant's water distribution system.*

The outer tissue is called **phloem**, and although it is part of the same vascular bundles as xylem, it does a very different job. Phloem consists of living cells, joined end to end. Food (including sugars dissolved in water) flows along the phloem tubes. The food is made in the leaves. It is then distributed to the roots, the growing tip, the flowers, the fruits and other parts of the plant via the phloem. *Phloem makes up the plant's food distribution system.*

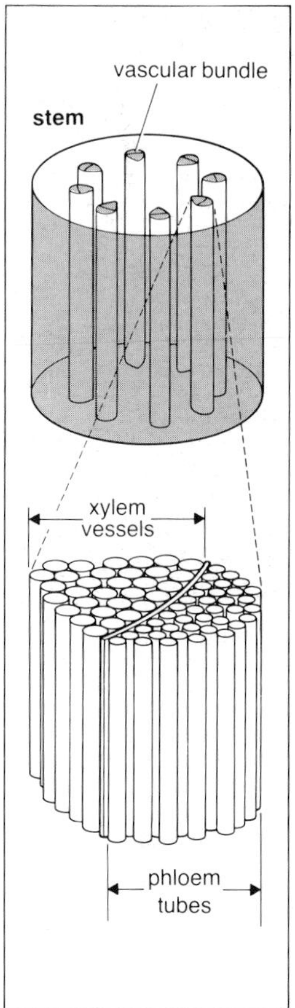

Figure 5.14 Vascular bundles in a plant stem.

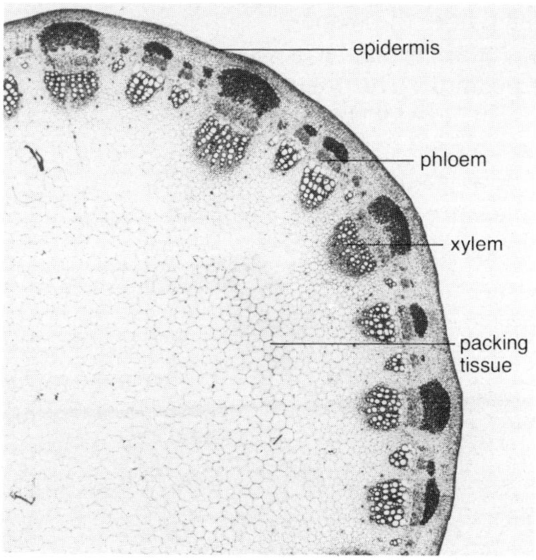

(*Left*) Transverse section of a sunflower stem.

- Xylem tubes in a plant's stem carry material in one direction only, upwards. The materials in the phloem tubes may be flowing up or down the stem. Explain this difference.
- When a ring of bark is removed from a tree, phloem vessels are removed, but not xylem. A tree 'ringed' in this way will slowly die. Why does the tree die, and why only slowly?

5.4 Speed and velocity

So far we have considered a number of examples of movement in living things. We can now investigate how to measure movement; both how *far* an object moves, and how *fast* it moves.

Distance and displacement

Suppose you put a woodlouse or some other small animal inside a covered glass dish (figure 5.15). The woodlouse will move around inside the dish, trying to find a way out. If you observed closely, you might be able to draw a chart of its movement over the course of, say, one minute. In that minute, the woodlouse would cover a fairly large distance, say, 37 cm. Because it has moved around in a haphazard way, the actual amount it has been *displaced*, from its starting point is fairly small, say, 3 cm.

The **distance** moved by an object is the total length of its path, whatever the direction. The *displacement* of a moving object is the distance it moves *in a particular direction*. In the woodlouse example, the *distance* travelled is 37 cm, but its overall *displacement* is only 3 cm from the centre of the dish to the finishing point. To tell where the woodlouse finishes we need to know its displacement from the starting position. The total distance moved is irrelevant, except to the woodlouse, who may end up tired.

As well as measuring how far the woodlouse goes, we can also measure how fast it moves, if we know how long it takes.

$$\text{speed} = \frac{\text{distance}}{\text{time}}$$

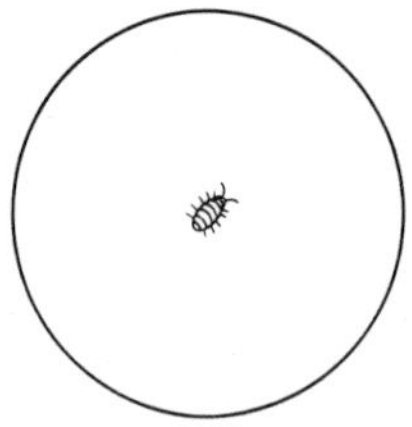

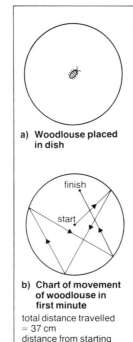

a) Woodlouse placed in dish

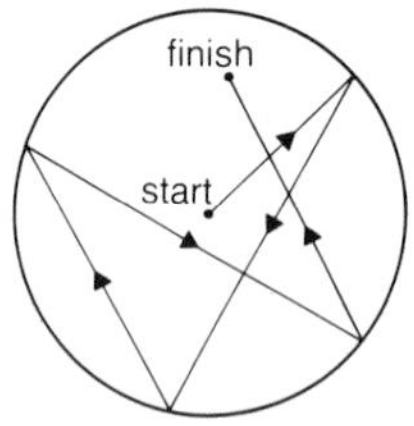

b) Chart of movement of woodlouse in first minute

total distance travelled = 37 cm
distance from starting point to finishing point = 3 cm

Figure 5.15 Investigating the movement of a woodlouse in a glass dish.

Obviously the woodlouse covered 37 cm in one minute, but its speed many have varied in this time, so we can only say that its *average* speed was 37 cm per minute.

Suppose we now release the woodlouse from its dish and put it on the ground. If it set off in a straight line, could you, without watching it, tell where it would be two minutes later? Assuming it travelled at the same average speed, 37 cm/min, you would know it would be 74 cm away after two minutes. But which direction? Unless you knew its direction, you would have to search all round a circle of radius 74 cm (figure 5.16). If it had set off due north at 37 cm/min you could locate it precisely. The speed of an object *in a particular direction* is called its **velocity**. In this example, the *speed* of the woodlouse is 37 cm/min; its *velocity* is 37 cm/min due north.

$$\text{velocity} = \frac{\text{displacement}}{\text{time}}$$

$$\text{speed} = \frac{\text{distance}}{\text{time}}$$

The units of speed and velocity are the same, distance per unit time. Thus speed is measured in centimetres per minute, or metres per second, or even miles per hour. Whenever a *velocity* is quoted, its direction must always be stated as well as its size.

Vectors and scalars

Quantities like displacement and velocity, that have both size and direction, are called **vector** quantities. Quantities like distance and speed, that have only size, are called **scalar** quantities.

Another example of a vector quantity is a force. A force must always act in a particular direction. Look at the photograph. If the woman wants to raise the glass to drink, she must exert a force on it. However, she must exert a force on the glass in the right direction, i.e. towards her mouth.

The glass contains a certain volume of beer – a pint. Volume is a scalar quantity: it has size, but no direction. It would be meaningless to talk about 'a pint of beer in a vertical direction', but sensible to talk about a force in a vertical direction.

(*Left*) When you raise a glass to drink, you must exert a force on it in a vertical direction.

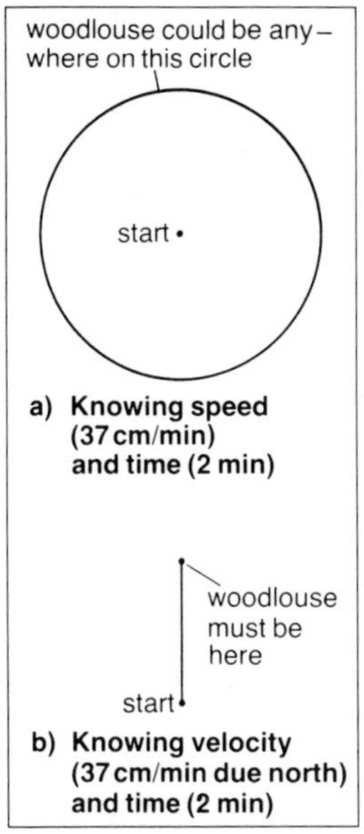

Figure 5.16 Find the woodlouse.

Distance–time graphs

A woman drives from Bristol to her home in Little Wittering (figure 5.17). The first part of her journey is along a dual carriageway, and here she travels at a steady, constant speed. She turns off the dual carriageway along a lane to her home, and along this lane her speed varies. If we measure the distance of the woman's car from a fixed point, say the village of Much Wittering, and we time her from that point, we can draw a distance–time graph of her journey (figure 5.18).

Notice that the first part of her journey, at steady speed along the dual carriageway, gives a straight line, with a constant gradient. Between the roundabout and home, the speed varied and the gradient of the graph varies. The gradient of the graph is a measure of distance divided by time, so

The gradient of a distance–time graph gives the speed.

If the speed is constant, the gradient will be constant; the graph is a straight line. If the speed varies, the gradient will vary.

Look at figure 5.18.

- Why does the graph level off at the point corresponding to the roundabout?
- What colour were the traffic lights?
- Were the level crossing gates closed?
- What was the car's speed along the dual carriageway?

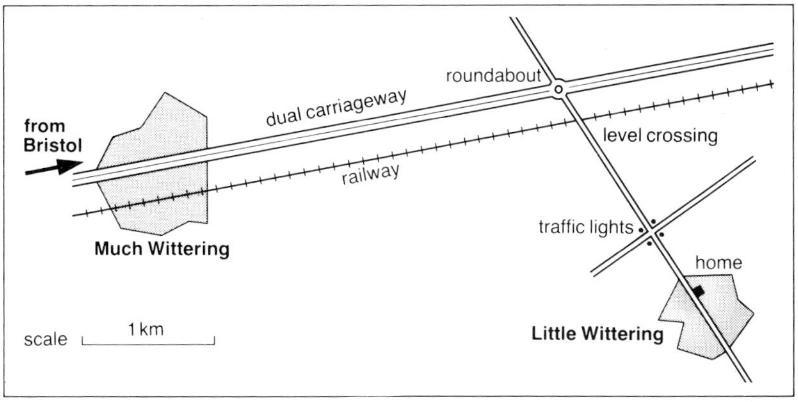

Figure 5.17 A journey from Bristol to Little Wittering.

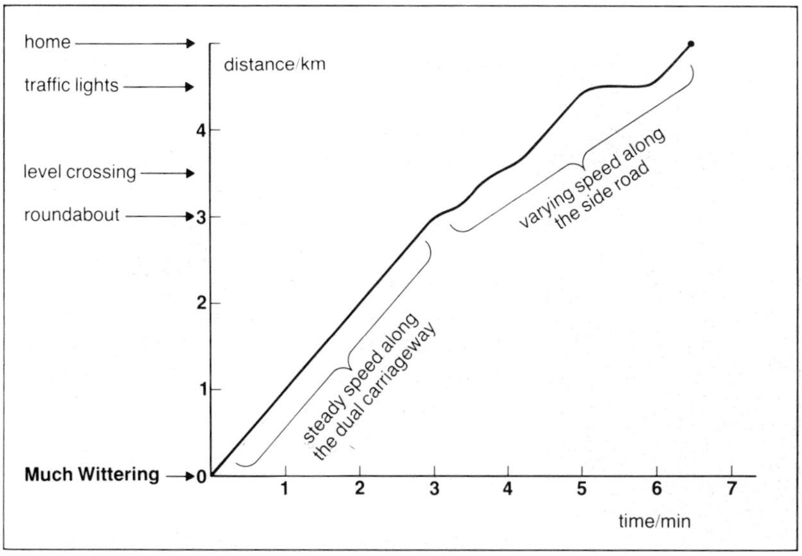

Figure 5.18 Distance–time graph for the journey.

Average speed

The first part of the graph in figure 5.18 shows a constant speed of 1 km/min, or 60 km/h. The second part shows a variable speed. If we wanted to know the speed at any point, we would have to find the gradient at that point of the graph. The best way to do this would be to draw a tangent at that point and find its gradient.

- From figure 5.18, estimate the speed of the car as it crossed the level crossing.

Of course, if you were travelling in the car itself, you could judge its speed at any point by looking at the speedometer. The speedometer works by measuring the rotation of the wheels at any instant. If the speedometer were broken, the best way of estimating your speed would be to measure how long it took to travel a certain distance. For example, telegraph posts are about 60 m apart, so you could time how long the car took to travel between telegraph posts. Suppose this time was three seconds.

$$\text{speed} = \frac{\text{distance}}{\text{time}}$$

$$= \frac{60}{3}\ \text{m/s} = 20\ \text{m/s} = 72\ \text{km/h}$$

This is only an average speed. Between the two posts the speed might have varied a bit. The closer the posts are together, the nearer the average speed will be to the actual speed at any instant. Average speed then, is found by dividing total distance by the time taken to move through that distance.

- Look at figure 5.18. Estimate the average speed of the car between the roundabout and home.

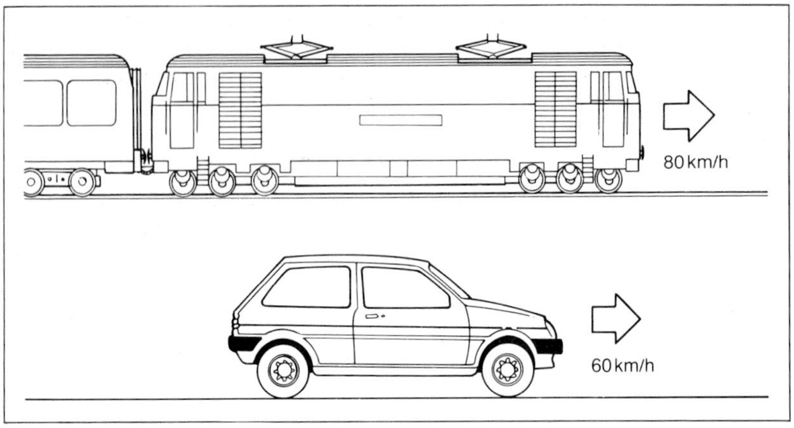

Figure 5.19 Relative speeds.

Relative speed

You will see from the map in figure 5.17 that a railway runs alongside the dual carriageway. Suppose a train is travelling in the same direction as the car, but at 80 km/h, while the car travels at 60 km/h (figure 5.19). If a passenger in the car watches the train, it will seem to move past the car at 20 km/h. *Relative to the car,* the train is moving at 20 km/h. *Relative to the ground* it is moving at 80 km/h. The *relative speed* of a moving body is its speed relative to something else, which may or may not be moving. In reality, everything moves, even the ground, which is moving relative to the Sun.

If the car and the train had been travelling in opposite directions, their speed relative to each other would be 60 km/h + 80 km/h = 140 km/h.

5.5 Changing speed – acceleration

When a moving object increases its speed we say it *accelerates*. Acceleration is the rate of change of speed:

$$\text{acceleration} = \frac{\text{change in speed}}{\text{time taken}}$$

When you see an advertisement for a motor car, you often see the car's acceleration figures quoted: '0–60 m.p.h. in 10 seconds', for example. This shows the rate of change of speed of the car at its peak performance.

Let us consider this example further. 60 miles per hour is about 100 kilometres per hour, or 30 m/s. So '0–60 m.p.h. in 10 seconds' means the car's speed increases from 0 to 30 m/s in 10 s:

$$\text{acceleration} = \frac{\text{change in speed}}{\text{time taken}}$$
$$= \frac{30-0}{10} = 3\ \frac{\text{m/s}}{\text{s}}$$

The acceleration of the car is therefore 3 metres per second every second. This is usually written 3 m/s^2. This means that the car increases its speed by 3 metres per second in every second.

- Is the acceleration of the car likely to be constant (steady)? (Remember the driver will have to change gear.)

Car advertisements often give acceleration figures.

Our new fuel injected
2·0 litre engine is so powerful that
we built a new model for it.
0–60 mph in 9·4 seconds
The new Sierra 2·0iS.
Ford

Suppose the driver applied the brakes as soon as the car reached 30 m/s, and the car stopped in 3 seconds. Once again the speed has changed. This time the speed decreases from 30 m/s to 0 m/s in 3 s, so

$$\text{acceleration} = \frac{\text{change in speed}}{\text{time taken}} = \frac{0-30}{3} = -10\,\text{m/s}^2$$

Figure 5.20 Speed–time graph for the journey.

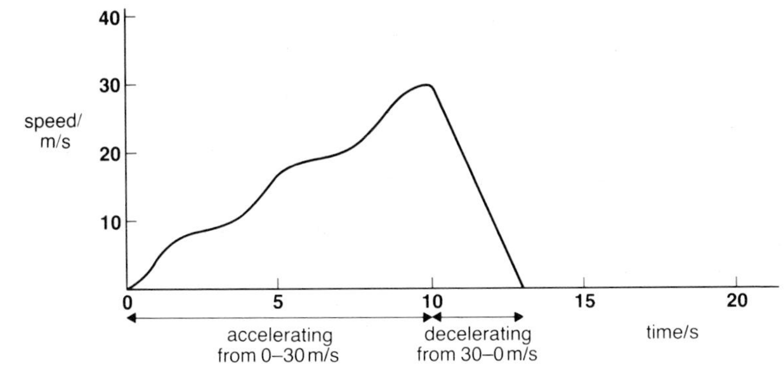

The negative sign shows that the speed has decreased. Usually, a negative acceleration is called **deceleration** or **retardation**.

Speed–time graphs

Figure 5.18 was a distance–time graph, showing rate of change of distance. We can also plot a speed–time graph, showing the rate of change of speed. Figure 5.20 is a speed–time graph for the motor car just described. Notice that in the first part, the graph is irregular, indicating that the acceleration varied. This is because the driver cannot accelerate while changing gear. Therefore the acceleration of 3 m/s^2 worked out earlier was an average value. In the second part, the graph is straight, indicating a constant deceleration.

- After how many seconds did the driver change out of first gear?
- If the driver had continued to accelerate past 30 m/s, instead of braking, what would the graph have looked like, assuming the car has four gears?

Summary

1 A force is needed to get a thing moving. Animals move by pushing against air, land or water, which push back and make the animal move.

2 Biological transport systems (mass–flow systems) are used to carry materials from one part of an organism to another part.

3 Blood is an important transport system in many animals. It also plays an important role in the defence of the body.

4 Blood circulates around the body in a system of blood vessels. Arteries carry blood away from the heart. Veins carry blood back to the heart. A system of tiny capillaries carries blood to all parts of the tissues.

5 The heart is a pump. The left side pumps blood to the body. The right side pumps blood to the lungs.

6 Red blood cells carry oxygen. White blood cells are important in the body's defence system.

7 Many plants have a vascular system to transport materials.

8 Xylem vessels make up the plant's water distribution system.

9 Phloem vessels make up the plant's food distribution system.

10 The movement of water through a plant from roots to leaves is called transpiration.

11 Speed = distance/time.

12 Average speed is found by dividing total distance moved by the time taken to cover that distance.

13 The speed of an object in a particular direction is called its velocity.

14 Quantities that have both size and direction are called vector quantities. Quantities that have only size are called scalar quantities. Speed is a scalar quantity; velocity is a vector quantity.

15 Acceleration is the rate of change of speed of an object.

Study questions

1 a) How is a fish's body adapted for swimming?
b) A fish swims steadily up a river against the current. The current is flowing at 0.5 m/s. Relative to the water, the fish's speed is 1.5 m/s. What is its speed relative to the river bed?
c) Use your answer to part (b) to calculate how far up the river the fish would move in one minute.

2 a) Why do very small organisms like *Amoeba* and *Euglena* not need a transport system, while larger ones like mammals and trees do?
b) The most important transport system in humans is the circulation of the blood. What jobs does blood do?
c) Blood contains red and white cells. How does each cell help blood do the jobs described in part (b)?

3 a) A small number of babies are born with a condition known as 'hole in the heart'. These children have a hole connecting the left and right sides of their hearts. Why is this a dangerous condition?
b) What is anaemia? People suffering from anaemia tend to feel unusually tired. Why is this?
c) When someone has a badly cut hand, one way of giving first aid is to tie a tight bandage, called a tourniquet, around the arm. Why is this done?

4 a) What is xylem?
b) What is phloem?
c) If you cut a flower or leaf off a plant, it soon wilts, unless put in water. Why does it wilt, and why does putting it in water stop wilting?
d) Why do cactus plants have a waxy coating on their leaves?

5 a) What is the difference in function between veins and arteries?
b) What differences are there in structure between veins and arteries?
c) In general, the blood in veins is less oxygenated than the blood in arteries. However, there is an exception to this rule. Which vein carries highly oxygenated blood?
d) When you are given an injection by the doctor the needle is put into a vein, not an artery. Give two reasons for this.

6 a) What is the difference between a vector quantity and a scalar quantity?
b) What is the difference between speed and velocity?
c) A cyclist is riding round a circular track. One circuit of the track is 300 m long, and the cyclist takes 6 minutes to make 10 circuits.
i) What is the cyclist's average speed?
ii) Why can we only call this speed an average?
iii) Why must we talk about speed, not velocity in this example?

7 A car accelerates from standstill along a road. After 10 seconds the car is travelling at 90 km/h.
a) What is the car's average acceleration?
b) If the car kept up the same acceleration for a further 2 seconds, what would its speed now be?
c) If the driver applied the brakes when the car was travelling at 90 km/h, and the car stopped in 3 seconds, what is the car's average deceleration?

8 A cyclist rides along a straight road through points A, B, C and D. The distance–time graph in figure 5.21 shows the cyclist's progress.
a) For what part of the journey was the cyclist travelling at constant speed?
b) What was the cyclist's speed between A and B?
c) What was the cyclist's average speed for the journey from the starting point to D?
d) What did the cyclist do after D?

Figure 5.21 Distance–time graph for a cyclist.

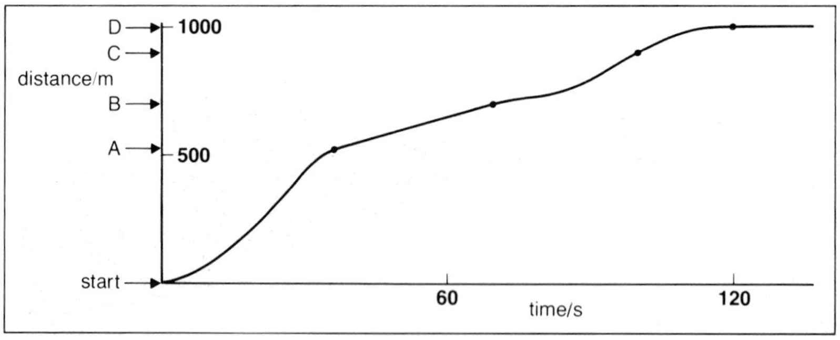

9 a) Land animals and land vehicles move in very different ways. Most land animals have legs, and most land vehicles have wheels. Why do few vehicles have legs, and why do no animals have wheels?
b) Give an example of an animal which moves by a similar method to a vehicle.

6 Forces and friction

Forces can stretch things and make things move. Gravitational forces hold our feet on the ground and frictional forces enable us to stop and start and move around easily.

6.1 What is a force?

How would you exert a force on something? You could push it, pull it, squeeze it, twist it, punch it or tap it. There must be thousands of different ways in which we have all felt and exerted forces. Every sport depends on the ability to apply precise forces to objects. This might mean lobbing a tennis ball, kicking a football or hitting a hockey ball.

What do forces do?

Try the following experiments with a rubber band or a thin strip of polythene.

- What is the effect of exerting a force on the material?
- What happens when the force is removed?
- Do all materials require the same force to make them change shape by the same amount?
- What happens to a rubber band when the stretching force is removed?
- Why is a rubber band described as 'elastic'?
- Is polythene elastic?

These experiments show that *forces can change the shape of objects*. When the force is removed, some materials remain deformed but elastic materials return to their original shape. The next experiment shows another way in which forces can act.

(*Left*) An Apollo rocket exerts a force of about 30 million newtons as it leaves the launch pad.

A weight lifter exerts a pull, and then a push in raising weights above his head.

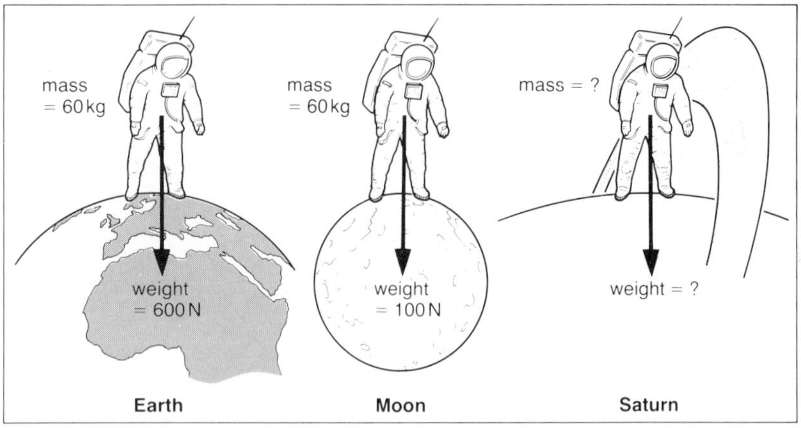

Figure 6.1 The mass and weight of an astranaut on the Earth, the Moon and Saturn. (Saturn is much bigger than the Earth and its gravitational pull is about four times greater than that on the Earth.) What are the astronaut's mass and weight on Saturn?

- Place a marble on a flat surface. Apply a small force to it. What happens?
- Repeat the experiment, but this time, whilst the marble is still moving, apply a force at right angles to its direction of motion. What happens?
- Try the experiment again with a smaller force and then with a force in the opposite direction to the marble's motion.

This simple experiment shows that *forces can cause stationary objects to move, and can change the motion of moving objects.*

6.2 Force, weight and mass

The effect of a force will depend on whether it is large or small. Therefore we must be able to measure the size of a force. So, what units do we use to measure forces? Forces are measured in **newtons** (see section 6.7). This name was chosen in honour of Isaac Newton, one of the first scientists to investigate the effects of forces.

It takes a force of about one newton (1 N) to lift an average-sized apple (mass 100 g) and a force of about 10 N to lift a one kilogram bag of sugar. These forces are minute in comparison with some of the forces exerted by machines. For example, the force (thrust) exerted by a Saturn V rocket as it leaves the launch pad is about thirty million newtons (3×10^7 N).

We all constantly experience one force. This is the **force of gravity**, which is caused by the pull of the Earth on our bodies. Scientists have shown that all lumps of matter attract each other, rather as magnets attract each other. The gravitational forces between everyday objects, like people and cars and houses, are too small to notice, but the force is very strong if one of the objects is as massive as the Earth. In fact, it is the gravitational force between the Sun and the Earth that holds the Earth in orbit around the Sun. The gravitational force between the Earth and the Moon holds the Moon in orbit and also causes the tides (section 1.3). The most important gravitational force as far as each one of us is concerned is that between the Earth and ourselves. This is called **weight**. The gravitational force between the Earth and an object is its weight. This is different from the mass of an object, which tells us how much matter there is in it. Mass is measured in kilograms (kg), but weight is measured in newtons (N).

On the Earth, a mass of 1 kg has a weight of about 10 N, because this is the force which the Earth's gravitation exerts on a 1 kg mass (see section 6.8). A mass of 2 kg weighs 20 N, and so on.

Weights are often stated, incorrectly, in the units of mass (kg, pounds, etc.), even though they are forces. In addition, many British shopkeepers, cooks and engineers continue to measure masses in pounds (lb) and ounces (oz). Bathroom scales often show masses in pounds and stones. However, the internationally agreed unit of mass is the **kilogram**.

1 kg = 1000 grams
1 tonne = 1000 kg
1 kg = 2.2 pounds (lb)

> *A can of baked beans has a mass of about 0.5 kg.*
> - What is its weight in newtons?
> - What is its mass in grams?
> - What would its mass be on the Moon?
> - What would its weight be on the Moon? (Hint: gravity on the Moon is only about one-sixth of that on the Earth.)

The Earth's mass is enormous, so it exerts a large pull on anything near its surface. If you could travel to the Moon, your mass in kilograms would stay the same because you still contain the same amount of matter (figure 6.1). The mass of the Moon is much less than the Earth's and its gravitational attraction is only one-sixth of the Earth's. This means that your weight on the Moon would be one-sixth of what it is on Earth.

6.3 Stretching springs

We can investigate the Earth's gravitational pull by hanging weights from a spring and measuring its extension (figure 6.2). The Earth pulls on the weights and this causes the spring to extend. Some results are shown in table 6.1.

> - Plot a graph of the stretching force (y-axis) against extension (x-axis) using the results in table 6.1.
> - Draw the 'line of best fit' through the various points.
> - Write down a rule to describe how the spring extends when you apply a force to it.

Table 6.1

Weight added, i.e. stretching force on spring/N	*Length of spring/cm*	*Extension of spring/cm*
0.0	34.5	0
0.4	37.0	2.5
0.8	39.7	5.2
1.2	42.2	7.7
1.6	45.0	10.5
2.0	47.5	13.0

The results in table 6.1 show that *the extension of the spring is proportional to the stretching force*. This is usually known as **Hooke's law** after the scientist Robert Hooke, who investigated springs about three hundred years ago. Hooke used his results from stretching springs to design a balance spring for watches.

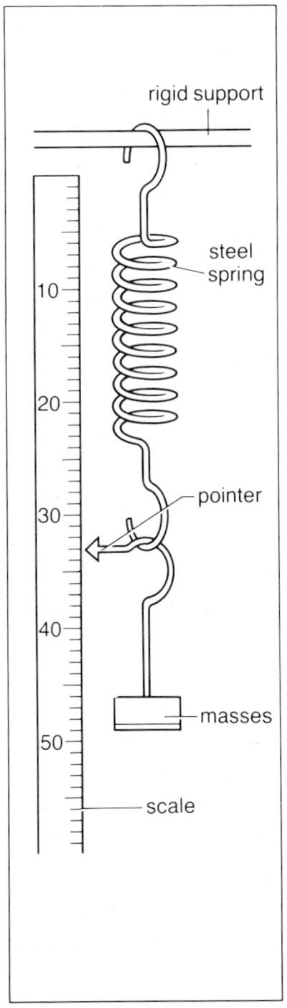

Figure 6.2 Investigating the extension of a spring.

This supermarket has provided a spring balance so that customers can check the weight of their groceries.

Using the proportional sign ($\propto$) we can write Hooke's law as

$$\text{Extension} \propto \text{stretching force.}$$

This means that if the force is doubled, the extension is doubled. If the force is trebled, the extension is trebled, and so on.

Using a spring and a graph of force against extension like the one you have just drawn, it is possible to weigh various objects.

> - Use your graph, or the results in table 6.1, to estimate the weight in newtons of an apple which extends the spring by 9.1 cm.
> - What is the mass of this apple in (a) kilograms and (b) grams? (Assume that 1 kg weighs 10 N.)
> - How does a spring balance work?

Bathroom scales and some kitchen scales are examples of spring balances. They have a spring which is either extended or compressed when an object is placed on them. In kitchen scales, a pointer is attached to the spring and this moves over a scale which indicates the weight (or the mass) of the article. In bathroom scales, the scale is attached to the spring and this moves below a fixed marker.

6.4 Force against force

Action and reaction

Objects do not always move, even though they have large forces acting on them. Why is this? Why, for example, do you not fall through the floor? The answer is that the floor exerts a force on you (a **reaction**) to balance your force (**action**) on it. This is often summarised briefly by saying

Action = reaction for stationary objects.

(*Above*) The wheel was one of the earliest inventions to overcome friction. This toy comes from Mesopotamia, and dates from about 2000 BC.

Friction

If you have tried to push a heavy sideboard along a flat floor, you will know how difficult it is to move it, however hard you push. The sideboard is prevented from moving because of **friction**, *the force which prevents one surface moving over another* (figure 6.3). For the sideboard there is friction between the base and the floor.

What causes friction?

If two touching surfaces are not absolutely smooth, the bumps on one surface will tend to settle into the hollows in the other. When we try to slide one object over the other, we have to raise it slightly so that its bumps move over the bumps of the adjacent surface.

Another source of friction occurs where the molecules of one surface get very close to molecules in the other surface. The forces of attraction between these molecules must be overcome in order to slide or roll one surface over the other.

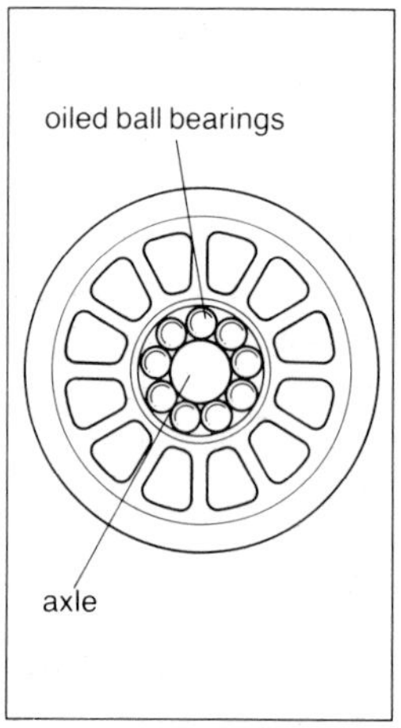

Figure 6.4 Reducing friction with oiled ball bearings.

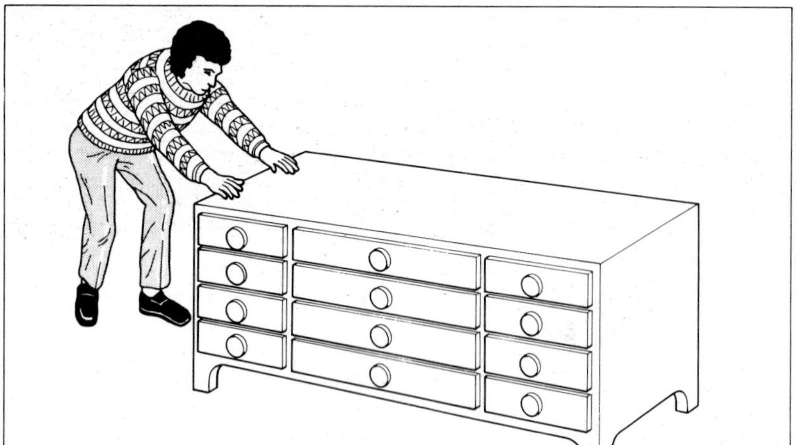

Figure 6.3 Would you rather push a sideboard over a deep-piled carpet, or over a polished floor?

- Think of three ways to reduce friction.
- Is it possible to eliminate friction completely when one surface moves over another?

6.5 Overcoming friction

Friction is bad because it resists movement, it wears things out and makes them hot. However, we cannot do without friction as you will see in section 6.6.

One of the earliest inventions to overcome friction was the wheel. This opened up new opportunities for travel and transport to early civilisations. Long before the wheel was invented, men and women used simple boats such as coracles and kyaks for long-distance transport. Water transport was so much smoother than transport on land because friction between a boat and water was much less than that between a dragged object and the ground. Eventually, however, the wheel was invented and this made transport on land much easier.

Bearings

Friction between a wheel and its axle can be reduced by oiling the surfaces in contact. Better still, the wheel can be mounted on the axle with ball bearings (figure 6.4). The ball bearings themselves roll, like little wheels – wheels within wheels!

Lubrication

Lubrication is essential when parts of machinery in contact are moving rapidly. In a car engine, for example, the bearing surfaces are lubricated continuously with oil,

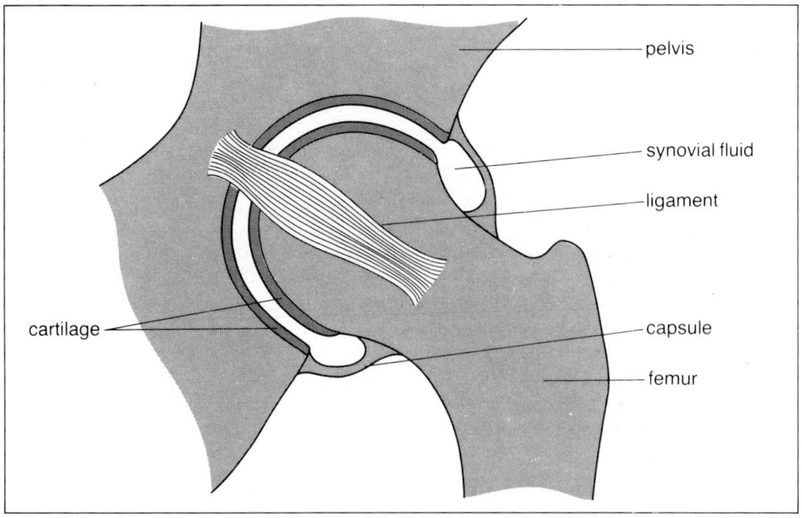

Figure 6.5 The hip joint illustrates how friction can be reduced at joints.

which is under pressure. If the oil supply fails, friction between the moving parts makes them so hot that they expand and 'seize up'. Lubricants like oil work by separating the two surfaces by a thin liquid layer.

In order to reduce friction still further, engineers have developed air-lubricated bearings. These are particularly useful in machine tools, such as metal cutters and grinders. Air is forced between the surfaces at high pressure. This keeps the surfaces apart; the air forms an elastic friction-free cushion between the bearings. Air lubrication is, of course, used in hover mowers, hovercrafts and aerotrains which travel over the land or over water on a cushion of air.

Our bodies, like machines, also have moving parts and it is important to reduce friction where bones slide over one another at **joints** (figure 6.5). To make them slide easily, the surfaces in contact are covered with a smooth, layer of elastic tissue called **cartilage** (gristle). The joint is enclosed within a tough **capsule containing synovial fluid** which acts as a lubricant. Experiments have shown that synovial fluid is about ten times more slippery that the best man-made lubricants. To stop the bones slipping apart, they are held together by tough elastic strands known as **ligaments**. These run from one bone to the other across the joint. Notice that both the ligaments and cartilage are elastic. This helps our joints to move smoothly.

Engineers must increase streamlining so that cars can run on less fuel. At General Motors, computer graphics simulate the airflow round a new design.

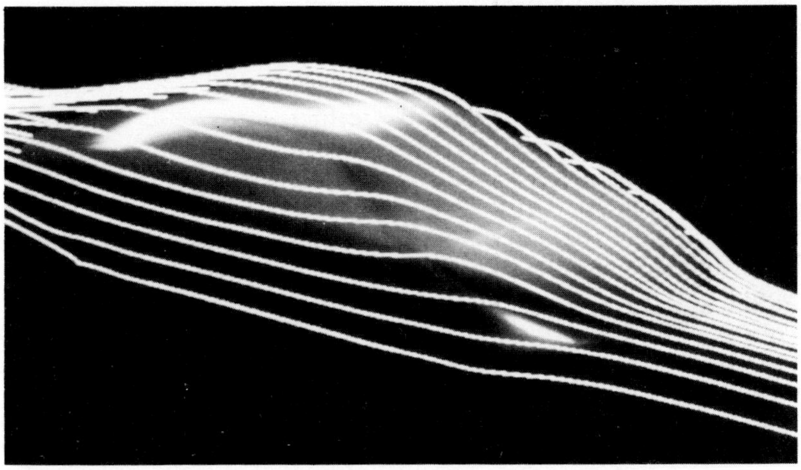

Streamlining

Fluids like air and water provide much less friction than solid surfaces, but air and water resistance can be very significant. The frictional force which fluids exert in resisting the forward movement of an object through them is known as **drag**. For example, the drag from air flowing past a fast moving car may be as much as 2000 N. Because of this, designers try to increase the **streamlining** of cars, trains, rockets and aeroplanes. By reducing drag and friction, vehicles can achieve the same speed using less fuel.

Streamlining in animals

Streamlining is very noticeable in animals. Over millions of years, different species have evolved and become better fitted to their environment and the way in which they live. Dolphins and seals evolved as sleek, streamlined animals capable of moving through water at high speed.

The dolphin evolved as a sleek streamlined animal capable of moving through water at high speed.

- Try to identify different activities of birds during flight, such as gliding, flapping and stalling. (You can use the photograph on p. 64.)
- How is the shape of the bird's head and body adapted to overcome drag?

Try to identify different activities of these gannets during flight, such as gliding, flapping and stalling.

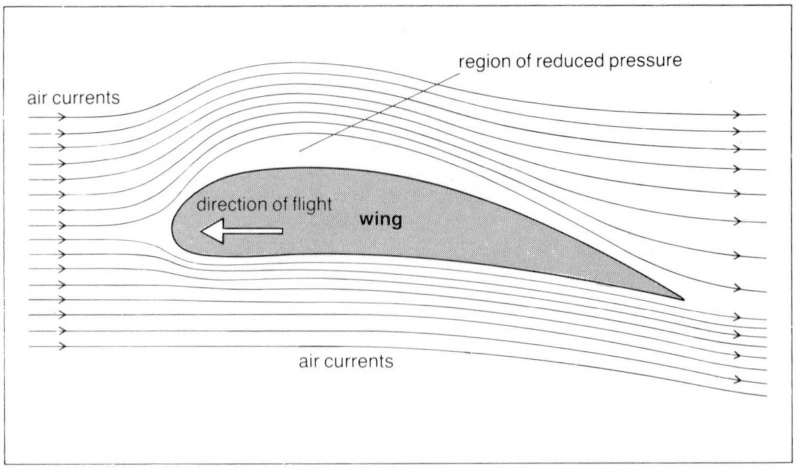

Figure 6.6 Air currents streaming past a bird's wing.

Using drag

Figure 6.6 shows the air currents streaming past a bird's wing during flight. As the air rushes over the top and bottom of the wing, it produces drag which hinders forward movement. The wing, however, is shaped so that the air is deflected away from the upper surface causing a reduction in pressure close to the top of the wing. The pressure on the underside of the wing is, therefore, greater than that on the top and the resultant **lift** keeps the bird in the air.

Figure 6.7 shows the forces acting on a bird's wing during flight. Gravity pulls the bird towards the ground, but lift acts upwards allowing the bird to stay in the air.

So far we have thought of the bird's wing is if it were stiff, like the wings of an aeroplane. Lift keeps the bird in the air, but how does the bird move forward? It pushes backwards against the air with its wings. Movement of the bird is, of course, hindered by drag, which is overcome as the bird pushes itself forward against the air by flapping its wings. In order to propel themselves in this way, birds have developed very large breast muscles which can make up half of the total mass of the bird in some species.

- Why does a bird need to flap its wings a great deal at the start of its flight?
- How are aeroplanes designed to overcome wind resistance (drag)?
- What provides aeroplanes with the force to overcome drag?

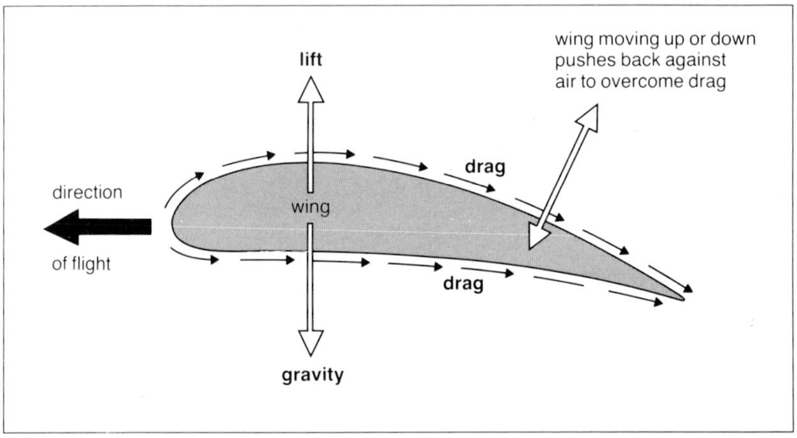

Figure 6.7 Forces acting on a bird's wing during flight.

6.6 Using friction

Although friction can be a nuisance, it is sometimes essential. Anyone who has tried to walk over smooth ice knows that movement is uncertain when friction is reduced. Friction between the soles of our shoes and the ground enables us to stop and start and move around easily and comfortably (figure 6.8).

Vehicles also rely on friction for their movement. Car tyres are designed to give as much friction as possible in all weather conditions. Vehicles are normally slowed down by making a tough brake lining press against a moving part of the wheel. If there were no friction, brakes simply would not work; once an object had started to move, it would be very difficult to stop it. In the absence of friction, nails would come loose, and everything, even furniture, would have to be fixed in position using glue or solder. Without friction, pencils would be unable to leave marks on the paper.

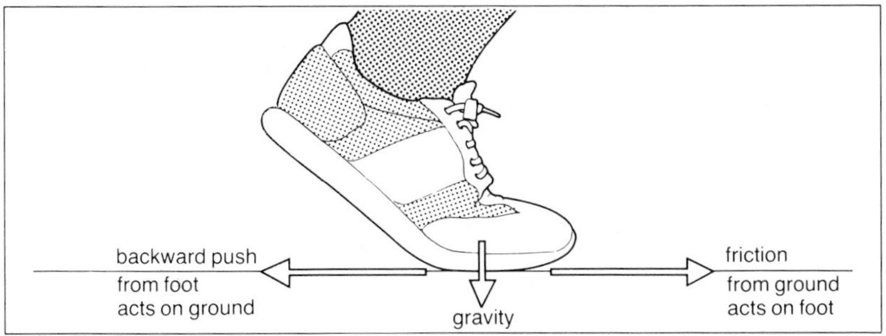

Figure 6.8 Friction from the ground opposes the backward push from our feet on the ground. It is this friction which helps us to move along. In the absence of friction it would be impossible to walk forward.

6.7 Newton's laws of motion

If you roll a ball along a flat surface, friction and air resistance will eventually bring it to rest. If these forces were absent, the ball would go on rolling with a constant speed and in a straight line forever. Provided there is no friction or drag to oppose its motion, an object does *not* require a force to keep it moving.

These simple ideas seem obvious to us now, but they were not fully understood until Sir Isaac Newton put forward his laws of motion in a book entitled *Principia Mathematica*.

Newton's first law of motion summarises the ideas suggested at the beginning of this section.

If an object is at rest it will remain at rest, and if it is moving it will continue to move in a straight line with constant speed unless an external force acts upon it.

This law explains some of the effects which you might experience in a motor car

- What are the missing words in the following paragraph?
  When a car moves off, the passengers tend to remain ______ until a ______ acts on them. This is produced by the seat backs which push the passengers forward. If the car brakes suddenly, the passengers tend to ______ and get thrown forward from their seats. Seat belts are therefore fitted to exert a ______ backwards and prevent the passengers hitting the windscreen.

Newton's first law is concerned with objects moving at constant speed or at rest. What happens when a force is applied and the object accelerates?

(*Right*) As the Red Devils fall, air friction (drag) increases as they move faster. Eventually, the upward 'drag' force equals their weight. The overall force on them is then zero and they continue to fall with a constant velocity, known as terminal velocity. Thank heavens for friction.

How does acceleration change as force increases?

You may know from experience that a car will accelerate more rapidly if two people push it instead of one. If three people push, then it accelerates even faster. When accurate experiments are carried out and care is taken to reduce friction, the results show that the acceleration doubles when the force doubles, and acceleration trebles when the force trebles (table 6.2).

- Look closely at experiments A, B and C in table 6.2. How does acceleration change as the force increases?
- What is the relationship between force and acceleration?
- Now look at experiments A, E and F where a constant force of 1 unit acts on vehicles of mass 1, 2 and then 3 units. How does the acceleration change when (a) the mass is doubled and (b) the mass is trebled?
- What is the relationship between mass and acceleration?

Table 6.2
The effect of force and mass on the acceleration of a vehicle

Experiment	*Number of units of force*	*Number of mass units*	*Acceleration* / cm/s^2
A	1	1	30
B	2	1	60
C	3	1	90
D	1	2	15
E	1	3	10

Newton's second law of motion

The last two experiments show that acceleration, a, is directly proportional to the force applied, F,

$$a \propto F$$

and that it is inversely proportional to the mass, m,

$$a \propto \frac{1}{m}$$

These results can be combined and written as:

$$a \propto \frac{F}{m}$$

$$\text{or} \quad F \propto m \times a$$

This is the mathematical expression of **Newton's second law of motion**, which states that:

> The acceleration of an object is directly proportional to the force acting on it and inversely proportional to the mass of the object.

Instead of writing $F \propto m \times a$ for the second law, we could write

$F = k \times m \times a$

where k is a constant. The unit of force, the newton, was chosen so that k equals one.

> One newton is defined as the force which causes a mass of 1 kg to accelerate at 1 m/s^2.

In this case, F = 1 N, m = 1 kg, a = 1 m/s^2. Substituting in $F = k \times m \times a$, we get:

$$1 = k \times 1 \times 1$$

$$\therefore \quad k = 1$$

So we can write:

$$F = m \times a$$

Remember that F must be in newtons, m in kilograms and a in metres per second squared when this equation is used, otherwise k is not equal to one The following example illustrates this point.

A car of mass 1 tonne accelerates from rest to 90 kilogrammes per hour in 5 seconds. What is

a) the average acceleration,
b) the force causing the acceleration,
c) (*Hard*) the distance travelled?

First, put all measurements in the correct units:

mass of car = 1 tonne = 1000 kg
initial speed of car = 0 m/s
final speed of car = 90 km/h

$$= \frac{90 \times 1000}{60 \times 60}\text{ m/s}$$

$$= 25\text{ m/s}$$

time of acceleration = 5 s

Now work out the answers.

a)
$$\text{average acceleration} = \frac{\text{change in speed}}{\text{time taken}} = \frac{25 - 0}{5} = 5\text{ m/s}^2$$

b) force causing acceleration:
$$F = m \times a = 1000 \times 5 = 5000\text{ N}$$

c)
$$\text{distance travelled} = \text{average speed} \times \text{time} = \frac{25}{2} \times 5 = 62.5\text{ m}$$

6.8 Acceleration due to gravity

When an object is dropped, it falls to the ground and accelerates due to the force of gravity from the Earth. Assuming there is no air resistance, all objects accelerate to the ground at the same rate. This acceleration due to gravity is given the symbol g and equals 9.8 metres per second every second. (g is often approximated to 10 m/s^2.)

Using $F = m \times a$, we can link this acceleration to the weight of the object. Since the weight of an object is equal to the force of gravity attracting it to the Earth, we can write

$$\text{weight of an object} = \text{force of gravity from Earth}$$

Using $F = m \times a$, we get

$$\text{weight of object} = \text{mass of object} \times \text{acceleration due to gravity}$$

$$\text{weight} = \text{mass} \times g$$

Thus the weight of an object with a mass of 1 kg is (1 × 10) N = 10 N, and the weight of a 5 kg mass is (5 × 10) N = 50 N.

Summary

1 Forces can change the shape of objects.

2 Forces can make things move

3 Forces can change the motion of moving objects.

4 The weight of an object is the force which the Earth exerts on it.

5 The mass of an object is the amount of matter inside it.

6 Weights and forces are measured in newtons. Masses are measured in kilograms.

7 The extension of a spring is proportional to the stretching force. This is Hooke's law.

8 Friction is the force which hinders one surface moving over another.

9 Drag is the friction on an object as it moves through a gas or a liquid.

10 Vehicles and animals are streamlined to overcome drag.

11 Newton's first law of motion states that: if an object is at rest, it will remain at rest, and if it is moving, it will continue to move in a straight line with constant speed unless and external force acts on it.
Newton's second law of motion states that: the acceleration of an object is directly proportional to the force acting on it and inversely proportional to its mass, $F = m \times a$.

Study questions

1 a) What do you understand by the terms (i) mass, (ii) weight, (iii) force and (iv) acceleration?
b) State Newton's first and second laws of motion.
c) It is possible to measure the mass of atomic particles by observing their acceleration in a known magnetic or electric field. In a particular experiment, an electron was found to accelerate at $10^{10}\,m/s^2$ under the influence of a force of $10^{-20}\,N$ from an electric field. What is the mass of the electron?

2 a) An astronaut on the surface of the Moon finds it much easier to lift a load on to a trolley than it was during training on Earth. Why is this?
b) When he pushes the trolley along horizontal ground there is little difference in the effort required on the Moon or the Earth. Why is this?

3 a) A journey to the Moon has just begun. What forms of energy does the rocket gain as it increases speed and rises?
b) From what source is this energy produced?
c) Why do the occupants feel pressed against their seats during 'lift off'?
d) On the way to the Moon, an astronaut climbs out of the craft to adjust an aerial. Why is he not left behind even when the space-ship is travelling at 4000 m/s?
e) If he now loses his grip on his spanner, what happens to it?
f) Why does the speed of the capsule increase as it approaches the Moon?

4 Two polishes for a tiled floor are advertised as 'non-slip'. What experiments could you make to find out which produced the less slippery surface, when applied according to the maker's instructions?

5 In making a spring balance, the spring is first tested by hanging known masses from it. The results for a particular spring balance are shown below:

load in grams	0	10	30	50
length of spring in cm	20	22.5	27.5	32.5

a) Plot a graph of the length of the spring against the load.
b) Name the force which is stretching the spring.
c) What load will make the spring 30 cm in length?
d) How would the results differ if the experiment were repeated on the Moon?

6 A trolley of mass 10 kg can be pushed at a constant speed by applying a force of 5 N to it. When the push is increased to 7 N, the trolley accelerates.
a) How large is the frictional force which hinders movement of the trolley?
b) What is the net force which accelerates the trolley?
c) What is the size of the acceleration?

7 A car of mass 750 kg accelerates from rest to 20 m/s in 10 s.
a) What is its average acceleration?
b) What force causes this acceleration?
c) Why is the total force exerted by the car on the road greater than the value in part (b)?

8 Investigate the effect of streamlining with paper darts. Make three darts with the same mass (i.e. same area of paper), but with different shapes (i.e. different length, wingspan or body size). Which shape and which design are the best for a paper dart?

9 A heavy stone was attached to a paper tape which could run through a ticker timer which produced 50 ticks per second. The stone was dropped vertically and about 1.5 m of clearly marked tape was obtained containing about 25 dots. Three sections of the tape are shown in figure 6.9.

a) Explain the meaning of the following terms: (i) speed, (ii) velocity and (iii) acceleration.
b) Did the stone reach a constant velocity or was it accelerating all the time? Explain your answer.
c) What is the time between one tick and the next?
d) How far does the stone fall between
   i) the 10th and 11th ticks,
   ii) the 20th and 21st ticks?
e) What is the average velocity of the stone between
   i) the 10th and 11th ticks,
   ii) the 20th and 21st ticks?
f) What time elapses between the 10th and 20th ticks?
g) What is the average acceleration of the stone between the 10th and 20th ticks?

Figure 6.9

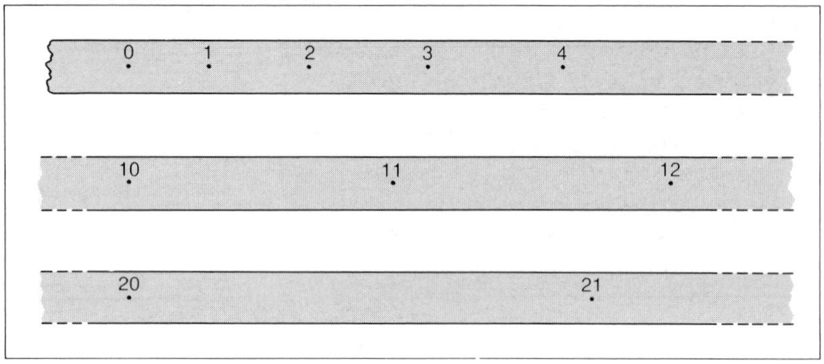

7 Pressure and pumps

Why can camels move over desert sand faster than horses?

Why are camels better than horses for transport in the desert? How do bicycle pumps and barometers work? The idea of pressure will help us to answer these and other questions.

7.1 What is pressure?

The word pressure is used in various ways. People talk about their blood pressure or their pressure of work, but to a scientist *pressure* describes how 'concentrated' a force is. If the force acts on a small area, the force is concentrated and pressure is high. If the force acts on a large area, its effect is spread out and pressure is low:

$$\text{pressure} = \frac{\text{force}}{\text{area}}$$

that is, pressure is the force per unit area. To see what this means, imagine a girl weighing 500 N standing on snow wearing

a) shoes with an area of $0.02\,\text{m}^2$ in contact with the snow,
b) skis with an area of $0.2\,\text{m}^2$ in contact with the snow.

When the girl is wearing shoes, the pressure she exerts on the snow is

$$\text{pressure} = \frac{\text{force}}{\text{area}} = \frac{500\,\text{N}}{0.02\,\text{m}^2} = 25\,000\,\text{N/m}^2$$

- Calculate the pressure the girl exerts on the snow when she wears skis.
- Why is she less likely to sink into the snow wearing skis?

Horses and camels have roughly the same weight, but a camel's foot has about three times the area of contact with the ground compared to a horse's hoof.

- Which is more suitable for riding in a sandy desert, a horse or a camel? Why?

The horse and the camel exert approximately the same total force on the ground. But the pressure caused by the horse is about three times that from the camel, because the horse's weight is concentrated on a smaller area.

The smaller the area over which a force acts, the greater the pressure. This is why drawing pins with sharp points can be pushed into a notice board easily, and why woodpeckers need strong, sharply pointed beaks for making holes in trees.

- Why do elephants have large, flat feet?
- Why is it more painful to walk barefoot on pebbles than on the pavement?

7.2 Pressure in liquids

The force of gravity pulls a liquid down into its container. This exerts pressure on the container and on any object in the liquid. At great depths, this pressure is so large that it would crush a human diver not wearing a protective suit.

- *Pressure in a liquid increases with depth.* As the liquid gets deeper, the weight of liquid pushing down increases and the pressure gets greater (figure 7.1). Because of this, dam walls are built thicker towards the base in order to withstand the higher pressure from water at the bottom of the reservoir.
- *Pressure at a given depth is the same in all directions.* A liquid pushes on every surface in contact with it, whichever way the surface is facing. At any particular depth in the liquid, pressure is the same in all directions; upwards, downwards or sideways. This can be demonstrated using the apparatus in figure 7.2.

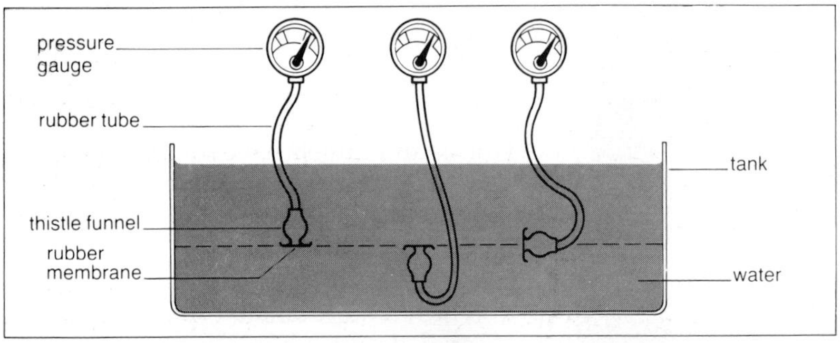

Figure 7.2 Provided the centre of the funnel is kept at the same depth below the surface, the reading on the pressure guage stays the same.

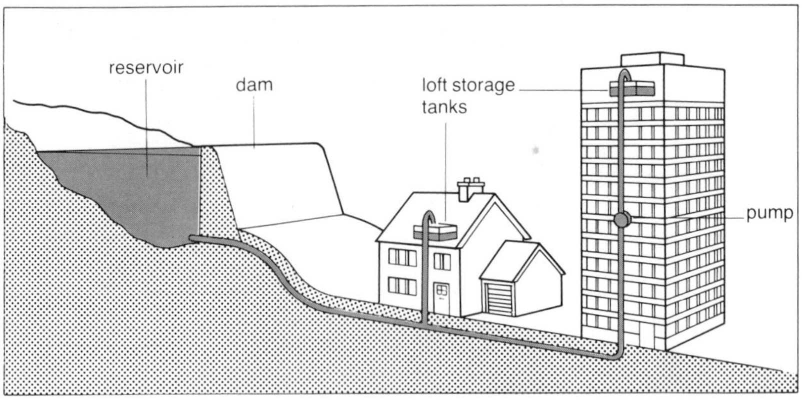

Figure 7.3

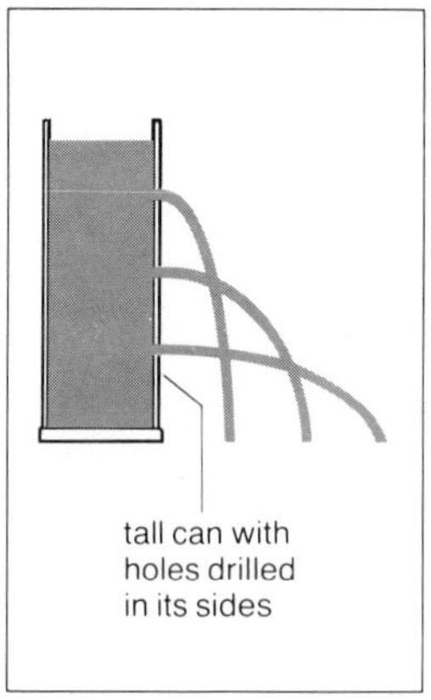

Figure 7.1 Water spurts out furthest from the lowest hole. Why is this?

Water supply systems

Most buildings in our towns and cities obtain their water from the public water supply system. The water comes from a reservoir on high ground and flows through pipes to the various places being supplied (figure 7.3).

- Why is the water pressure greatest at the lowest lying places in the region supplied?
- Why is the water pressure sometimes less in dry, summer months?
- Why is it sometimes necessary to *pump* the water up to storage tanks in tall buildings? (See figure 7.3.)

Hydraulic machines

The word **hydraulic** relates to water or other liquids in pipes. Unlike gases, liquids cannot be squashed into a smaller volume. Any pressure on a trapped liquid in a pipe will therefore be felt throughout the whole liquid. These properties make liquids useful for transmitting pressure in hydraulic machines such as hydraulic jacks, fork lift trucks and car brakes.

Figure 7.4 shows the principle on which these machines work. Suppose a force of 100 N (easily exerted by a human arm) is applied to the small piston X, whose area is $\frac{1}{1000}\,\text{m}^2$:

$$\text{pressure on oil} = \frac{\text{force}}{\text{area}}$$

$$= \frac{100\,\text{N}}{\frac{1}{1000}\,\text{m}^2} = 100\,000\,\text{N/m}^2$$

This pressure is transmitted through the liquid and acts on piston Y. Since

$$\text{pressure} = \frac{\text{force}}{\text{area}}$$

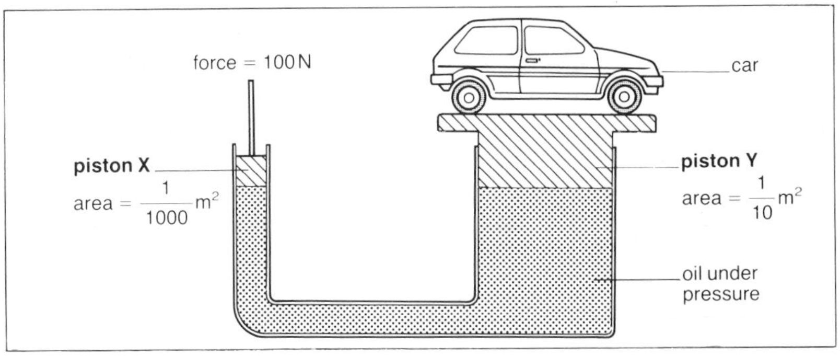

Figure 7.4 The principle of hydraulic machines.

Pressure is transmitted through a liquid trapped in a pipe. Using pistons of different area, the hydraulic jack is a force multiplier.

it follows that

force = pressure × area

Therefore, for piston Y,

$$\text{force on piston Y} = \text{pressure on piston Y} \times \text{area of piston Y}$$
$$= 100000 \times 1/10$$
$$= 10000\,\text{N}$$

This simple machine has 'magnified' a force of 100 N on piston X into a force of 10 000 N on piston Y. This could lift a car of 1000 kg, i.e. one tonne.

Figure 7.5 shows the hydraulic braking system in a car. When the brake pedal is pushed down, piston A moves into the master cylinder and pressure is exerted on the brake fluid. This pressure is transmitted through the brake fluid to pistons B and C which force the brake pads against the discs attached to the wheel.

- How will the force of the brake pads on the wheels change if
  a) piston A is made larger in area?
  b) pistons B and C are made larger in area?
- Hydraulic brakes will not work properly if air gets into the brake fluid system. Why is this?
- How would you modify the hydraulic jack in figure 7.4 so that it can be used as a hydraulic press?

Figure 7.5 The disc brake on a car wheel.

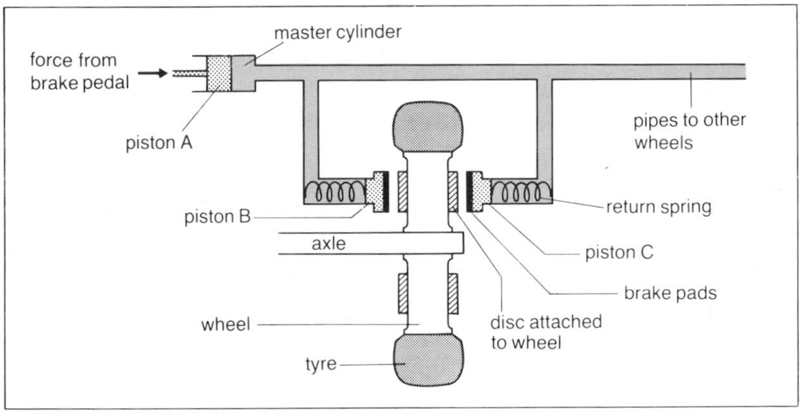

7.3 Blood pressure

The circulation of blood around the body through arteries, capillaries and veins (section 5.2) is an example of a hydraulic system.

- Hold one hand above your head and let the other hang down for about thirty seconds. Then look at the veins and the colour on the back of each hand. Why does the hand that hangs down have the fatter veins and the pinker colour?

The contrast in colour and vein size is due to a difference in **blood pressure** in the two hands.

Blood is forced around your body by your heart, which acts like a pump. The heart contracts roughly seventy times a minute. Every time this happens, blood is forced out of the heart into the arteries. As the heart relaxes, its walls move outwards and blood is sucked into it from the veins. (The circulation of the blood and the pumping action of the heart is discussed more fully in section 5.2.)

Every time the heart contracts and blood is forced into the arteries, the blood pressure rises to a higher value, known as the **systolic pressure**. At the end of each pulse, the heart muscle relaxes and the blood pressure falls to a lower value, known as the **diastolic pressure**. At this point, the heart begins to contract again, the pressure starts to rise and the cycle is repeated. We are all aware of this cycle when we feel our pulses or notice that our hearts are beating after strenuous exercise.

- Put your finger above the artery in your wrist. Can you *feel* the throb of your pulse?
- Count the number of heart beats in one minute.
- How could you *hear* someone's heart beat?
- If the heart beats faster, blood pressure increases. Exercise makes the heart beat faster. What else has this effect?

A healthy person will have a reasonably high blood pressure to keep the blood moving around the body, but the blood pressure must not be too high as this will put undue strain on the heart muscles and arteries. If a person is unwell, their blood pressure may become unusually high or low. These abnormal values can help a doctor in deciding what is wrong with someone.

The instrument used to measure blood pressure consists of a thin, airtight tube attached to a *manometer*. A manometer is a U-tube containing mercury with a scale at the side (figure 7.6). As the pressure in the airtight tube and in the left-hand limb of the U-tube increases, the mercury is pushed higher up the right-hand limb. The difference in the height of the mercury in the two limbs of the U-tube is proportional to the excess pressure in the left-hand limb.

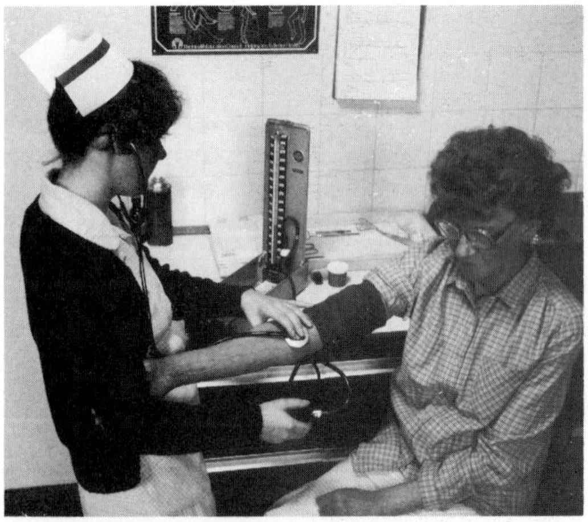

The nurse listens to the pulse with a stethoscope as the blood pressure is measured on the manometer.

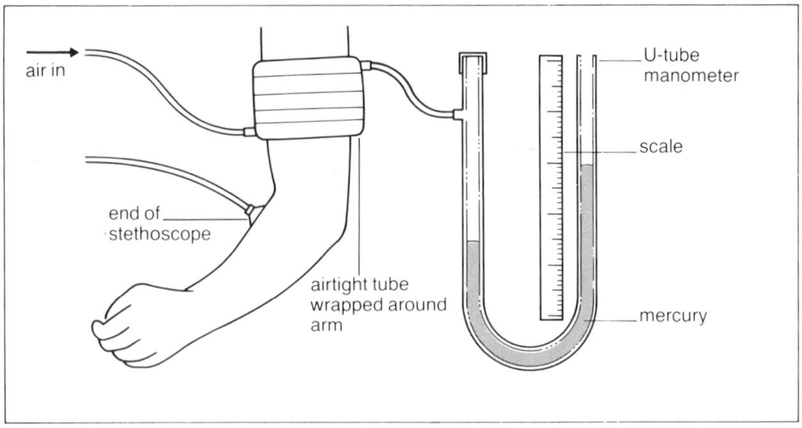

Figure 7.6 Measuring someone's blood pressure.

The airtight tube is wrapped around the patient's arm and then inflated until the pressure in the tube is great enough to stop the flow of blood down the main artery to the forearm. The doctor now listens to the pulse in the patient's lower arm with a stethoscope and slowly releases air from the tube. When the pressure in the tube is the same as the systolic pressure (the peak pressure) of the blood, the heart can just force blood past the band. A gentle, repetitive thud can then be heard in the stethoscope. The pressure in the tube is measured using the manometer. More air is then released from the tube until blood can pass along the artery *all the time*. This corresponds to the diastolic pressure (the lower pressure), and the gentle thud in the stethoscope disappears.

In a healthy teenager, the systolic and diastolic pressures are equivalent to about 115 mm and 75 mm of mercury. These values change with age, exercise, stress, drugs and disease.

- Which factors cause the blood pressure to increase?

7.4 Floating and sinking

Why do certain things, like boats and wood float on water, while other things like stones sink? How do fishes float in water?

The pressure in a liquid increases with depth. When an object is lowered into the water, the top of the object experiences atmospheric pressure. The bottom of the object experiences atmospheric pressure *plus* the pressure caused by the additional depth of water (figure 7.7). This excess pressure on the bottom surface of the object produces an overall upwards force called an **upthrust**.

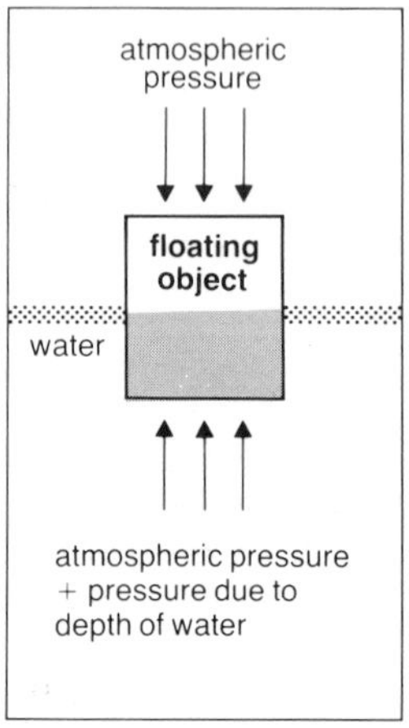

Figure 7.7

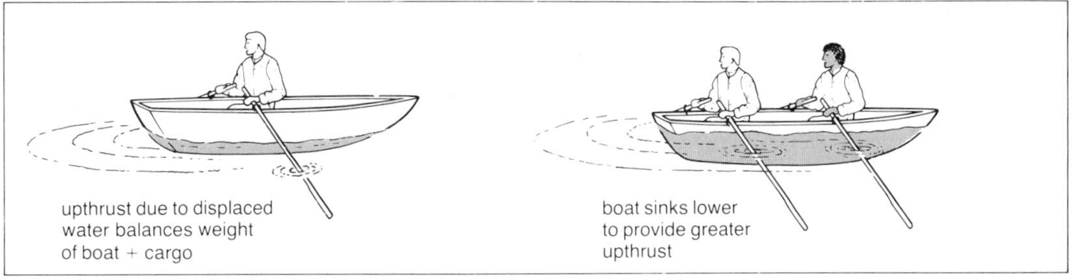

Figure 7.8

As the object sinks further into the water, the difference in pressure between the top and the bottom of the object increases and therefore the upthrust increases. The object stops sinking into the water when the upthrust is just large enough to support its weight:

Upthrust on floating object = weight of object.

If the floating object in figure 7.7 were removed, it would be replaced by a volume of water equal to the shaded part. Thus, the upthrust at the bottom of the floating object must be enough to support the volume of water which the object has displaced.

Upthrust on floating object = weight of water displaced.

This statement applies to any object floating in either a gas or a liquid, and it is known as the **law of floatation**.

When a boat is lowered into water, it sinks down until the upthrust is just enough to support its weight. If the boat is loaded with a heavy cargo, a greater upthrust is required to support the greater weight. The boat, therefore, sinks lower, displacing more water and increasing the upthrust (figure 7.8). If the cargo is too heavy, the upthrust cannot support the weight of the boat even when all the boat is immersed. The boat sinks!

Have you noticed how a goldfish comes to the surface to gulp air? Most fishes have an air-filled cavity in their body called a **swim bladder**. When extra air enters this cavity, the volume of the fish increases. This means the fish floats upwards towards the surface. By letting air out of the swim bladder, the fish can make itself sink. You may have noticed goldfish blowing bubbles in order to sink.

- When you are next at the swimming baths, see if you can make yourself float or sink in water according to whether your lungs are full of air or empty.

7.5 Pressure in gases

Our life is vitally affected by the weather. Holidays, agriculture, building construction and many other activities can be severely disrupted by bad weather. The study of the weather is called **meteorology** and one of the most useful measurements that meteorologists can make in studying the weather is atmospheric pressure.

Atmospheric pressure

The atmosphere is like a deep ocean of air. This air is attracted by the Earth's gravity and presses down on everything beneath it. Consequently, the pressure from the atmosphere decreases as you rise further and further above sea level. Like the pressure of a liquid, it acts in all directions.

On the Earth's surface, atmospheric pressure is about 100 000 N/m^2; roughly the weight of an elephant pressing on every square metre.

Tennis fans waiting for the rain to stop at Wimbledon. Meteorologists try to predict the weather so that we can plan our activities better.

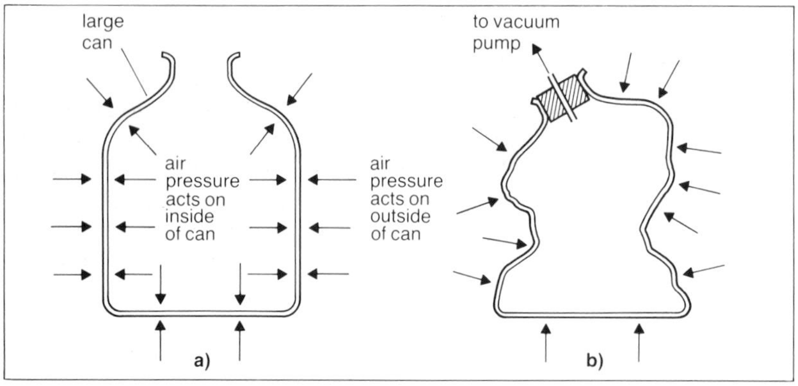

Figure 7.9 The collapsing can experiment.

- Why do we not feel the pressure of the atmosphere?
- Why do we not collapse and get crushed by this pressure?
- Look closely at figure 7.9. What happens to the pressure inside the can when air is pumped out of it?
- What is the name for a space from which all the air has been withdrawn?
- Why does the can collapse in diagram (b)?

In section 3.2, we saw that the pressure of a gas is caused by particles of the gas bombarding the sides of their container. In figure 7.9a, particles of gas are bombarding the inside and the outside of the can. The pressure is equal on both sides and the can keeps its shape. When the gas is removed from inside, there are very few particles bombarding the inner surface and the inside pressure is almost zero. Air particles, however, continue to bombard the *outside* of the can and this pressure causes the can to collapse. It is the pressure of blood and other fluids inside your body that balances atmospheric pressure and stops the atmosphere crushing you.

The part of the human body most sensitive to pressure is the ear. Look at figure 19.9 (section 19.3). Notice the ear drum separating the middle-ear cavity from the outside atmosphere. When you go up in an aeroplane or a lift, or go up a mountain, atmospheric pressure falls. Unless the pressure in the middle ear falls too, the eardrum will bulge outwards due to the greater pressure within. This causes discomfort. The narrow tube called the Eustachian tube leading from the middle ear to the throat is designed to let air in and out of the middle ear. This equalises pressure on each side of the eardrum. Sometimes you can feel a 'popping' sensation as it opens. It is possible to reduce the pressure in the middle ear and relieve the discomfort by swallowing, which opens the Eustachian tube. Similar things occur when the pressure *outside* increases, for example, when you dive underwater, or when you come down in an aeroplane.

Measuring atmospheric pressure

Atmospheric pressure is measured by instruments called **barometers**.

The mercury barometer

A simple accurate barometer can be made by filling a long, thick-walled glass tube, which is sealed at one end, with mercury. When the tube is *completely* filled with mercury, it is corked and turned upside down into a dish of mercury (figure 7.10). When the cork is removed, the level of the mercury in the tube falls until the pressure from the column of mercury in the tube is balanced by the pressure from the atmosphere acting on the mercury in the dish. A metre scale is placed at the side of the barometer to measure the height of the mercury column above that in the dish. This gives the atmospheric pressure in 'millimetres of mercury'. The higher the atmospheric pressure, the higher the mercury column.

At sea level, atmospheric pressure varies between 730 and 770 mm of mercury depending on the weather. On the top of Mount Everest, atmospheric pressure may be as low as 250 mm of mercury.

Mercury barometers take up a lot of space. They must be nearly a metre long. They also require the use of liquid mercury, which gives off a poisonous vapour. Scientists have therefore looked for more convenient ways of measuring atmospheric pressure.

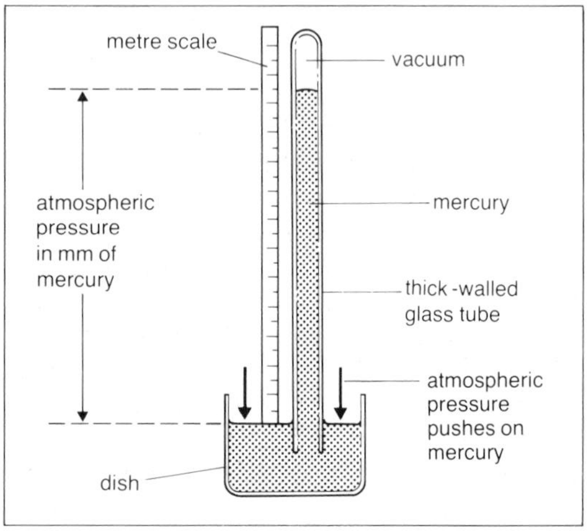

Figure 7.10 The mercury barometer.

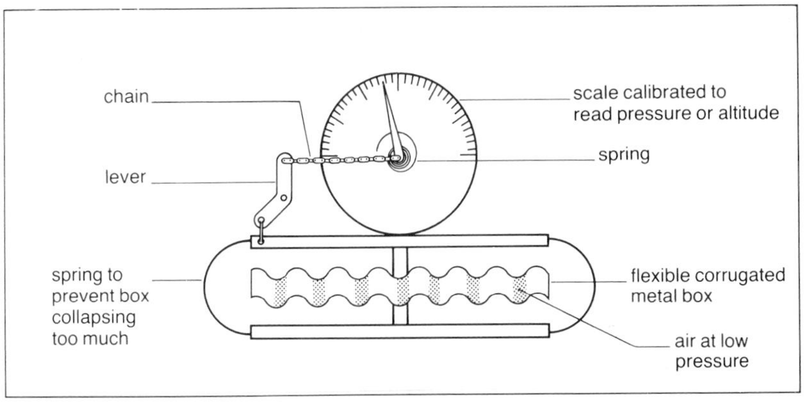

Figure 7.11 The aneroid barometer.

The aneroid barometer

The aneroid barometer is more portable and easier to use than the mercury barometer. This is because it does not use any liquid. The main part of the instrument is a small corrugated metal box containing air at low pressure. The box is made of thin metal so that any changes in the atmospheric pressure cause the top and bottom of the box to move in or out. The movement of the box is magnified by a lever and chain joined to a pointer which moves over a circular scale (figure 7.11).

Aneroid barometers are used as pressure gauges and also as altimeters in aircraft. Since atmospheric pressure decreases with height, the scale of the barometer can be made to read the altitude of the aeroplane directly.

7.6 Weather maps

Weather forecasts used to be quite unreliable. Nowadays, meteorologists measure atmospheric pressure, wind speeds, temperature and humidity. These measurements, combined with photographs from Earth satellites and powerful computers, have made their work much more accurate.

The atmospheric pressure at a particular place varies according to the weather. Changes in atmospheric pressure can be used to predict the coming weather. A large number of readings of atmospheric pressure are made over the whole surrounding area. The readings are then recorded on a weather map. Lines are drawn on this map linking places of equal atmospheric pressure (figure 7.12). These lines are called **isobars**. If the isobars are extended far enough they form closed curves which look like contour lines. When the isobars enclose a region of low pressure, the system is called a **depression** or a **cyclone**. If they enclose a region of high pressure, the system is known as an **anticyclone**.

Meteorologists express pressure in millibars. One millibar is $100\,N/m^2$, and standard atmospheric pressure equals 1013 millibars. On a weather map, the isobars are usually drawn at intervals of 4 or 8 millibars. When the isobars are close together on the weather map, atmospheric pressure changes rapidly over a short distance. Consequently, there are high winds, as the air moves rapidly from a high pressure to a low pressure region. When the isobars are widely spaced, the wind velocity is usually light and variable.

We might expect winds to blow straight across the isobars from the areas of high pressure to areas of low pressure. Unfortunately the Earth's rotation must also be considered. In the northern hemisphere, winds tend to blow clockwise around an anticyclone and anticlockwise around a depression.

In Britain, the weather is largely dictated by depressions which form in the North Atlantic and then travel towards the north east. The depression normally has associated **fronts**, or boundaries, separating regions of air at different temperatures. A **warm front** separates colder air from advancing warmer air. A **cold front** separates warmer air from advancing colder air. Generally, the cold front of the depression overtakes the warm front, since the warm less dense air rises above the colder air. As the warm moist air rises, it cools and water vapour in it condenses giving rain. Eventually, the warm and cold fronts unite forming an **occluded front**. When this happens, the pressure rises and the depression dies away.

Figure 7.12 The Atlantic weather map at noon on a June day.
Key
warm front
cold front
occluded front
isobar

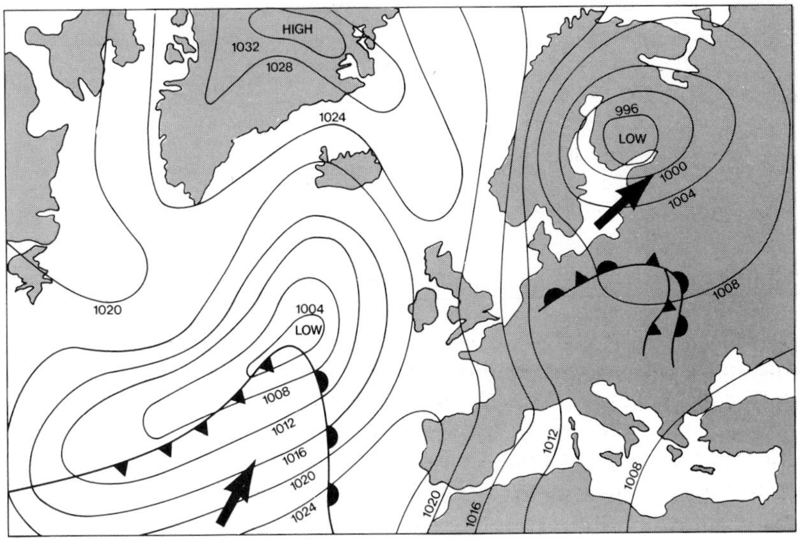

Anticyclones occur much less frequently than depressions over Britain. The isobars associated with anticyclones are more widely spaced than those in depressions and the winds are light and variable in direction. Since winds are moving away from the anticyclone, the clouds tend to disappear leaving clear blue skies. In Britain, the average number of days with anticyclones is greatest during September and, surprisingly, it is least during July and August. So much for summer holidays!

- Redraw figure 7.12 as a sketch map.
- On your map, write the letter A at the centre of any anticyclone and the letter D at the centre of any depression.
- Write the letter R at one point where you might expect rain to be falling.
- Join up points at standard atmospheric pressure with a dashed line.
- How are wind directions shown on the weather map?
- What is the interval between the isobars?

Figure 7.13

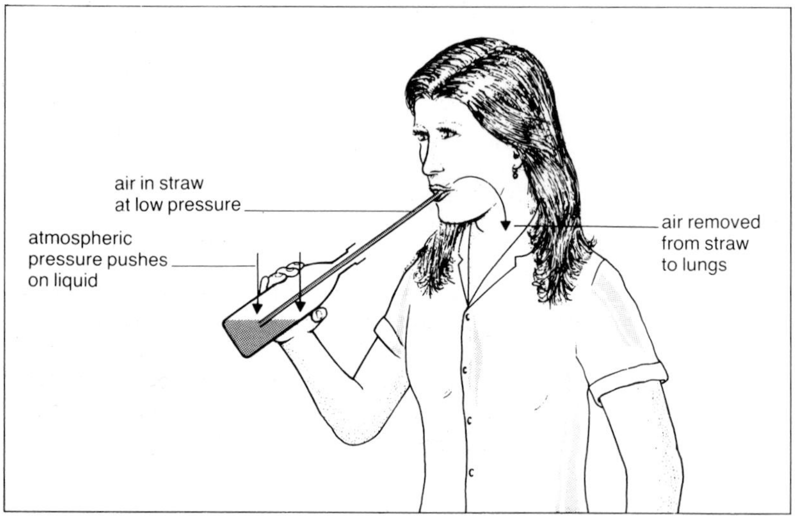

7.7 Pumps

Pumps are used to transfer liquids and gases from one place to another. An understanding of what happens when you drink through a straw will help you to appreciate the way in which simple pumps work (figure 7.13). When you suck on the straw, you draw air into your lungs from inside the straw. The atmospheric pressure on the liquid in the bottle is now greater than the pressure of the air inside the straw. This forces liquid into your mouth. All pumps are pressure differences to move liquids or gases from one place to another. One of the simplest pumps in everyday use is the syringe (figure 7.14).

- What happens to the pressure inside the syringe when the piston is pulled out?
- Why does liquid flow up into the syringe?
- What important uses do syringes have?

Figure 7.14 The syringe.

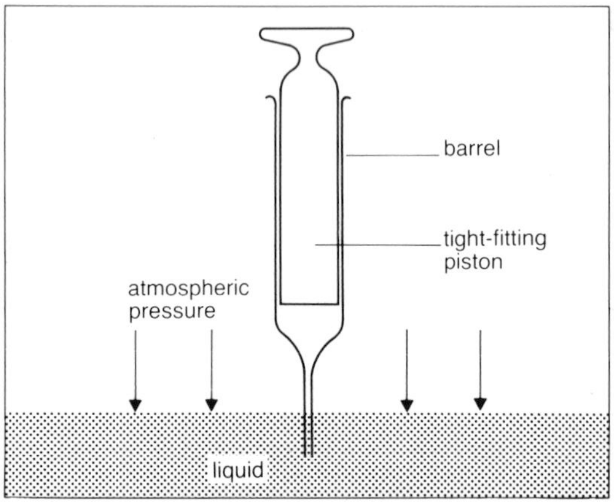

The bicycle pump

The bicycle pump also works in a simple way (figure 7.15). Like the syringe it consists of a piston which moves in a cylinder. When the piston is pushed in, air pressure between the piston and the valve increases. The washer is pressed against the walls of the cylinder, providing a seal. When the pressure of the air between the washer and the valve exceeds that of the air inside the tyre, air is forced past the valve and into the tyre.

When the piston is pulled out, atmospheric pressure forces air past the sides of the washer, into the pump ready for the next stroke.

Figure 7.15 (Below) The bicycle pump.

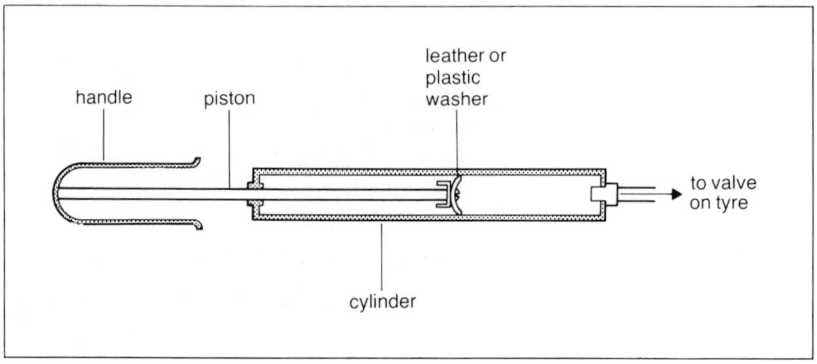

The lungs as pumps

Our bodies cannot work without a continuous supply of oxygen. When we breathe in, air enters the lungs which have a rich blood supply. Oxygen is absorbed into the blood. At the same time, carbon dioxide passes from the blood into the lungs and this is expelled when we breathe out. In order to help this exchange of gases, the chest acts like a pump transferring gases in to and out of the lungs (figure 7.16). The lungs are situated inside the chest (**thorax**). The sides of the thorax are bounded by the **rib cage**, and there are muscles linking the ribs. At the bottom of the thorax there is a flexible sheet of muscular tissue called the **diaphragm** which is stretched between the lowest pair of ribs. Figure 7.16 shows what happens when we breathe in and out.

When we breathe in, muscles pull the diaphragm downwards and the ribs upwards and outwards. The thorax increases in size and air is drawn into the lungs. When we breathe out, the diaphragm relaxes and moves upwards and the ribs move inwards. The thorax returns to its original size, so the pressure inside it increases and air is forced out of the lungs.

Figure 7.16 Breathing in and breathing out.

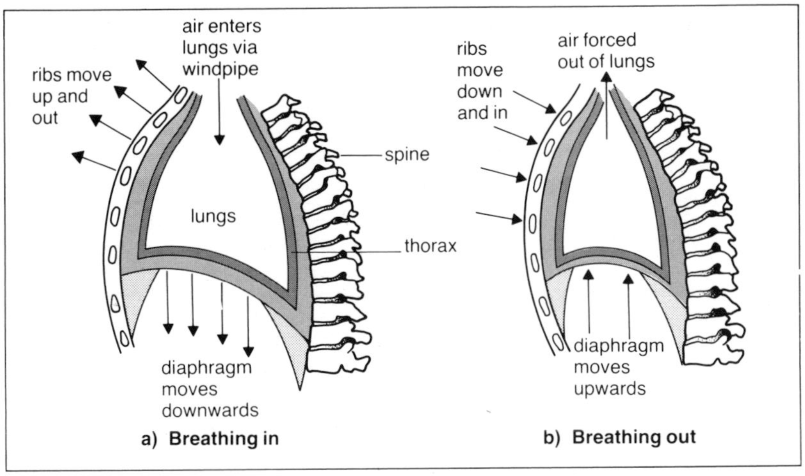

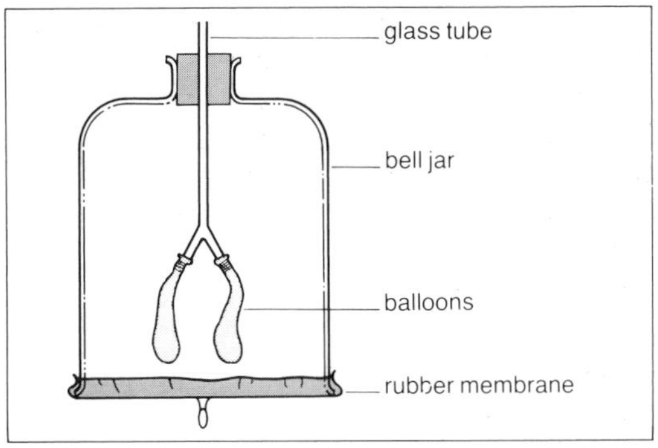

Figure 7.17

Figure 7.17 shows a model which can be used to explain breathing. When the rubber membrane is pulled down, the balloons expand. When the membrane is released, the balloons contract.

- The glass tube represents the wind pipe (trachea). What do the bell jar, the balloons and the rubber membrane represent?
- What happens to the pressure inside the bell jar when the membrane is pulled down?
- Why do the balloons expand when the membrane is pulled down?
- What happens to the pressure inside the bell jar when the membrane is released?
- Why do the balloons contract when the membrane is released?

In the model shown in figure 7.17, the space between the balloons and the walls of the bell jar is quite large. In the body, the corresponding space (called the **pleural cavity**) is relatively small, and it is filled with liquid *not* air.

Summary

1 Pressure = force/area.

2 Pressure in a liquid increases with depth.

3 Pressure at a given depth in a liquid is the same in all directions.

4 Blood is forced around your body by your heart, which acts like a pump.

5 Manometers and barometers are used to measure pressure.

6 The upthrust on a floating object equals the weight of the object.

7 The upthrust on an object floating in a fluid (liquid or gas) equals the weight of fluid displaced.

8 A region of low atmospheric pressure is called a depression or a cyclone. A region of high atmospheric pressure is called an anticyclone.

9 The lungs and ribs act like a pump in transferring gases into and out of the body.

Study questions

1 A drawing pin with a point of area $10^{-8}\,m^2$ is pushed into a notice board with a force of 50 N.
   a) What pressure does the point exert on the notice board?
   b) If the same pressure must be exerted by the point of a nail (area $10^{-7}\,m^2$) before it can be pushed into the board, what force must be applied to the head of the nail?

2 An elephant weighing 60 000 N and a girl weighing 600 N are standing on a circus platform. One of the elephant's feet has an area of $600\,cm^2$. The girl is wearing high-heeled boots and each heel has an area of $0.6\,cm^2$.
   a) What pressure does the elephant exert on the platform if it stands on one leg?
   b) What pressure does the girl exert on the platform if she spins around on one heel?
   c) Are the elephant's feet or the girl's boots more likely to damage the wooden platform?

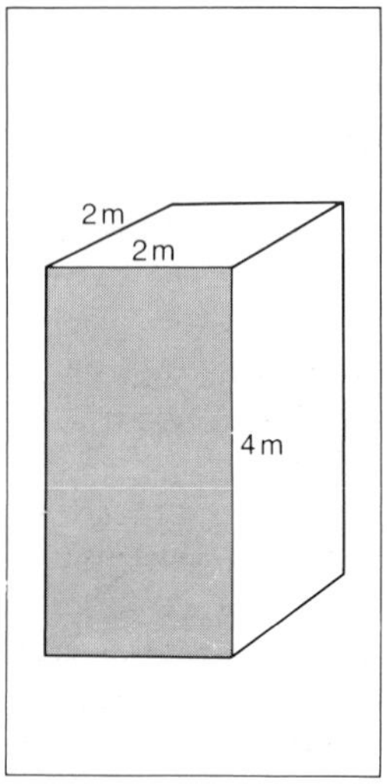

Figure 7.18

3 Figure 7.18 shows a large block of concrete.
   a) What is its volume?
   b) What is its mass? (Density of concrete = $2500\,kg/m^3$.)
   c) What is its weight? (Assume 1 kg has a weight of 10 N.)
   d) What pressure does the concrete exert on the ground
      i) when standing as shown,
      ii) if the shaded side is on the ground?

4 a) What is meant by the term *pressure*?
   b) Why is it difficult to cut with a blunt knife?
   c) Why does a car tyre look 'flat' when some of the air has leaked out?
   d) A bottle of milk is shaken so that the cream mixes thoroughly with the milk. Will the pressure on the bottom of the bottle change when the milk and cream are thoroughly mixed? Explain your answer.

5 A dentist's hydraulic chair weighing 1200 N is raised on a metal pillar with a cross-sectional area of $0.01\,m^2$. The pillar forms the large piston of a hydraulic lift. The dentist's foot pedal operates a small piston of cross-sectional area $0.001\,m^2$, which forms the other part of the hydraulic lift.
   a) What total force must be applied to the chair to lift a man weighing 800 N sitting in it?
   b) What pressure is required to support the metal pillar when the man sits in the chair?
   c) What force must be applied to the plunger to support the man in the chair?

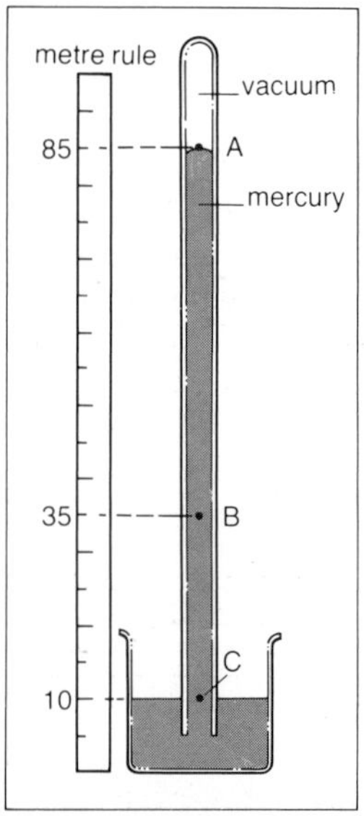

Figure 7.19

6 a) Why is there an upthrust on a floating boat?
   b) A sailor climbs aboard a floating yacht. What happens to
      i) the position of the yacht in the water,
      ii) the upthrust on the yacht,
      iii) the amount of water displacement by the yacht?
   c) Why does the yacht float lower in fresh water than in the sea?
   d) Wood floats on water, yet stones sink. Why is this?
   e) How do submarines rise and sink in water?

7 a) Explain how you are able to drink milk through a straw.
   b) Why would this not work if there was a hole in the side of the straw?
   c) Draw a diagram of a simple manometer suitable for measuring the pressure of air in your lungs when you blow hard. Say exactly what you would measure and how you would express the result.

8 a) State *three* essential features of a clear glass tube which is to be used in making a simple barometer.
   b) Describe how you would use such a tube to set up a simple barometer.
   c) Why should mercury never be left in a dish open to the atmosphere?
   d) Figure 7.19 shows a simple barometer. What is the pressure (in cm of mercury) at (i) A, (ii) B and (iii) C?
   e) What atmospheric pressure is indicated by the barometer in figure 7.19?
   f) If the height of mercury in the tube suddenly decreased, what change would you expect in the weather?
   g) Normally, liquids find their own level. What, then, holds the mercury up in the tube?
   h) What would happen if the tube were slowly tilted through 60°?
   i) What difference would it make to the height of mercury in the tube if the tube was twice as wide?
   j) What difference would there be if the mercury was replaced by water? Explain your answer.

8 Machines – more power to the elbow

A fishing rod is a simple machine. By using the rod and line, it is possible to land a fish from further away, and pull in a different direction than without the rod.

Machines make life easier for us. They enable us to exert bigger forces and to move objects through greater distances than we would be able to do alone. Even our own bodies are complicated machines.

8.1 What is a machine?

Standards of living have advanced because men and women have used machines to help them in doing jobs. By using a crowbar, a workman can exert a larger force on a stone than he could with his hands alone. By using a rod and line a fisherman can land a fish from a greater depth of water and exert his pull on the fish from a different direction.

Crowbars and fishing rods are examples of simple machines. Most of us use dozens of different machines every day. Some of these machines, like scissors, nutcrackers and screwdrivers, are relatively simple. Other machines, like typewriters, washing machines and power drills are very complex.

Machines enable us

- to exert larger forces,
- to move objects through larger distances,
- to exert forces in different directions,
- to work faster.

Without machines, many jobs would be impossible. Other jobs would be difficult and would take longer to carry out.

8.2 Simple machines

A see-saw is a simple machine. Figure 8.1 (overleaf) shows two children on a see-saw.

- If the boy and girl are exactly the same weight and the boy sits 4 m from the pivot or **fulcrum**, where must the girl sit to balance the seesaw horizontally?
- Now, suppose the boy weighs 300 N and the girl weighs 600 N, where must the girl sit to balance the seesaw if the boy stays 4 m from the fulcrum?

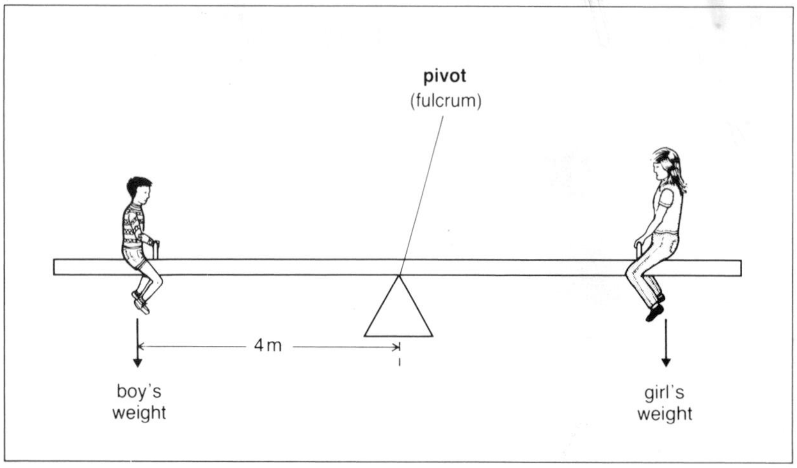

Figure 8.1 Children on a seesaw.

The seesaw acts like a **lever**: a device which can turn about a pivot or fulcrum. The boy and the girl each produce a 'turning effect' on the see-saw. The turning effect produced by a force is called its **moment**.

$$\text{moment of a force about a fulcrum} = \text{force} \times \text{distance from fulcrum to line of action of force}$$

Notice that the moment increases if the force increases, or if the force acts at a greater distance from the fulcrum.

In figure 8.1, the girl's weight causes a moment which acts downwards on the right and tries to turn the seesaw in a clockwise direction. The boy's weight causes a moment which acts downwards on the left and tries to turn the seesaw in an anticlockwise direction. The seesaw balances when these two moments are exactly equal.

If the boy weighs 30N,

$$\text{anticlockwise moment due to boy} = \text{force due to boy's weight} \times \text{distance of boy from fulcrum}$$
$$= 300 \times 4$$
$$= 1200\,\text{Nm}$$

If the girl weighs 600N and the seesaw balances:

clockwise moment = anticlockwise moment

$$600 \times \text{distance of girl from fulcrum} = 1200$$

$$\Rightarrow \text{distance of girl from fulcrum} = \frac{1200}{600} = 2\,\text{m}$$

These results with the seesaw illustrate the **law of moments**, which is sometimes called the **principle of levers**.

When something is balanced on a fulcrum, the clockwise moments are equal to the anticlockwise moments.

Levers

Have you ever used a screwdriver to remove the lid from a tin of paint? The lid cannot be opened by hand because the force needed to prise off the lid is too great. It can, however, be done using a screwdriver as a lever (figure 8.2). A large force can be exerted on the lid by pushing on the handle of the screwdriver with a much smaller force. The applied force is called the **effort** and the resisting force from the object being moved (in this case the tin lid) is called the **load**.

Look at figure 8.2 carefully. Suppose that the tin lid offers a resistance (load) of 1000N. What force (effort) must be applied to the screwdriver to remove the lid? Using the law of moments and taking moments about the fulcrum,

clockwise moment = anticlockwise moment

$$\text{effort} \times \text{distance of effort from fulcrum} = \text{load} \times \text{distance of load from fulcrum}$$

$$\Rightarrow \text{effort} \times 20 = 1000 \times 0.5$$

$$\Rightarrow \text{effort applied to screwdriver} = \frac{1000 \times 0.5}{20} = 25\,\text{N}$$

This is the smallest force needed to overcome the load – the resistance of the lid to being moved.

The force applied to the screwdriver is only 25N, but the force exerted on the tin lid is 1000N. The screwdriver is a **force multiplier**; it is a machine which enables us to exert larger forces. Notice, however, that although the load is much greater than the effort, the effort must move much further than the load. A small movement of the lid needs a large movement of the screwdriver handle. Three other examples of levers are shown in figure 8.3.

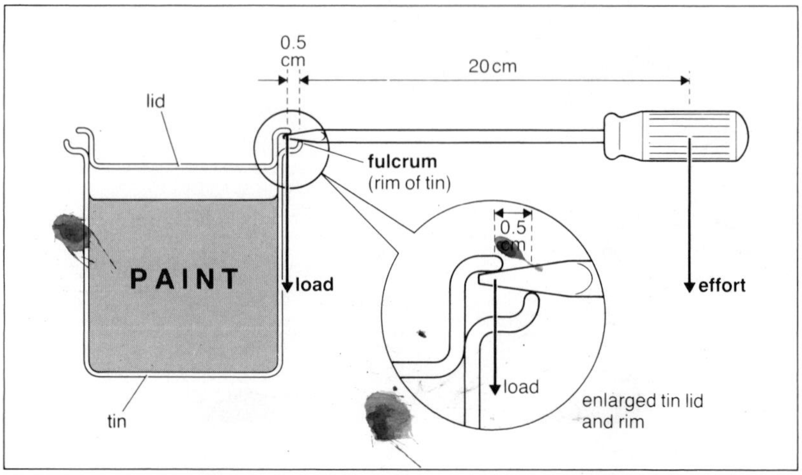

Figure 8.2 Removing a tin lid with a screwdriver.

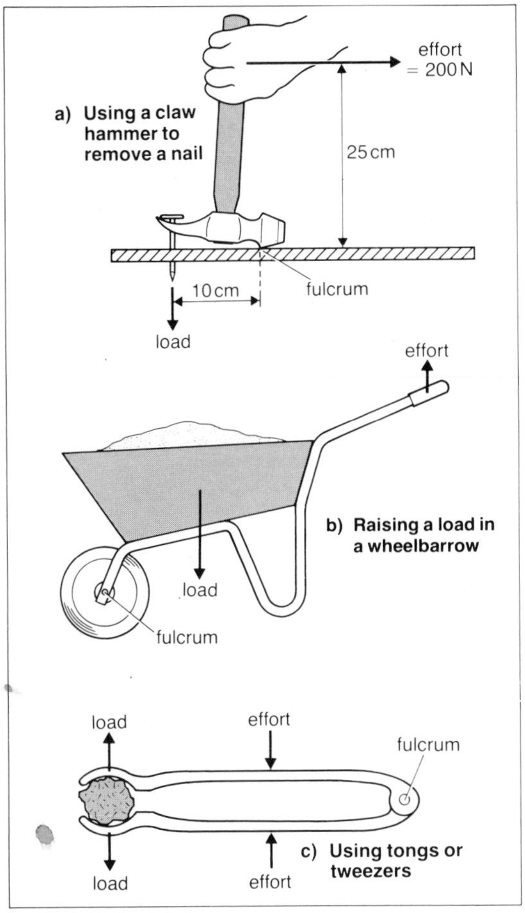

Figure 8.3 Three examples of levers.

- Use the law of moments to decide which of the examples in figure 8.3 are force multipliers. (In these cases, the load will be greater than the effort.)
- If an effort of 200 N is applied as shown to the handle of the claw hammer, what load (resistance) from the nail can be overcome?

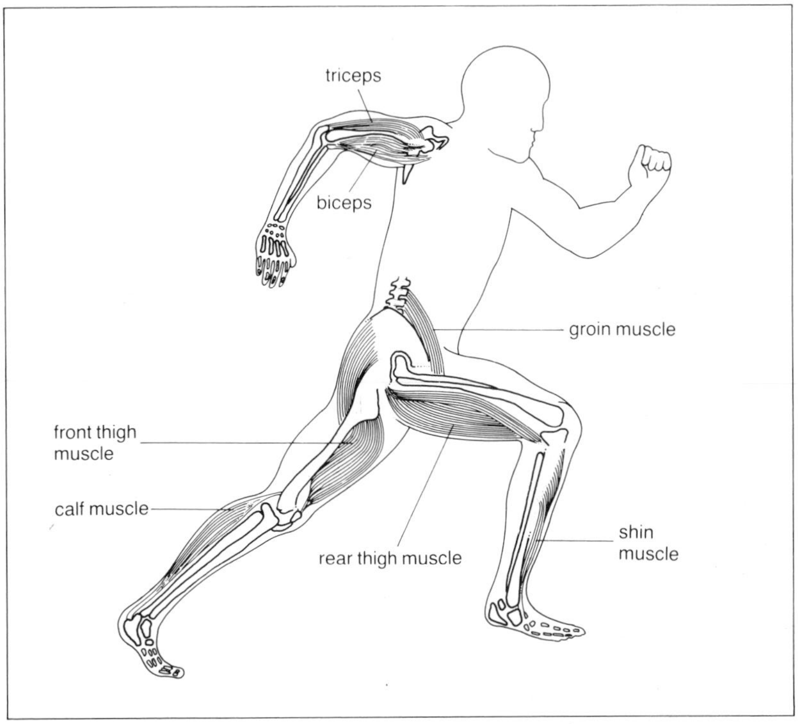

Figure 8.5 Muscles used in running.

Figure 8.4 Muscles and bones in the arm.

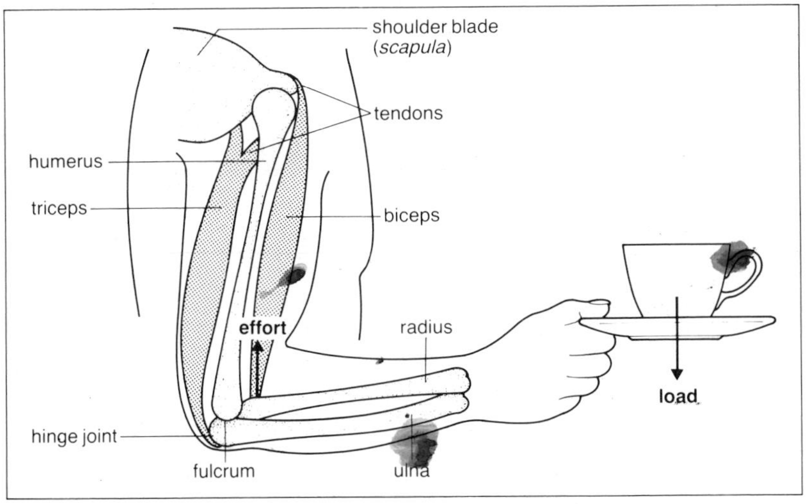

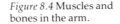

Levers in your body

Some of the bones in our bodies also act as levers. Look closely at figure 8.4, which shows the muscles and bones in the human arm. The joint at the elbow is called a **hinge joint**. This allows movement in only one plane, unlike that at the shoulder which is a **ball and socket joint**, allowing movement in any plane.

Two main muscles move the arm, the **biceps** and the **triceps**. These muscles produce opposite effects, so when one contracts the other relaxes. Although these muscles act in opposite directions, they work in a co-ordinated way. When the biceps contracts, the radius is pulled towards the shoulder and your arm bends at the elbow. When the triceps contracts, the ulna is pulled down and the arm straightens. Muscles, such as the biceps, which bend limbs are called **flexors**. Muscles, like the triceps, which straighten limbs are called **extensors**.

When we lift an object, such as the cup and saucer in figure 8.4, the arm acts as a lever. The fulcrum is at the elbow and the effort is provided by the biceps. The biceps moves a short distance, but the cup and saucer move up through a much larger distance. The arm is a **distance multiplier**; it is a machine which enables us to move loads through larger distances than the efforts themselves move. Figure 8.5 shows the muscles used in running.

8.3 The human machine: bones and muscles

The muscles and bones in our bodies act like a machine. The bones form a **skeleton** which provides a framework inside the body (figure 8.6). Bones contain living cells surrounded by a hard, outer layer of calcium carbonate and calcium phosphate. This structure makes the bones strong and rigid. The bones in the skeleton have three main functions.

- **They support the body**. Without bones and a skeleton we would collapse into a soft, flabby heap.
- **They protect vital organs**. For example, the skull protects the brain and the vertebrae protect the spinal cord.
- **They allow movement**. Various bones in the skeleton are connected to one another at **joints** so that we can move easily.

  Two important types of joint are the ball and socket joint and the hinge joint (section 8.2). The bones are held together by **ligaments**. These are tough, elastic strands which stretch across the joint from one bone to the other.

Look at figure 8.6.
- Which organs are protected by (a) the rib cage and (b) the pelvis?
- How many bones are there in one leg, excluding the foot and ankle?
- Find two ball and socket joints in the skeleton.
- Find two hinge joints in the skeleton.

Refer back to section 6.5 if you cannot answer the next two questions.
- What is the name for the gristly elastic material between bones which acts as a shock absorber?
- What is the name for the liquid which lubricates our joints like the moving parts of machines?

All vertebrates have skeletons inside their bodies like ourselves. You will have noticed this from eating meat, poultry or fish. Interior skeletons like these are called **endoskeletons**. Many animals, though, have an *exterior* skeleton, a hard outer shell enclosing the soft inside. Think of a crab, with its hard outer shell. This is an exterior skeleton, or **exoskeleton**. In fact all arthropods (insects, crustaceans, spiders etc.) have exoskeletons.

Exoskeletons have the advantage that they protect the animal and help it to conserve water. The disadvantage is that the exoskeleton must be shed and replaced by a new one as the animal grows.

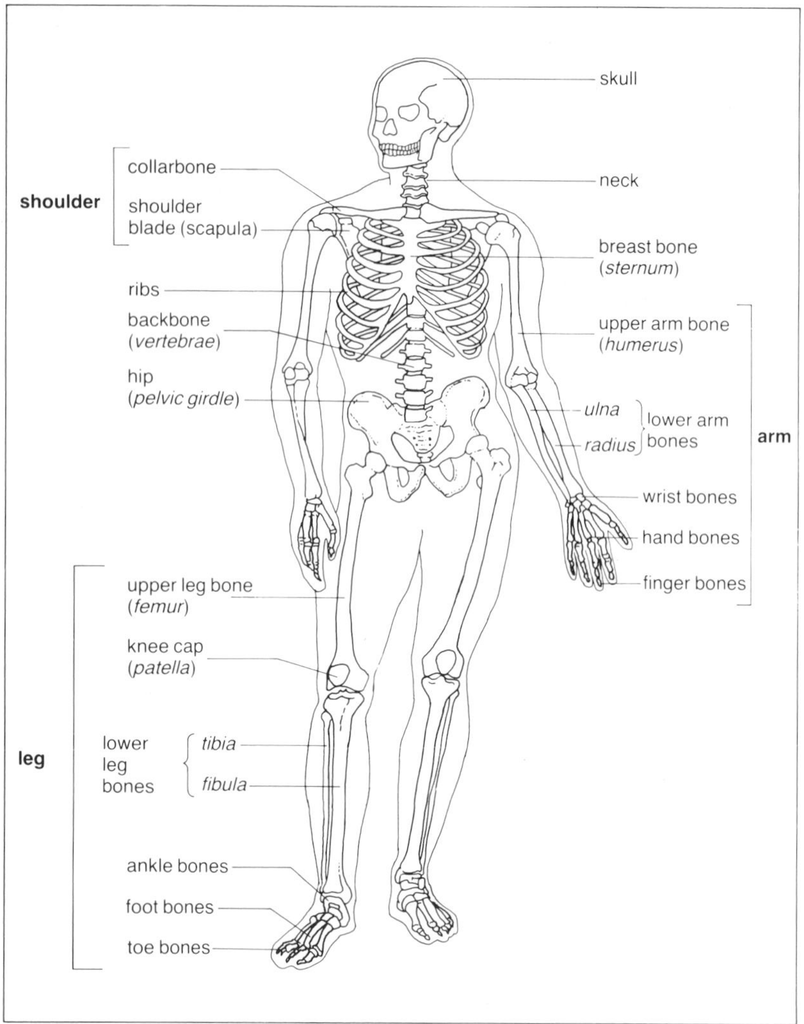

Figure 8.6 The main bones in the human skeleton.

Our bodies contain over two hundred bones, many of which act like the levers and supports of a machine. But, bones on their own are not enough. The human machine will only move when forces act on the bones. These forces are provided by **muscles**.

Muscles are attached to bones by strong fibres called **tendons**. For example, the Achilles tendon joins the calf muscle to the heel bone and the hamstring tendon joins the rear thigh muscle (the 'hamstring') to the tibia (shinbone).

When muscles contract, they pull on bones. As this happens, the muscle normally gets shorter and fatter. After contracting, a muscle cannot lengthen itself again. It has to be pulled back to its original shape by a second muscle. Pairs of muscles which act in this way, like the flexors and extensors in our limbs (section 8.2), are called **antagonistic muscles**. In these pairs, one muscle pulls the limb one way and the other pulls it back.

Hold your arm out straight. Find the biceps and triceps muscles.

- Clench your fist and bend your arm upwards. Does the biceps muscle contract or relax?
  Does the triceps muscle contract or relax?
- What happens to the triceps when the biceps contracts?
- What happens to the biceps when the triceps contracts?

Although the human body can be compared to a machine, it is, of course, very complex. It can carry out a much greater variety of jobs than any manufactured machine. It is also a cleverly controlled machine in which various organs maintain balanced conditions inside the body. For example, the blood supply tries to maintain a balance between the food we eat, the chemicals required by our bodies for warmth and movement and the waste products which we eventually excrete.

The machine-like activities of our bodies are also seen in the way in which the heart and lungs act as pumps; one transferring a liquid (blood) (section 5.2), the other transferring gases (section 7.7).

8.4 Work, energy and power

Work

Work is done whenever we exert a force on something and cause it to move. This happens when we throw a stone, push a trolley or lift a bag. Bulldozers do work when they move soil. Vehicles do work when they climb hills, overcoming the force of gravity. When a vehicle travels along a flat road, it does work overcoming the force of friction.

When a force of one newton moves one metre, the work done is one joule (1 J).

- How much work is done when a force of 2 N moves 1 m?
- How much work is done when a force of 2 N moves 2 m?
- How much work is done when a sack is dragged 4 m against a frictional force of 100 N?

The last three questions should help you to see that the work done by a force can be obtained from:

work done =	force	× distance
joules (J)	newtons (N)	metres (m)

What is the source of energy for this steam engine? What forms of energy does it interconvert?

From this equation you will see that work cannot be done unless something moves.

Scientists have agreed to use the word **joule** for the units of work, in honour of the English physicist, James Prescott Joule (1818 – 1889). Joule devoted his life to the study of heat, work and energy.

- How much work is done when a 2 kg (20 N) bag of sugar is lifted 0.5 m from a table on to a shelf?
- How much work must you do in climbing the stairs? (Suppose your weight is 700 N and the stairs are 2 m high.)

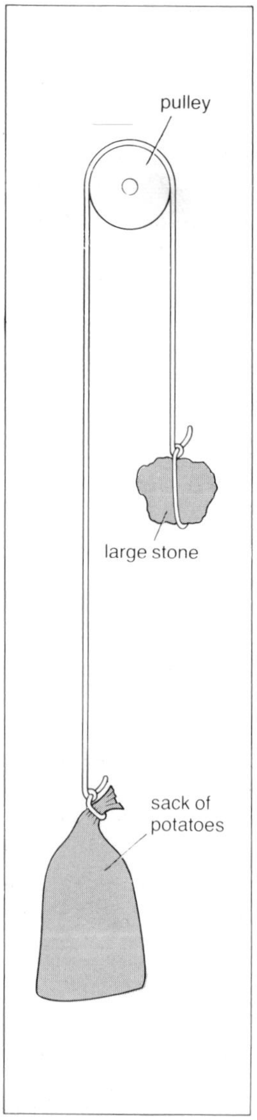

Figure 8.7 Using a falling stone to do work. As the stone falls, the sack is raised.

Energy

Energetic people can usually do lots of work. Scientists use the word *energy* in a similar way. When a machine or an object does work, it uses energy.

Energy is like 'money in the bank'. It can be saved up and then used to do work later. The work done can be compared to moving money from the bank to the shop where you want to buy something.

Energy is the ability of an object or a machine to do work.

Energy can be measured in terms of the amount of work done. Therefore, the units of energy, like those of work, are joules.

When a machine works, energy is not lost, but converted from one form into another. There are several forms of energy and some of these are described below.

Potential energy

When a stone is lifted above the ground it is given potential energy. Work has been done in lifting the stone against the force of gravity and the stone could do work when it falls (figure 8.7). Two factors affect the potential energy of the stone: its weight (the force of gravity overcome in lifting it) and its height above the ground. The greater its weight and height, the greater is its potential energy. *Anything that is lifted or pushed or pulled into a position from which it can do work is said to possess potential energy.* Other examples of objects which possess potential energy are the water behind a dam, a wound-up watch spring and a stretched rubber band.

Kinetic energy

When a stone falls from rest, it loses height and potential energy. As the stone falls, its speed increases and it is capable of doing work if it hits something. The energy of the moving stone is described as kinetic energy. Two factors affect the kinetic energy of the moving stone: its mass and its speed. The greater its mass and speed, the greater its kinetic energy. *All moving objects possess kinetic energy.*

Heat

When a moving object, like a stone or a hammer, hits the ground, friction results and heat is produced. Sometimes sparks fly. Kinetic energy in the moving object is being converted into heat.

When a substance is heated up, its molecules move faster and their kinetic energy increases. The hot, fast-moving molecules can be used to do work. For example, the fast-moving molecules in steam can be used to drive a turbine.

Chemical energy

When fuels burn, substances in the fuel combine with oxygen in the air and heat is produced. The heat comes from energy locked in the bonds between atoms in the fuel, and this is chemical energy. Foods, like bread and meat, also contain chemical energy which can be released in your body when the food combines with oxygen. The chemical energy in the food may be converted into heat to keep you warm, or into kinetic energy and potential energy in your muscles as you move around.

Electrical energy

The energy in an electric current can be used to do work. Electrical energy can be used to drive a motor and raise a heavy load such as a lift. Electricity is one of the most important ways of transmitting energy from one place to another.

Wave energy

Light waves, radio waves and sound waves also carry energy. The energy in sunlight is important in processes like photography and photosynthesis. When light hits a photographic film, it is absorbed by the chemicals on the film and turned into chemical energy. This makes a reaction occur on the photographic film (section 20.5).

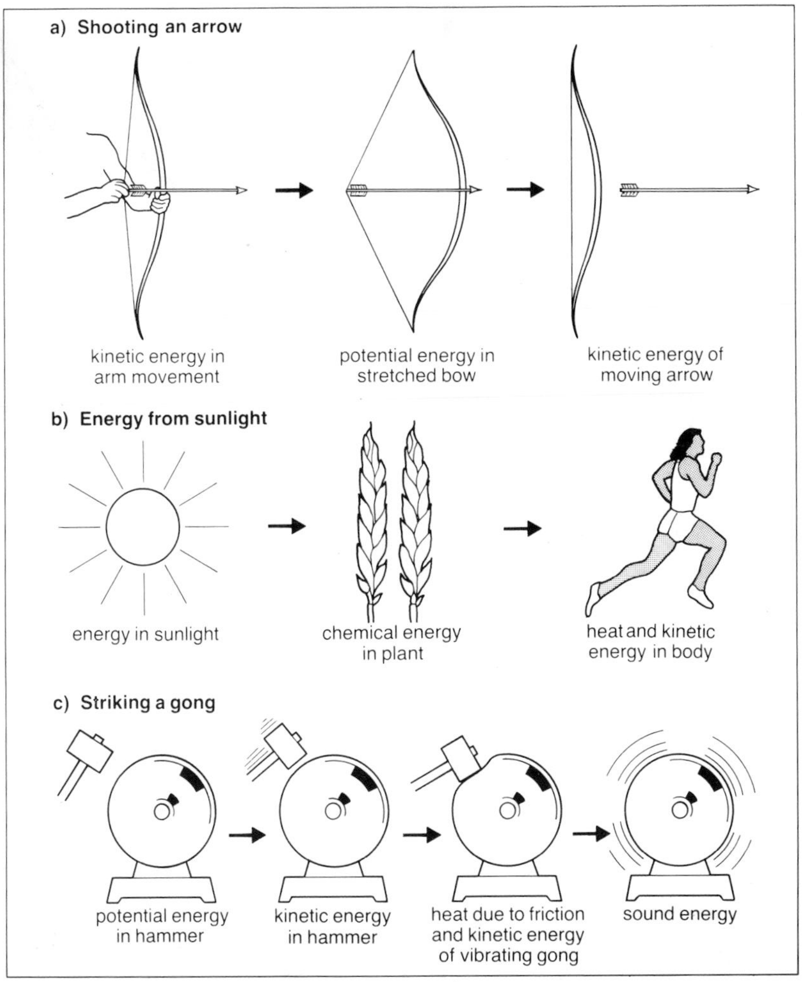

Figure 8.8 Some examples of energy conversions.

Nuclear energy

The energy stored in the nuclei of atoms is called nuclear energy. This energy is released mainly as heat and light when a nuclear reaction occurs in a nuclear (atomic) power station, or in an atomic bomb.

Figure 8.8 shows some examples of energy conversions.

- What form of energy do the following possess?
  a) a stretched violin string,
  b) a pendulum at the bottom of its swing,
  c) a pendulum at the top of its swing,
  d) a lump of plutonium,
  e) a litre of petrol,
  f) gamma rays,
  g) molten iron,
  h) noisy traffic
- What energy conversions occur when
  a) a hammer is used to hit a nail,
  b) a battery is used in a small torch,
  c) a guitar is plucked?

Power

Both engineers and athletes often talk about power. Engineers are concerned about the power of machines and athletes are interested in the power they can develop in running, jumping or throwing.

We can appreciate the power of a machine by considering a crane lifting bricks. The first thing we need to know about the crane is what load it can lift. Suppose the crane can lift 10000 kg. This means that it can overcome a gravitational force of 100000 N (assuming $g = 10\,\text{m/s}^2$). If the crane lifts 10000 kg through 10 m,

$$\begin{aligned}\text{work done by crane} &= \text{force} \times \text{distance}\\ &= 100000 \times 10\\ &= 1000000 \text{ joules}\\ &= 10^6\,\text{J}.\end{aligned}$$

This is all very well, but the crane would not be much use if it took an hour to lift the load. In order to estimate the usefulness of the crane, we also need to know how *quickly* it can do the work. If the crane does this work in 10 seconds,

$$\text{work done by crane per second} = \frac{10^6\,\text{J}}{10\,\text{s}} = 10^5\,\text{J/s}$$

The work done per second by the crane is known as its **power**:

$$\text{power} = \frac{\text{work done}}{\text{time taken}}$$

The power of a machine is the rate at which it can do work.

The crane's power is 10^5 J/s. Although power can be expressed in joules per second, scientists have agreed to use the word **watt** (W) for the unit of power in honour of James Watt, who was the first scientist to investigate the power of machines.

One watt is a rate of working of one joule per second.

We can therefore express the power of the crane in the example above as 10^5 watts or 10^5 W.

Energy, power and energy conversions are discussed further in chapter 12.

8.5 More about machines

Look closely at figure 8.9 which shows a crowbar being used to lift a heavy boulder. Taking moments about the pivot, we get:

$$\text{effort} \times \text{distance of effort from pivot} = \text{load} \times \text{distance of load from pivot}$$

$$\Rightarrow \text{effort} \times 100 = 2000 \times 10$$

$$\therefore \text{effort} = \frac{2000 \times 10}{100} = 200\,\text{N}$$

By applying an effort of only 200N at one end of the crowbar, it is possible to move a boulder (the load) which is ten times heavier. Scientists summarise this by saying that the **mechanical advantage** of the crowbar is 10. By comparing the load moved with the effort exerted, it is possible to obtain the mechanical advantage of any machine.

$$\text{mechanical advantage} = \frac{\text{load}}{\text{effort}}$$

Machines, like the crowbar, which allow heavy loads to be moved by smaller efforts have a mechanical advantage greater than one. These machines are force multipliers. Unfortunately, however, the effort has to move further than the load in these machines. In order to move the boulder 1cm (figure 8.9), the other end of the crowbar must be pushed though 10cm.

Figure 8.10 shows a diagram of the human forearm lifting a load of 10N.

- What is the clockwise moment of the load around the elbow joint?
- What effort is needed in the biceps to raise the 10N load?
- What is the mechanical advantage of the forearm?
- How much does the lower end of the biceps contract when the load is raised 15cm?

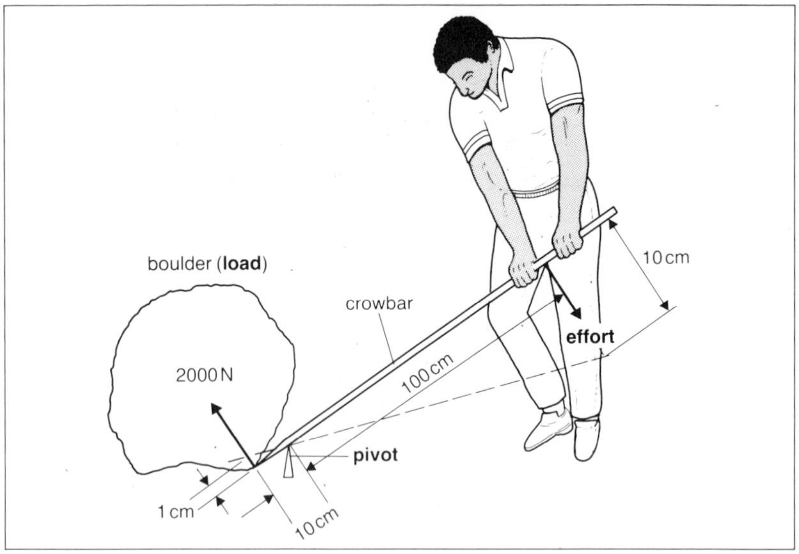

Figure 8.9

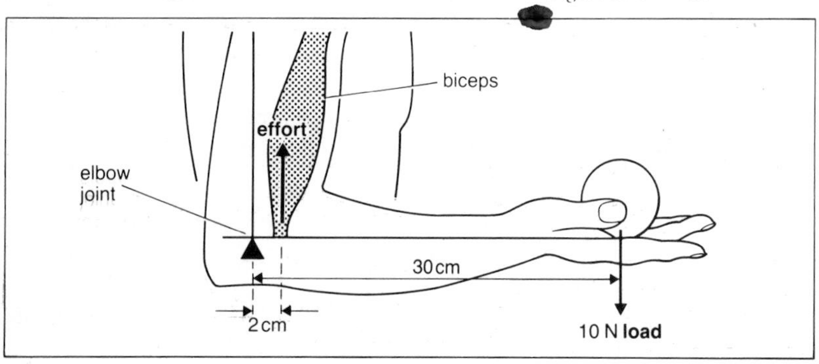

Figure 8.10

The effort exerted by the biceps muscle is 150N, which is much greater than the 10N load. The mechanical advantage is therefore less than one. This means that the arm is not as good at moving big loads as the crowbar, but it is much more mobile. A small movement in the biceps will raise the load through a much larger distance. When the load is raised 15cm, the lower end of the biceps moves only 1cm.

8.6 The efficiency of a machine

Machines can make jobs much easier, but no machine is perfect. Work is done by the effort on the machine and the machine then does work in moving the load. Energy is therefore transferred from the effort (energy input) to the load (energy output). In practice, it is impossible to transfer all the energy from the effort to the load. *Some energy is always wasted in overcoming friction and in moving and lifting the machine itself.*

Different machines waste different amounts of energy, so we use the term **efficiency** to show how well a machine transfers energy from the effort to the load.

$$\text{efficiency} = \frac{\text{energy output}}{\text{energy input}}$$

This means that

$$\therefore \text{efficiency} = \frac{\text{work done on load}}{\text{work done by effort}}$$

and since work is force × distance:

$$\text{efficiency} = \frac{\text{load} \times \text{distance load moves}}{\text{effort} \times \text{distance effort moves}}$$

Figure 8.11 shows a sailor hoisting the sail by using a pulley to change the direction of her effort.
The load from the sail is 40 N, but the yachtswoman must pull with an effort of 50 N in order to overcome the load of the sail and the friction between the rope and the pulley.

- What is the frictional force between the rope and the pulley?
- What is the mechanical advantage of the pulley?
- What length of rope does the sailor pull in if the top of the sail is raised 1 m?
- What is the efficiency of the pulley?

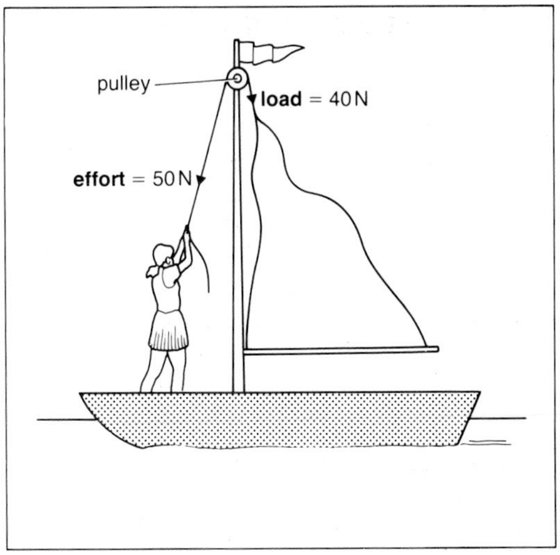

Figure 8.11 (Above) A sailor hoisting the sail using a pulley.

The muscle which raises a bird's wing works like a pulley. There are two flight muscles attached to the wing (figure 8.12). Muscle 1 pulls the wing down and muscle 2 pulls it up. The muscle which raises the wing has a tendon which runs through a hole at the point where the wing bone is attached to the main skeleton. In pulling the wing up, this muscle works like a pulley.

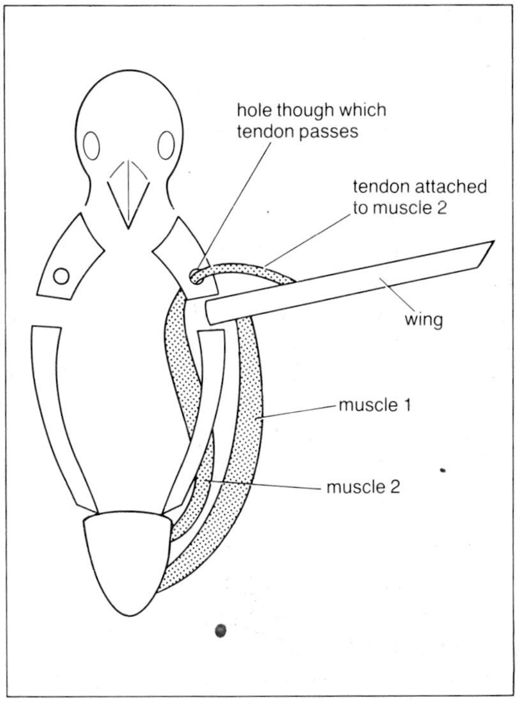

Figure 8.12 When muscle 2 contracts, the tendon pulls the wing upwards.

A much more complicated pulley system, called a **block and tackle**, is shown in figure 8.13. Blocks and tackles are used in cranes and consist of two blocks, each with one or more pulleys. In figure 8.13, the pulleys have been drawn one above the other, but normally they are arranged side by side in the pulley blocks.

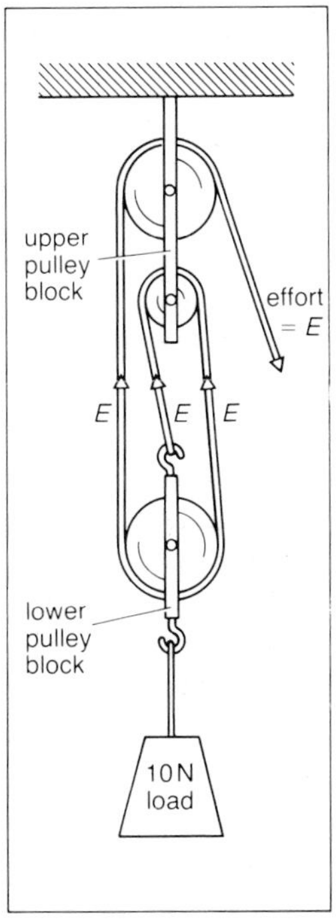

Figure 8.13 Using a block and tackle pulley system

Suppose a load of 10 N is suspended from the lower pulley block and an effort E is required to pull in the rope. Since the lower pulley block is supported by three parts of the rope, the total upward force is $3E$. Assuming the pulleys are frictionless and weightless, this upward force of $3E$ balances the downward weight of the load. This means

$$3E = 10\,\text{N}$$

So an effort of $3\frac{1}{3}$ N will raise the 10 N load.

$$\text{mechanical advantage} = \frac{\text{load}}{\text{effort}} = \frac{10}{3\frac{1}{3}} = 3$$

If the load is raised one metre, each of the three ropes supporting the lower block must shorten by one metre. This means that the end of the rope, where the effort is applied, must be pulled down a total of three metres. Thus, the effort is only one-third of the size of the load, but the effort must move three times as far as the load.

So far, we have assumed that the pulley system is 100% efficient (i.e. efficiency = 1). In practice, the pulleys are neither weightless nor frictionless, and it will require a greater effort than $3\frac{1}{3}$ N to raise the 10 N load.

Suppose that the effort actually required is 5 N.

- What is the mechanical advantage now?
- How far does the effort move when the load is raised 1 m?
- What is the efficiency?

8.7 Engines: special machines

Machines enable us to transfer energy from one thing to another and from one form to another. For example, in a hair dryer, electrical energy is changed into heat. Some machines convert the energy in chemicals (chemical energy) to heat and kinetic energy. These special machines are called **engines**. They include petrol engines, jet engines and even your body – a human engine!

The energy needed to keep you warm and enable you to move around comes from chemical energy in the foods you eat. Food is digested in the gut and broken down to smaller molecules. These smaller molecules then pass into the bloodstream and are carried round your body. Energy is released when the food molecules combine with oxygen in the cells of your body.

food + oxygen → carbon dioxide + water + energy

Figure 8.14 The four strokes in an internal combustion engine.

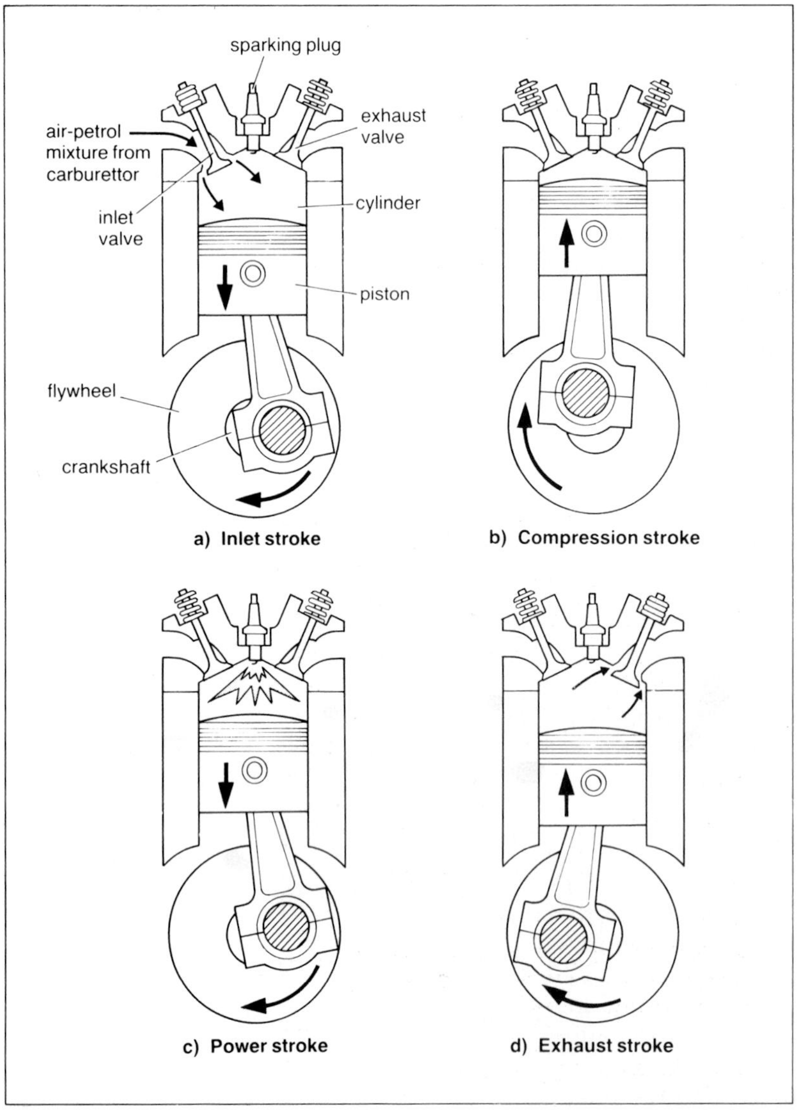

Table 8.1
The energy obtained from various foods

Food	*Energy released /kJ*
one chocolate biscuit	200
a pint of beer	500
a portion of chips	700
a slice of bread	200
a teaspoon of sugar	80
a lettuce	50
a small pat of butter (4 g)	150

This process is called **respiration** (section 14.5). An average fifteen year-old requires about 11 000 000 joules (11 000 kilojoules) per day to remain active and healthy. Table 8.1 shows the amount of energy obtained from various foods. About half of the energy from our food is used to keep us warm and maintain essential processes like breathing and digestion. The rest of the energy is needed so that our muscles can do work. The more work we do, the more food we need. The importance of foods as body fuels is discussed more fully in chapter 15.

Figure 8.14 shows a somewhat less complicated engine than the human body. The four-stroke petrol engine (sometimes called the **internal combustion engine**) converts the chemical energy in petrol into kinetic energy in a moving vehicle. It is called a **four-stroke** engine because there are four different events, or strokes. These strokes are continually repeated as the piston moves up and down its cylinder.

On the **inlet stroke**, the piston moves down and a mixture of air and petrol enters the cylinder from the carburettor (figure 8.14a). The inlet valve is open, but the exhaust valve is closed. The carburettor ensures that the air and petrol are mixed in the right proportions for explosion.

As the crankshaft passes the bottom of its cycle, the inlet valve closes, the piston starts to rise and the **compression stroke** begins (figure 8.14b). As the piston moves upwards, the mixture of air and petrol vapour inside the cylinder is compressed.

When the piston reaches its highest point in the cylinder, a spark crosses the points of the sparking plug and the **power stroke** begins (figure 8.14c). The petrol/air mixture explodes, producing hot, expanding gases which force the piston down and turn the crankshaft and the flywheel. The heavy flywheel helps the crankshaft to rotate more smoothly despite the sudden explosions on the power stroke.

Once the crankshaft reaches the bottom of its path, the piston starts to rise and the **exhaust stroke** begins (figure 8.14d). The exhaust valve opens and the burnt gases are pushed out of the cylinder. Once the piston reaches the top of its path, the inlet stroke begins again and the cycle of events is repeated.

The engines in most cars contain four cylinders in which all the pistons turn the same crankshaft (figure 8.15). However, the pistons and the sparking are arranged so that each cylinder is always on a different stroke in the cycle from the other three, This means that one cylinder is always on the power stroke and so the crankshaft and flywheel revolve more smoothly.

- What is the function of (a) the carburettor and (b) the sparking plugs?
- Why do engines have heavy flywheels?
- Why do most car engines have at least four cylinders?
- How many times does the crankshaft rotate for a complete cycle of the four strokes in one cylinder?

Some small engines, such as those in lawnmowers, mopeds and small motor boats, have **two strokes**. In these engines, the inlet stroke and the compression stroke are combined. The power stroke and the exhaust stroke are also combined.

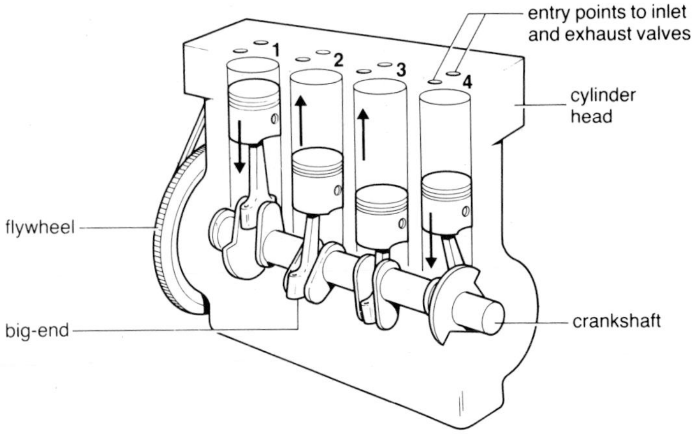

Figure 8.15 A four-cylinder engine. Notice the positions of the pistons. If the order of firing is 1 – 3 – 4 – 2 and the piston in cylinder 1 is on the power stroke, what is happening in the other cylinders?

When petrol explodes in the cylinder of an engine, chemical energy in the petrol is converted into kinetic energy in the molecules of the hot product gases. Eventually this energy is converted to kinetic energy in the moving vehicle.

petrol + oxygen → carbon dioxide + water (steam) + energy

If the petrol does not burn fully, then carbon monoxide is produced as well as carbon dioxide. All car exhaust fumes contain some carbon monoxide, which is very poisonous.

The efficiency of internal combustion engines is only about 30%. So only about one-third of the chemical energy in the petrol becomes kinetic energy in the moving vehicle. The remaining two-thirds is used in overcoming friction or is lost as heat.

Summary

1 Machines convert energy from one form to another. They enable us to exert bigger forces, to move objects through larger distances and to work faster than we can do alone.

2 Moment of a force = force × distance from fulcrum to line of action of force.

3 The law of moments. When an object is balanced: clockwise moments = anticlockwise moments.

4 The muscles and bones in our bodies act like a machine. Bones in the skeleton have three main functions. They support the body, they protect vital organs, they allow movement.

5 Work done = force × distance.

6 Energy is the ability of an object or machine to do work.

7 The power of an object or a machine is the rate at which it can do work.

8 Mechanical advantage = load/effort.

9 Efficiency = energy output/energy input.

10 Engines are machines which convert chemical energy into heat and kinetic energy. They include the human body and the internal combustion engine.

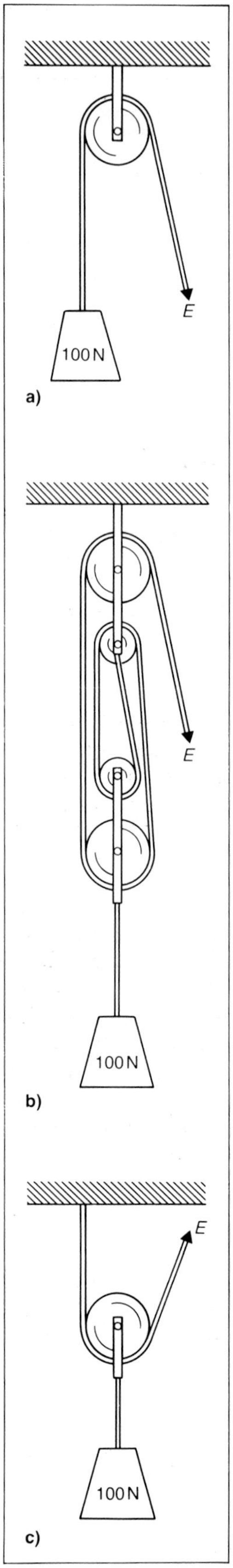

Figure 8.16

Study questions

1 a) Give one example in each case of the way in which work may be done by
   i) steam,
   ii) the force of an explosion,
   iii) electricity.
  b) About 5% of the electrical energy supplied to a light bulb is turned into light. What becomes of the remainder?

2 a) Why can a machine never be 100% efficient?
  b) A person lifts a load by raising her forearm from the elbow. Draw a simple diagram of the arrangement showing the load, the effort and the fulcrum (pivot).
  c) What advantage does this arrangement have as a machine?
  d) What disadvantage does this arrangement have as a machine?

3 a) Solar energy (energy from the Sun) is often called the Earth's main source of energy. Why is this?
  b) Nuclear energy and tidal energy may be used by people. Suggest *one advantage* and *one disadvantage* possessed by each of these forms of energy.
  c) When a person pedals a bicycle, much of the energy is wasted. Mention *three* ways in which energy losses occur.
  d) Describe *two* ways in which the efficiency of a bicycle may be improved.

4 a) Calculate the effort *E* which will raise the load of 100 N in each of the pulley systems shown in figure 8.16. (Assume that the pulley systems are weightless and frictionless.)
  b) What length of rope must be pulled in by effort *E*, if the 100 N load in system b rises 1 m?
  c) Suppose pulley system c weighs 10 N.
   i) What is the total load to be lifted?
   ii) What effort would lift this load?
   iii) What length of rope must be pulled in by effort *E*, if the 100 N load in system c rises 1 m?
  d) Which of these three pulley systems are force multipliers? Explain your answer.

5 a) A metre rule just balances at the 20 cm mark when a weight of 2 N is hung at the 5 cm mark.
   i) Draw a diagram of the balanced metre rule.
   ii) What is the moment of the 2 N weight about the balance point?
   iii) Why does the metre rule not tip over under the action of the 2 N weight?
   iv) Calculate the weight of the metre rule.

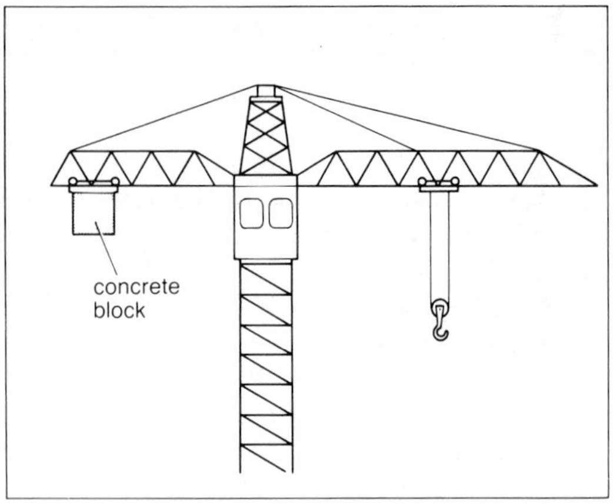

Figure 8.17

  b) Figure 8.17 shows the top of a large crane.
   i) What is the purpose of the concrete block?
   ii) How should the position of the concrete block change when the crane is lifting a heavy load?

6 A girl of mass 60 kg runs up a flight of stairs 12 m high in 10 seconds.
  a) What is the girl's weight in newtons ($g = 10\,m/s^2$).
  b) What work does the girl do in lifting her body to the top of the stairs?
  c) What average power does the girl develop during the ten seconds?

7 A farmer wishes to bridge a river, 10 m wide, using a uniform plank 15 m long and 500 kg in mass (figure 8.18). The farmer presses down at the end of the plank so that it does not turn about the point X.
  a) Explain what is meant by (i) the moment of a force and (ii) the principle of moments.
  b) What is the weight of the plank in newtons? ($g = 10\,m/s^2$)
  c) Calculate the force *F* which just allows the plank to reach the other side of the river in a horizontal position.

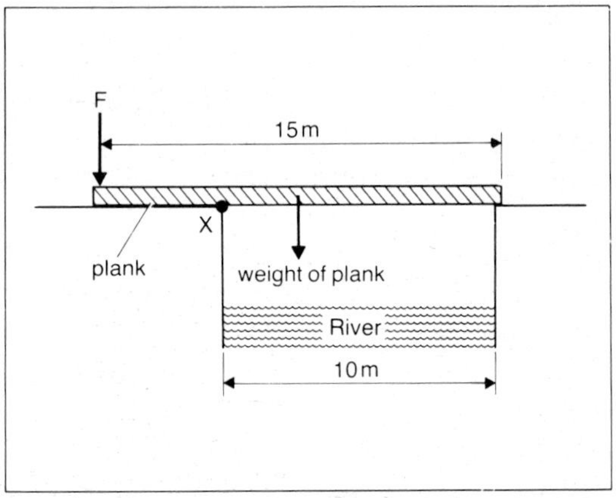

Figure 8.18

9 Electric charge

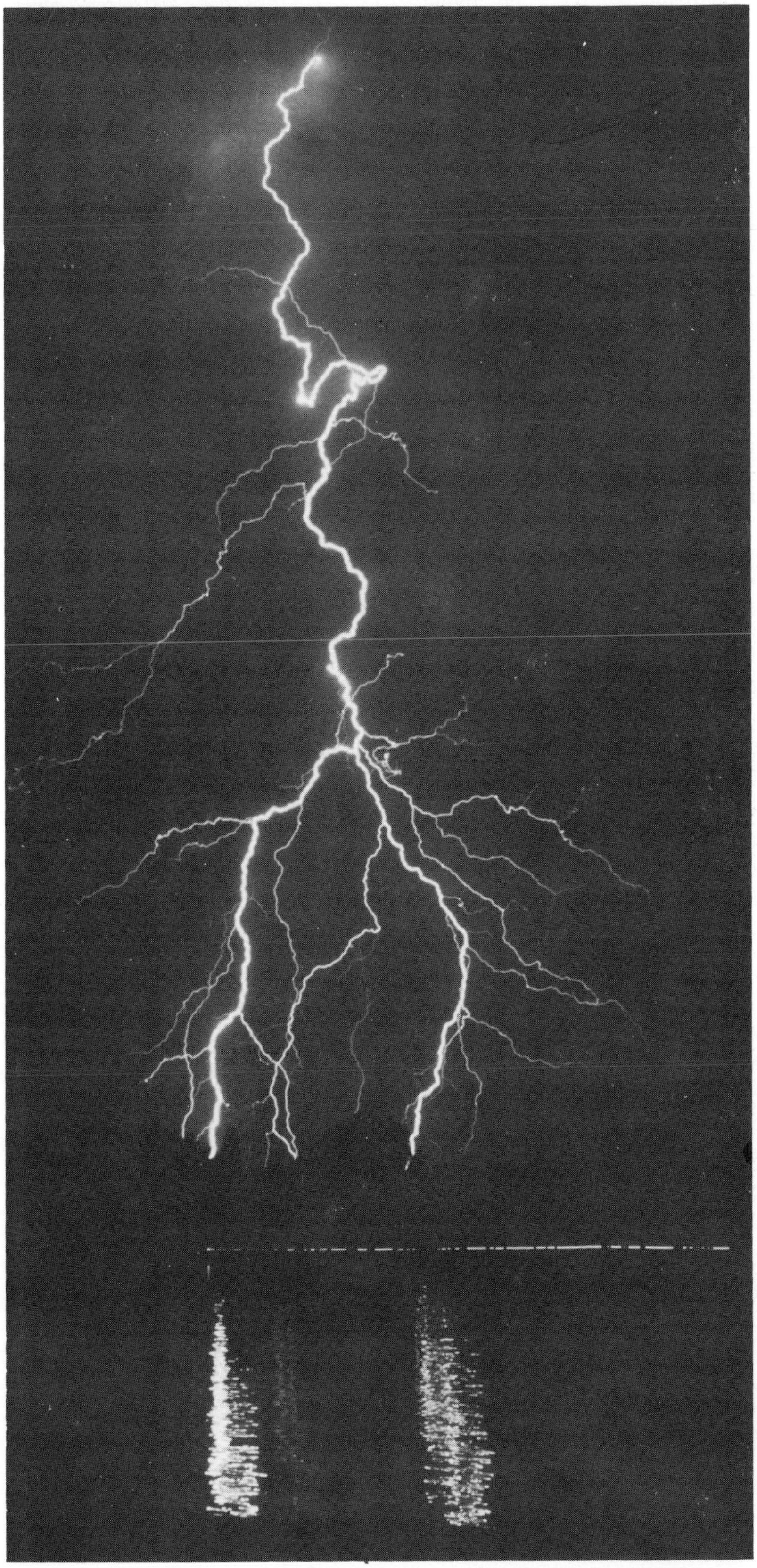

Electric charges cause lightning flashes, they make dust stick to records, and they enable us to use many thousands of electrical gadgets.

9.1 Invisible forces

Comb your hair quickly and then use the comb to pick up tiny pieces of paper.

- Why does the comb pick up bits of paper?
- What are the invisible forces acting on the paper?
- The comb has become *charged*, but where did the charge come from?
- Rub your hand over the comb and see if it will pick up the paper now.

Finding out about charges

Table 9.1 (overleaf) summarises what happens when strips of polythene and cellulose acetate (a clear plastic) are rubbed with a woollen cloth and then brought together, but with one strip free to move (figure 9.1). If the charged strips are made of the same material they always *repel*. But when one charged strip is polythene and the other is cellulose acetate, they *attract* each other.

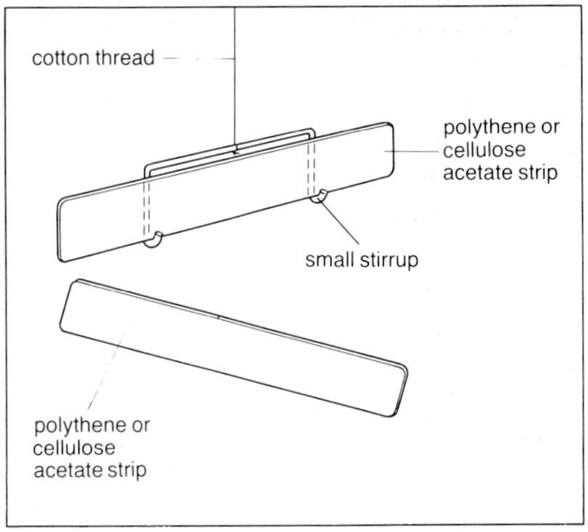

Figure 9.1 (Above) Simple experiments with charged strips of polythene and cellulose acetate.

Two pieces of polythene rubbed with the same woollen cloth must have the same charge, and these repel each other. The same applies to two pieces of cellulose acetate. But the polythene strips attract the cellulose acetate, so these two must be charged differently.

This experiment suggests that there are two kinds of electric charge. Halfway through the eighteenth century, Benjamin Franklin suggested the terms **positive** and **negative** for the two kinds of charge.

> *Polythene becomes negatively charged when it is rubbed with wool.*
> - What kind of charge do you think the wool might have?
> - What kind of charge does cellulose acetate get when it is rubbed with wool?

Franklin and Millikan – ideas about charge

Franklin explained his experiments with charged objects by imagining that the electric charge was a kind of 'fluid', which could be rubbed off one material onto another.

By 1900, scientists thought that Franklin's 'electric fluid' consisted of tiny charged particles, which they called *electrons*. Between 1910 and 1916, the American scientist, Robert Millikan, obtained more information about these charged particles. He found that the charge on one electron was 1.6×10^{-19} coulombs. (The coulomb as a unit of charge is explained more fully in section 10.4.)

Inside atoms

Scientists now believe that atoms are composed of three particles: **protons**, **neutrons** and **electrons**. These are the *building blocks* for atoms. The centre of the atom, called the **nucleus**, contains protons and neutrons. Protons have positive charge, and neutrons have no charge. Electrons occupy the outer parts of the atom and move around the nucleus.

The negative charge on one electron just balances the positive charge on one proton. Thus, atoms have equal numbers of protons and electrons, giving them equal amounts of positive and negative charge. For example, carbon atoms have 6 protons, 6 electrons and 6 neutrons (figure 9.2), whereas sodium atoms have 11 protons, 11 electrons and 12 neutrons.

Table 9.1

Which strip was in the stirrup?	*Which strip was brought close?*	*Result*
polythene	polythene	strips move apart *(repulsion)*
cellulose acetate	cellulose acetate	strips move apart *(repulsion)*
polythene	cellulose acetate	strips move closer *(attraction)*
cellulose acetate	polythene	strips move closer *(attraction)*

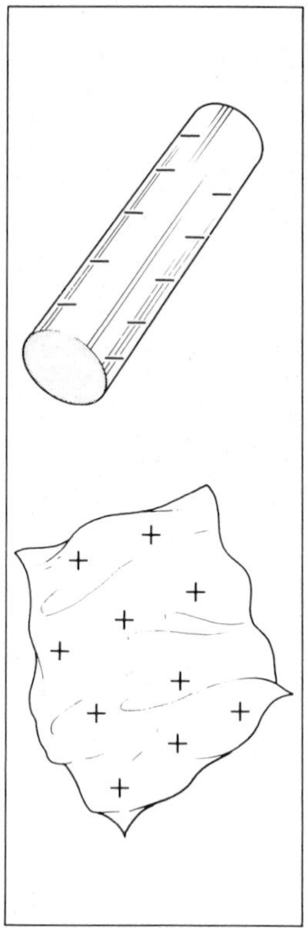

Figure 9.3 Charging a polythene strip by rubbing with a cloth.

Charging by rubbing

When a strip of polythene is rubbed with a cloth, the strip pulls electrons off the particles in the cloth. The polythene then has more electrons than protons and therefore it has a negative charge over all. The cloth has fewer electrons than protons and so it has a positive charge over all (figure 9.3).

When cellulose acetate is rubbed with wool, the cellulose acetate is left with a positive charge.

> - Have electrons moved from the cellulose acetate to the wool, or vice versa?
> - What is the charge on the wool?
> - Does the wool now have more protons than electrons, or vice versa?

Like charges repel, unlike charges attract

When you bring your charged comb near a tiny piece of paper, the negative charge on the comb repels electrons from the area of the paper nearest to it (figure 9.4). This part of the paper therefore becomes positive and

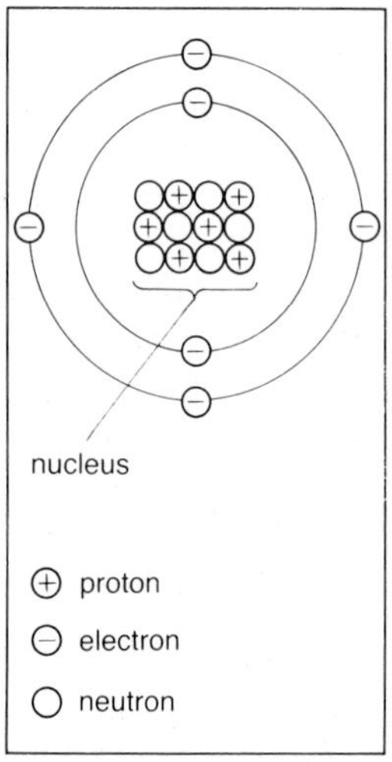

Figure 9.2 (Above) Electrons, protons and neutrons in an atom of carbon.

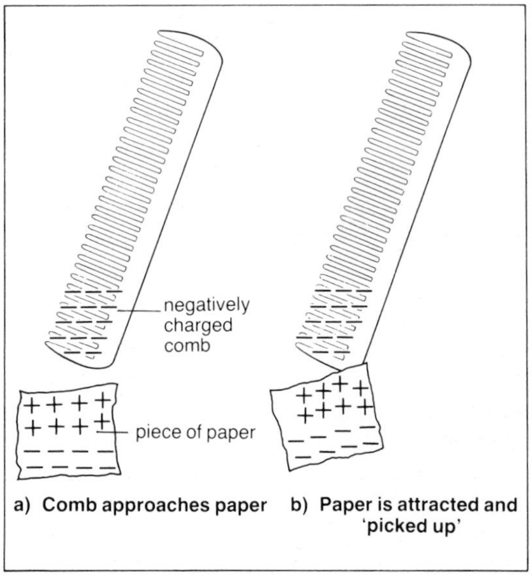

Figure 9.4 (Above).

it is attracted to the comb because *unlike charges attract*. If the paper is light enough it can be picked up.

This attraction between unlike charges also makes dust stick to records and it causes tiny crackles and sparks when you take off nylon or Terylene clothing. As you move around, your clothes rub on each other and leave one layer negative and the other positive. Tiny crackles and sparks result when electrons jump through the air from the negative garment to the positive one.

A similar process occurs during lightning. Millions of electrons rush through the air, from a region of negative charge to one that is positive, causing a flash of light. If the underside of a cloud is positively charged, it will **induce** a negative charge on the ground below. A lightning flash will occur when electrons jump from the ground to the cloud. The electrons are most likely to jump from the highest point below the cloud such as a tall tree, a chimney or a church spire. Air in the path of the enormous lightning spark suddenly gets very hot and then cools and contracts. This produces a sound wave which is heard as thunder.

- Why do you see lightning before you hear thunder?

Many tall buildings are fitted with lightning conductors to reduce the possibility of damage. Lightning conductors consist of a thick metal cable running from a pointed rod at the highest point of the building to a metal plate buried in the ground. If a positively charged thunder cloud passes over the building, negative charge is induced on the pointed rod. Electrons collect on the point of the conductor and cause air particles nearby to become negatively charged. These negative particles are attracted to the positive charge on the cloud. This reduces the charge on the cloud and a lightning flash becomes less likely.

Insulators and conductors

Materials such as polythene which hold their charge on rubbing and do not allow electrons to pass through them are called **insulators**.

Materials that allow electrons to pass through them are known as **conductors**. Conductors have electrons that are easily dislodged. In insulators the electrons cling to their parent atoms.

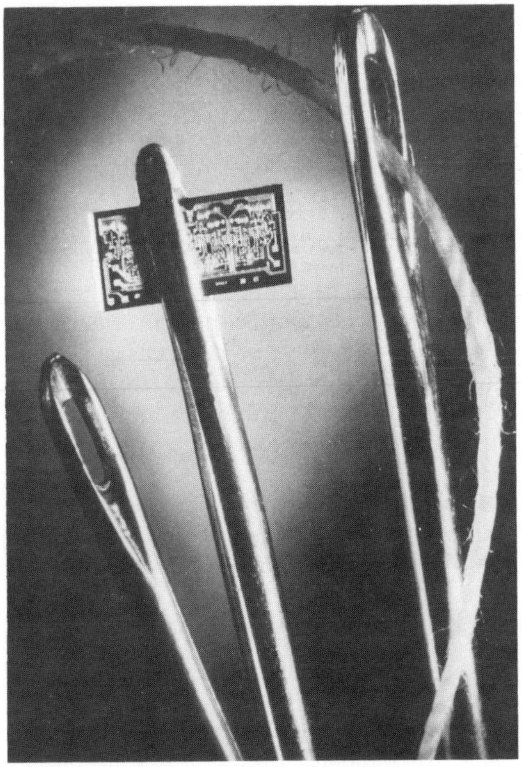

The silicon chip going through the eye of an ordinary sewing needle contains over 120 circuit components.

- What materials are used as conductors in electric wires and cables?
- What materials are used as insulators for electric wires and cables?

9.2 Charge transfer

Metals such as copper, iron and aluminium, which are good conductors and easily made into wire, are used for cables, fuses and wiring in electrical devices. Plastics such as polythene, cellulose acetate and PVC are often used to insulate wires and cables.

A few substances with special conducting properties are called **semiconductors**. Silicon and germanium containing a trace of impurity are two of the best known semiconductors. Devices made from these substances can provide a very high resistance to the flow of electrons in one direction and a very low resistance to the flow of electrons in the other direction. Semiconductors of this kind form an important part of any transistor. In some cases, hundreds of these tiny transistors can be built up on a small flat plate forming a silicon chip.

Electric wires and cables are often made of copper because electrons can move through it easily – it is a good conductor. *An electric current is a flow of electrons*. Look at

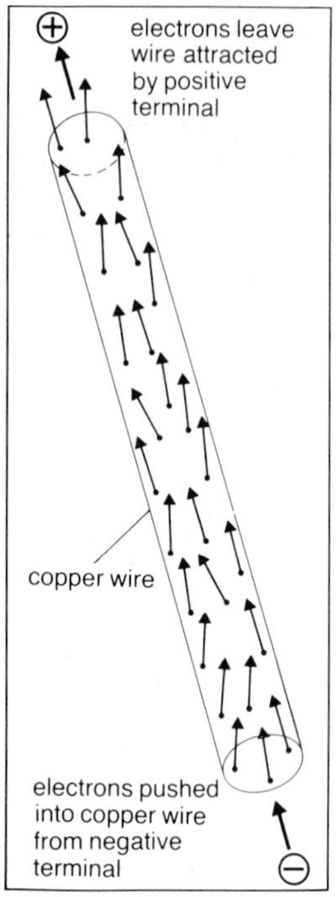

Figure 9.5 Movement of electrons along a wire.

figure 9.5. Some of the electrons in the copper can move freely through the metal. They are pulled (attracted) towards the positive terminal of the battery as extra electrons are pushed (repelled) into the copper wire from the negative terminal (figure 9.5).

Which solids conduct electricity?

The apparatus in figure 9.6a can be used to test whether a solid conducts electricity. The circuit includes two dry cells, a switch, and an ammeter to measure the current. When two or more cells are connected in this way, they make a **battery**.

- What happens if the solid conducts when the switch is closed?
- Which of the following solids will conduct?
  a) sulphur b) steel c) aluminium
  d) salt

Experiments show that *the only common solids which conduct electricity well are metals and graphite*. No solid compound will conduct electricity. This experiment is, therefore, a useful means of testing for metals.

Scientists use **circuit diagrams** to show the various parts of a circuit quickly and conveniently. Each piece of equipment is shown by a symbol. Figure 9.6b shows a circuit diagram for the apparatus in figure 9.6a.

- What is the symbol for (a) a switch, (b) a bulb and (c) an ammeter?
- Figure 9.6b shows the symbol for a battery of two cells. What is the symbol for one cell?
- Does the longer stroke represent the positive or the negative side of the cell?

Figure 9.6 Testing the conductivity of a solid.

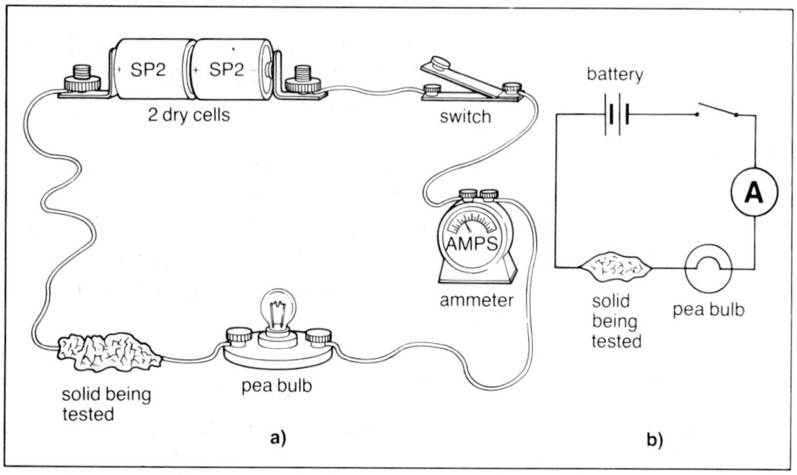

Can charge move through liquids?

Experiments show that *compounds containing both metals and non-metals such as sodium chloride, lead bromide and copper sulphate will conduct electricity when they are molten (liquid) and when they are dissolved in water (aqueous)*. Liquids and aqueous compounds made of non-metals, such as water (H_2O), alcohol (C_2H_5OH) and sugar do *not* conduct electricity.

Figure 9.7 shows what happens when molten sodium chloride conducts electricity. The electrode connected to the positive side of the battery is called the **anode**, that connected to the negative side of the battery is called the **cathode**. The battery pulls elecrons off the anode and pushes them on to the cathode. When the liquid conducts electricity, pale-green chlorine is produced at the anode and a shiny bead of sodium forms at the cathode. Compounds, like sodium chloride, that conduct electricity are called **electrolytes**. When an electric current passes through these electrolytes, they decompose at the electrodes. This decomposition of a molten or aqueous compound by electricity is called **electrolysis**. The energy which causes the chemical changes during electrolysis is provided by the battery.

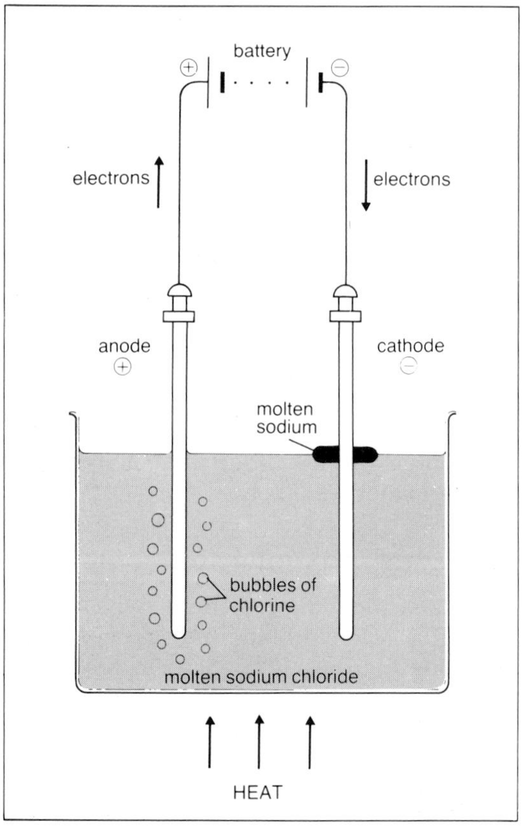

Figure 9.7 (Above) The electrolysis of sodium chloride.

How does the electric current flow through the electrolyte?

Sodium particles in the electrolyte must be positive since they are attracted to the cathode, which is negative. At the same time chlorine is produced at the anode.

- What is the charge on the anode?
- Are chloride particles positive or negative?

The formula of sodium chloride is NaCl so we can think of this as positively charged Na^+ particles and negatively charged Cl^- particles. Since sodium chloride is neutral, the positive charge on one Na^+ balances the negative charge on one Cl^-.

Charged particles, like Na^+ and Cl^-, which move to the electrodes during electrolysis are called **ions**. When Na^+ ions reach the cathode, they combine with the negative electrons on the cathode forming neutral sodium atoms.

$$\underset{\text{sodium ion in electrolyte}}{Na^+} + \underset{\text{electron from cathode}}{e^-} \rightarrow \underset{\text{sodium atom}}{Na}$$

When Cl^- ions reach the anode they lose their extra electron to the positive anode and form neutral chlorine atoms.

$$\underset{\text{chloride ion in electrolyte}}{Cl^-} \rightarrow \underset{\text{electron given to anode}}{e^-} + \underset{\text{chlorine atom}}{Cl}$$

In this way Na^+ ions remove electrons from the cathode, whilst Cl^- ions give up electrons to the anode. The electric current is being carried through the molten sodium chloride by ions. The electrolysis of other molten and aqueous substances can also be explained in terms of ions.

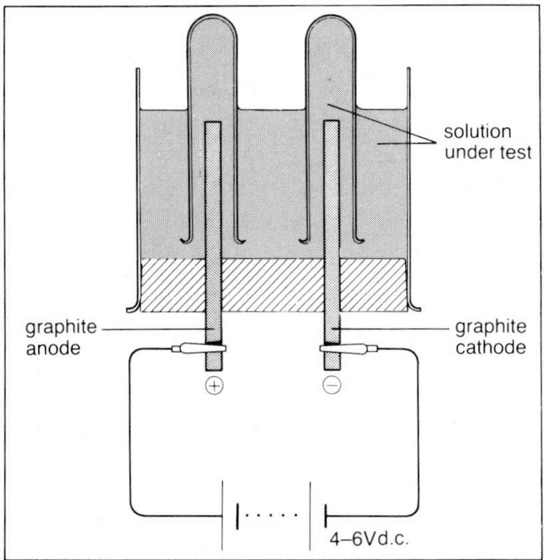

Figure 9.8 Investigating the products at the electrodes.

9.3 Charges on ions

What happens when ionic substances conduct electricity? Which ions are positive and which are negative? Figure 9.8 shows the apparatus which can be used to investigate the products at the electrodes when aqueous solutions of ionic compounds are electrolysed. The results of four experiments are shown in table 9.2.

Table 9.2
Products at the electrodes during electrolysis

Solution tested	*Product at anode*	*Product at cathode*
potassium iodide	iodine (turns solution brown)	hydrogen gas (burns with a pop)
copper chloride	chlorine gas (bleaches litmus paper)	copper (brown deposit)
zinc bromide	bromine (turns solution brown)	zinc (grey deposit)
silver nitrate	oxygen (relights glowing splint)	silver (dark grey deposit)

Look at table 9.2.

- What kind of element is produced at the anode?
- What kind of element is usually produced at the cathode?
- What elements do you think will form at the anode and cathode when aqueous sodium chloride is electrolysed?

When molten or aqueous compounds of a metal with a non-metal conduct electricity:

- metals or hydrogen are formed at the negative cathode,
- non-metals (except hydrogen) are formed at the positive anode.

Since the negative cathode will only attract positive charges and the positive anode will only attract negative charges, this means that:

Metals and hydrogen have positive ions.

Non-metals (except hydrogen) have negative ions.

Measuring the charge on an ion

The amount of charge required to deposit one mole of copper (63.5 g) can be measured using the apparatus in figure 9.9. The rheostat is used to keep the current constant and quite low. If the current is too large, the copper deposits too rapidly and will not stick to the cathode.

- Make sure the copper cathode is clean and dry and then weigh it.
- Connect up the circuit and pass the current for at least 45 minutes.
- Now, remove the cathode, wash it in distilled water and then acetone.
- When it is completely dry, reweigh it.

Here are some typical results:

Mass of copper cathode before electrolysis = 46.36 g
Mass of copper cathode after electrolysis = 46.48 g
∴ Mass of copper deposited = 0.12 g
Time of electrolysis = 60 min = 3600 s
Current = 0.1 A

The quantity of charge passed is equal to current × time (see section 10.4)

$$\text{quantity of charge passed} = 0.1\,\text{A} \times 3600\,\text{s} = 360 \text{ coulombs}$$

From these results:

0.12 g of copper is deposited by 360 coulombs

$$\therefore\ 1\,\text{g of copper is deposited by } \frac{360}{0.12} \text{ coulombs}$$

$\Rightarrow$ 1 mole of copper (63.5 g) is deposited by

$$\frac{360}{0.12} \times 63.5 \text{ coulombs} = 190500 \text{ coulombs}$$

Accurate experiments show that one mole of copper is deposited by 193 000 coulombs. This is the quantity of charge which passes through a one-bar electric fire in thirteen hours. Table 9.3 shows the quantity of charge required to produce one mole of atoms of five different elements. Notice that twice as much charge is required to produce one mole of copper as one mole of sodium. Exactly three times as much charge is required for one mole of aluminium.

When molten liquids and aqueous solutions are electrolysed, the quantity of electric charge needed to produce one mole of atoms is always a multiple of 96 500 coulombs (the quantity is 96 500, or 193 000 = 96 500 × 2, or 289 500 = 96 500 × 3). Because of this, 965000 coulombs is called the **Faraday constant** in honour of Michael Faraday. Faraday was the first scientist to

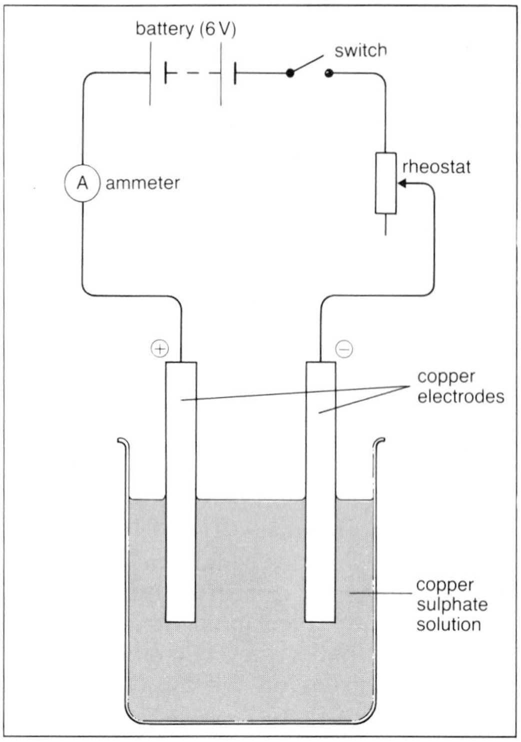

Figure 9.9 Electrolysis of copper sulphate solution.

carry out measurements on the masses of elements produced during electrolysis.

During electrolysis, the positive charge on one mole of sodium ions is 'neutralised' by 96 500 coulombs of negative charge from electrons on the cathode. Since one electron carries of 1.6×10^{-19} coulombs, the number of electrons carrying 96 500 coulombs will be

$$\frac{96500}{1.6 \times 10^{-19}} = 6 \times 10^{23}$$

6×10^{23} electrons is one mole of electrons. Thus, one mole of sodium ions requires one mole of electrons, or in other words one sodium ion requires one electron. We can write this as:

$$\underset{\text{sodium ion}}{Na^+} + \underset{\text{electron}}{e^-} \rightarrow \underset{\text{sodium atom}}{Na}$$

Twice as much charge is required to produce one mole of copper, so the copper ion can be written as Cu^{2+}.

> *Look at table 9.3.*
> - What is the charge on one aluminium ion?
> - What is the charge on one silver ion?
> - What is the charge on one lead ion?

Table 9.4 shows a list of some ions with their charges. *Most metal ions have a charge of* 2^+. The only common metal ions without a charge of 2^+ are Na^+, K^+, Ag^+, Al^{3+}, Fe^{3+} and Cr^{3+}.

Table 9.3
The quantity of charge required to produce one mole of some elements

Element	*Number of Coulombs required to produce 1 mole of atoms*
copper	193 000
sodium	96 500
silver	96 500
lead	193 000
aluminium	289 500

Table 9.4
The charges on some common ions

Positive ions			Negative ions	
+1	+2	+3	−1	−2
hydrogen H^+ sodium Na^+ potassium K^+ silver Ag^+	copper Cu^{2+} lead Pb^{2+} iron(II) Fe^{2+} zinc Zn^{2+} magnesium Mg^{2+}	aluminium Al^{3+} iron(III) Fe^{3+} chromium Cr^{3+}	bromide Br^- chloride Cl^- hydroxide OH^- iodide I^- nitrate NO_3^-	oxide O^{2-} sulphide S^{2-} carbonate CO_3^{2-} sulphate SO_4^{2-} sulphite SO_3^{2-}

9.4 Ionic compounds

Common salt, lime, limestone and fertilisers all contain ions, they are called **ionic compounds**. How do their ions form, what are their structures like and what properties do they have in common?

The Seven Sisters chalk cliffs in East Sussex are made of an ionic compound. Chalk is calcium carbonate, $CaCO_3$.

Forming ionic compounds, electron transfer

When metals react with non-metals, they form ionic compounds. For example, when sodium burns in chlorine, the elements combine to form sodium chloride, which contains sodium ions and chloride ions.

$$\underset{\text{sodium atom}}{Na} + \underset{\text{chlorine atom}}{Cl} \rightarrow \underbrace{\underset{\text{sodium ion}}{Na^+}\ \underset{\text{chloride ion}}{Cl^-}}_{\text{sodium chloride}}$$

Each sodium atom gives up one electron during the reaction and forms a sodium ion.

$$Na \rightarrow Na^+ + e^-$$

The electron is taken by a chlorine atom to form a chloride ion.

$$Cl + e^- \rightarrow Cl^-$$

When ionic compounds form, metal atoms lose electrons and form positive ions, whereas non-metal atoms gain electrons and form negative ions.

The reactions between metals and non-metals can be imagined as competitions for electrons. Metals are keen to form positive ions and have a weak attraction for electrons compared to non-metals, which gain the electrons to form negative ions. This is like the business world of supply and demand. Metals supply the electrons which non-metals demand.

When calcium reacts with oxygen to form calcium oxide, the calcium atoms readily give up electrons forming Ca^{2+} ions. These electrons are grabbed by oxygen atoms, forming oxide ions (O^{2-}):

$$\left.\begin{array}{l} Ca \rightarrow Ca^{2+} + 2e^- \\ O + 2e^- \rightarrow O^{2-} \end{array}\right\} Ca + O \rightarrow \underset{\substack{\text{calcium oxide} \\ \text{(lime)}}}{Ca^{2+}O^{2-}}$$

Formulae and structure of ionic compounds

- Ionic compounds are held together by strong forces of attraction between positive ions and negative ions. This is called **ionic bonding**.
- The strong ionic bonds hold the ions tightly together. The ions cannot move and this is why solid ionic compounds do not conduct electricity.

When ionic compounds form, the charges on the positive ions just balance the charges on the negative ions. Thus, we could predict that the formula of sodium chloride would be Na^+Cl^- (NaCl). *By balancing the charges on ions, we can predict the formula of any ionic compound.* Table 9.5 (overleaf) gives some examples.

The formula shows the ratio of the numbers of ions present in the ionic compound.

- What is the formula of (a) iron(III) chloride, (b) calcium sulphate and (c) copper oxide?
- What ions are present in the following compounds: (a) Ag_2S, (b) $Pb(OH)_2$, (c) $AlBr_3$ and (d) $FeCl_2$?

Table 9.5
Predicting the formulae of ionic compounds

Name of compound	*Ions in compound*		*Formula*	
lime (calcium oxide)	Ca^{2+}	O^{2-}	$Ca^{2+}O^{2-}$	CaO
iron ore (iron(III) oxide)	Fe^{3+}	O^{2-}	$(Fe^{3+})_2(O^{2-})_3$	Fe_2O_3
copper sulphate	Cu^{2+}	SO_4^{2-}	$Cu^{2+}SO_4^{2-}$	$CuSO_4$
calcium chloride	Ca^{2+}	Cl^-	$Ca^{2+}Cl^-_2$	$CaCl_2$
chalk (calcium carbonate)	Ca^{2+}	CO_3^{2-}	$Ca^{2+}CO_3^{2-}$	$CaCO_3$

X-ray analysis and electron microscope photographs show that the ions in different ionic compounds can be arranged in various patterns. One of the most important structures for ionic compounds is the **simple cubic structure**. Sodium chloride (common salt) and calcium oxide (lime) are good examples of ionic solids with simple cubic structures. The cubic shape of NaCl crystals can be seen clearly under a microscope.

Figure 9.10 shows a diagram of the structure of sodium chloride. Each dot shows the centre of an ion. Notice that the ions are arranged in a cubic pattern. Although figure 9.10 shows only a small number of ions, there are millions of ions in even the tiniest crystal of sodium chloride. Because of this, the structures of sodium chloride and other ionic compounds are described as **giant ionic structures**.

Figure 9.10 The structure of sodium chloride.

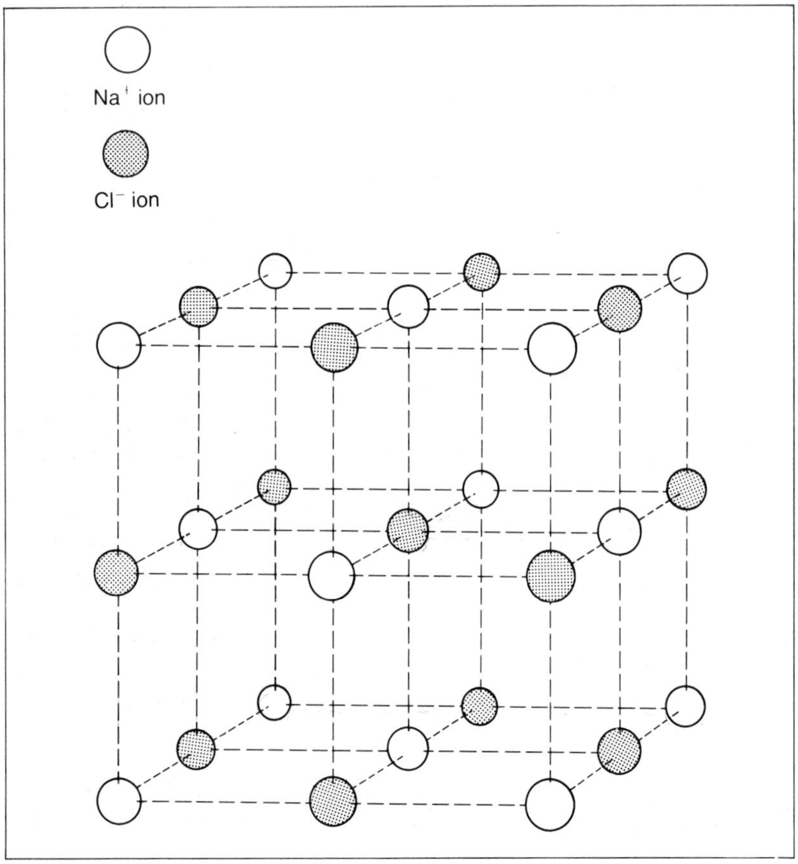

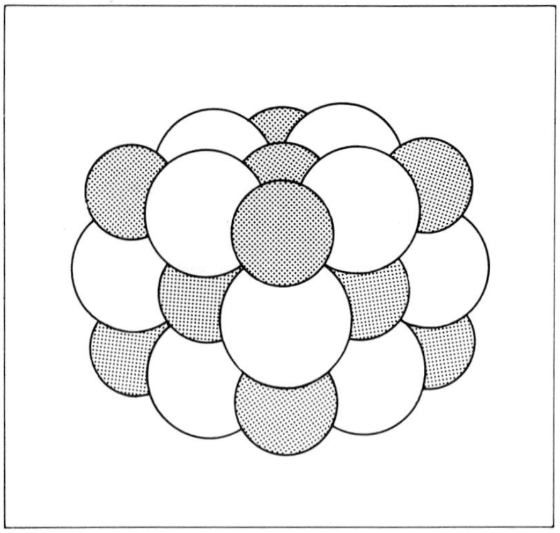

Figure 9.11 A model of the structure of sodium chloride.

Figure 9.11 shows a model of the structure of sodium chloride. Unlike figure 9.10, the whole ions are shown, not just their centres.

- How many Na^+ ions surround each Cl^- ion?
- How many Cl^- ions surround each Na^+ ion?
- Why are ionic substance so hard?

Forming molecular compounds, electron sharing

Metals can be mixed with each other to form alloys, but they *never* react with each other to form compounds. For example, copper and zinc form the alloy brass, but the two metals cannot react chemically because they both want to lose electrons.

Unlike metals, two non-metals can react with each other and form a compound, even though they both want to gain electrons. These non-metal/non-metal compounds consist of molecules, and do not contain ions. They are therefore called **molecular compounds**. Water (H_2O), hydrogen chloride (HCl) and sugar ($C_{12}H_{22}O_{11}$) are examples of simple molecular compounds.

When two non-metals react to form a molecule, the regions of electrons in the non-metal atoms overlap so that each gains negative charge. The electrons in the region of overlap belong to both atoms. Each positive nucleus attracts the electrons in the region of overlap and this holds the two atoms together. This type of bond formed by electron sharing between two atoms is known as a **covalent bond** (figure 9.12).

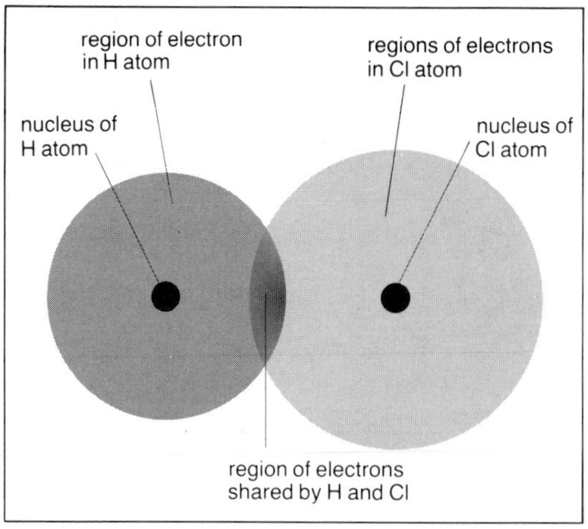

Figure 9.12 A simple model of a molecule of hydrogen chloride.

Notice that covalent bonding, like ionic bonding, involves the attraction between opposite charges. Covalent bonds hold the atoms together *within* a molecule. There are also bonds holding the different molecules to one another in molecular solids like sugar and molecular liquids like water. These bonds *between* different molecules are known as **intermolecular bonds**.

In a sample of water, there are strong covalent bonds between the two hydrogen atoms and the oxygen atom *within* each molecule of H_2O. There are also weak intermolecular bonds *between* the different molecules of H_2O (section 26.2).

Typical properties of ionic and simple molecular compounds.

Salt (NaCl) and sugar ($C_{12}H_{22}O_{11}$) have very different properties because of the way in which they are bonded. The differences between them are typical of the differences between ionic compounds and simple molecular compounds (table 9.6).

Table 9.6
Typical properties of ionic and simple molecular compounds

	Ionic compounds (e.g. NaCl, CaO)	*Simple molecular compounds (e.g. H_2O, sugar)*
Structure	giant structure of positive and negative ions	separate small uncharged molecules
Bonding	attraction of positive ions for negative ions, strong ionic bonds	strong covalent bonds hold atoms *within* the molecules; weak molecular bonds *between* separate molecules
Properties		
Melting point	high, solids at room temperature	low, usually liquids or gases at room temperature
hardness	hard solids	soft when solid
conduction of electricity	conduct when molten or aqueous, but not when solid	do not conduct when molten or aqueous, or when solid

Table 9.7
The activity series of metals

sodium	very reactive metals
magnesium	↑
aluminium	
zinc	increasing reactivity
iron	
lead	
copper	↓
silver	unreactive metals

9.5 Using electrolysis

Electrolysis is used in industry to manufacture and purify certain metals, and for electroplating.

Manufacturing metals by electrolysis

Reactive metals, high in the activity series (table 9.7), such as sodium, magnesium and aluminium, cannot be obtained by reducing their oxides with carbon (coke). These metals can only be obtained by electrolysis of their *molten* compounds. It is no use electrolysing aqueous solutions of their compounds because hydrogen (from the water) would be produced at the cathode in preference to the metal. For example, when aqueous sodium chloride is electrolysed, hydrogen is produced at the cathode, *not* sodium.

Metals, like copper and silver, which are low in the activity series, can be obtained either by reducing their compounds or by electrolysing their *aqueous* compounds. When their aqueous compounds are electrolysed, the metal rather than hydrogen (from the water), is produced at the cathode.

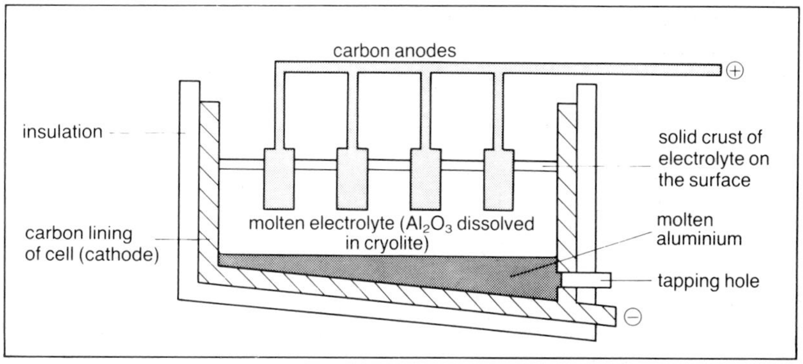

Figure 9.13 The electrolytic cell for the manufacture of aluminium.

Manufacturing aluminium by electrolysis

Aluminium is manufactured by the electrolysis of molten aluminium oxide, obtained from bauxite. Pure aluminium oxide will not melt until 2045°C, so it is dissolved in molten cryolite (Na_3AlF_6), which melts below 900°C. Figure 9.13 shows a diagram of the electrolytic cell that is used.

Aluminium ions (Al^{3+}) are attracted to the carbon cathode lining the cell, where they accept electrons to form aluminium.

$$Al^{3+} + 3e^- \rightarrow Al$$

The molten aluminium collects at the bottom of the cell and is tapped off from time to time.

Oxide ions (O^{2-}) are attracted to the carbon anodes, to which they give electrons leaving oxygen atoms:

$O^{2-} \rightarrow O + 2e^-$

The oxygen atoms then combine in pairs to form oxygen gas (O_2).

In order to keep the cost of aluminium production as low as possible, extraction plants are usually sited near sources of cheap hydroelectricity.

Purifying copper by electrolysis

Metals low in the activity series can be purified by electrolysis of their aqueous solutions. Pure copper, for electrical wires and cables, is obtained by the electrolysis of copper sulphate solution. The impure copper acts as the anode and the cathode is a thin sheet of pure copper (figure 9.14).

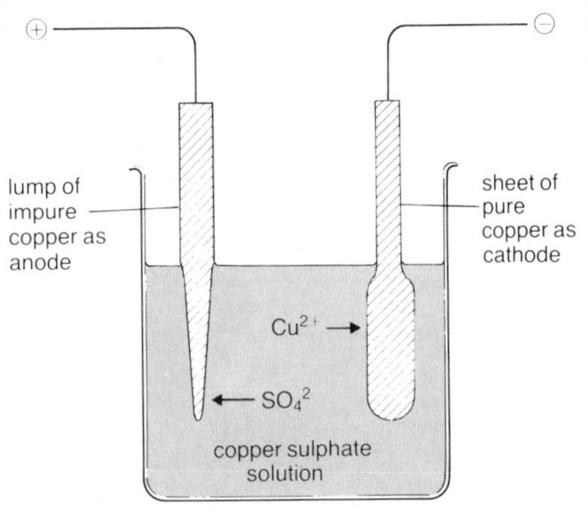

Figure 9.14 Purifying copper by electrolysis.

- Write the formulae of the ions present in the solution.
- Which ions are attracted to the cathode?
- Write an equation for the reaction at the cathode.

Sulphate ions are attracted to the anode, but they are *not* discharged. Instead, copper atoms in the impure anode give up two electrons and go into solution as copper ions.

$Cu(s) \rightarrow 2e^- + Cu^{2+}(aq)$

The overall result of the electrolysis is a transfer of copper from the anode into the solution and then onto the cathode. As the crude copper is purified, the lump of impure copper dissolves away and pure copper deposits on the cathode.

Purified copper cathodes being lifted out of an electrolytic cell at a copper processing plant in Zambia.

Electroplating

The method used to purify copper is also used for copper plating. If the cathode in figure 9.14 was made of iron, it would still become coated with copper. Parts of the steel bodywork of cars and bicycle frames are protected from corrosion by copper plating them. Car bumpers and kettles are protected in a similar way, but in this case, a layer of nickel or chromium is plated on top of the copper. This increases the protection and gives a shiny finish.

Although it is simple to deposit a metal during electrolysis, it is difficult to deposit a hard, even layer which does not flake off. In order to achieve good electroplating:

- the object to be plated must be clean and free of grease,
- the electric current must be very low so that a hard coating forms slowly,
- the object to be plated must be rotated to give an even coating,
- the temperature and concentration of the electrolyte must be carefully controlled, otherwise the coating will be deposited either too rapidly or too slowly.

The metal coating is deposited on the cathode during electrolysis. The electrolyte must contain ions of the metal which will form the coating. Figure 9.15 shows a nickel alloy fork being electroplated with silver.

Electroplating is also used in making records. First, grooves are cut into a soft plastic disc with a machine that is activated by sound waves. This original disc is given a coating of graphite to make it conduct. It is then electroplated with a thick layer of metal. Finally, the metal plating is stripped off the disc so that it can be used to stamp out copies of the original.

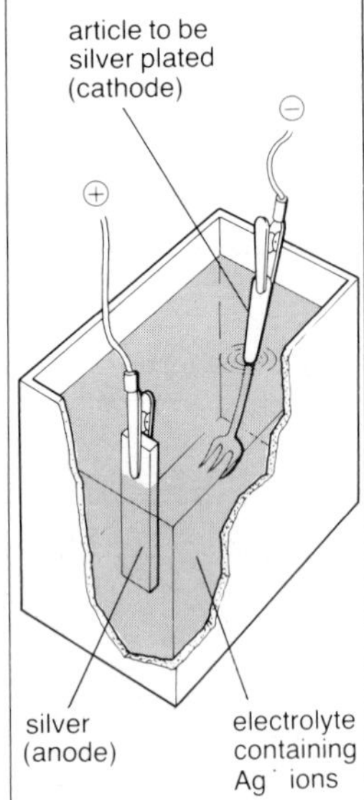

Figure 9.15 Electroplating a nickel alloy fork with silver.

9.6 Electric cells

Electric cells and batteries are a convenient source of electrical energy. The electricity which they provide is used to power calculators, torches and milk floats.

When electric cells are used, chemical energy stored in the materials of the cell is converted into electrical energy. This is just the reverse of electrolysis, in which electrical energy is converted into chemical energy in the new materials produced at the electrodes.

$$\text{chemical energy} \underset{\text{electrolysis}}{\overset{\text{use of electric cells}}{\rightleftarrows}} \text{electrical energy}$$

Figure 9.16 shows a simple arrangement that you could use to generate electricity. The bulb lights and the electric current in the circuit can be measured by an ammeter. Arrangements such as this, which generate electric currents are called **cells**. A battery is composed of several cells connected in series.

When the circuit in figure 9.16 is complete, zinc dissolves away from the zinc strip.

$Zn(s) \rightarrow Zn^{2+}(aq) + 2e^-$

The electrons flow through the circuit as an electric current and the bulb lights up. When these electrons reach the copper strip, they combine with hydrogen ions in the lemon juice and produce hydrogen gas.

$2H^+(aq) + 2e^- \rightarrow H_2(g)$

One of the most widely used cells is the **dry cell** (figure 9.17). This is used torches, bicycle lamps, radios and pocket calculators. When the terminals are connected, the zinc case acts as the negative terminal giving up electrons which form the electric current from the cell.

$Zn \rightarrow Zn^{2+} + 2e^-$

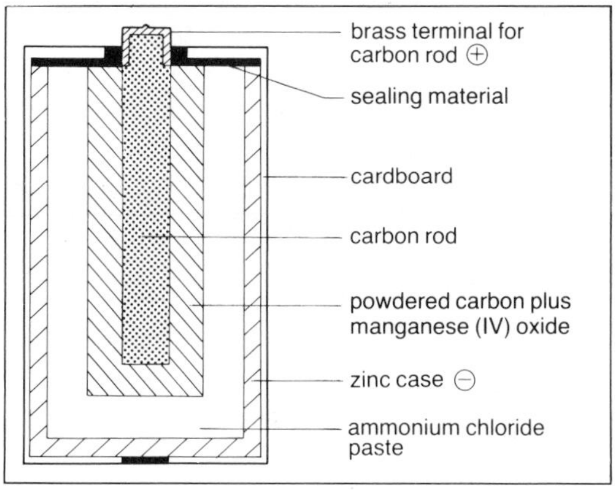

Figure 9.17 A dry cell.

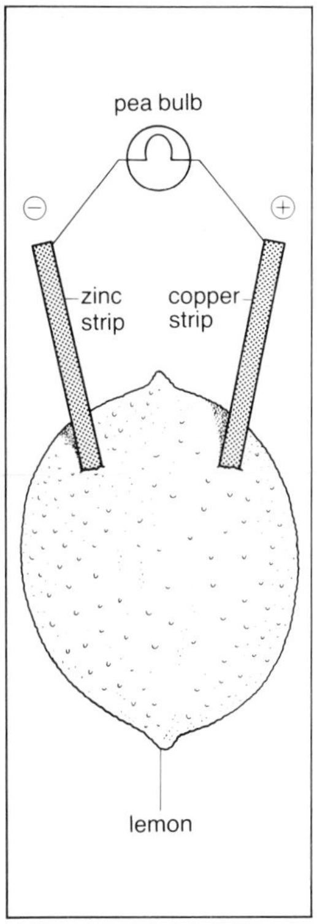

Figure 9.16 A simple cell.

An important advantage of the dry cell is that there is no danger of liquid spilling out since the electrolyte is a thick paste of ammonium chloride.

One dry cell can produce about 1.5 volts, but batteries of these cells can give up to 100 volts. When current is drawn from the cell, the zinc in the casing becomes Zn^{2+} ions, which dissolve in the paste. In time, the zinc casing falls apart and the paste oozes through the outer cardboard.

The lead–acid accumulator

When dry cells produce electricity, they are used up. They cannot be *recharged* and used again. Cells like this which cannot be recharged are called **primary cells**. On the other hand, **secondary cells** or **accumulators** can be recharged and used over and over again.

Lead–acid accumulators are used in car batteries. The negative terminal in a lead–acid accumulator is a lead plate, whereas the positive terminal is a lead plate covered in lead(IV) oxide (PbO_2). The electrolyte is fairly strong sulphuric acid. One lead–acid cell can produce about two volts.

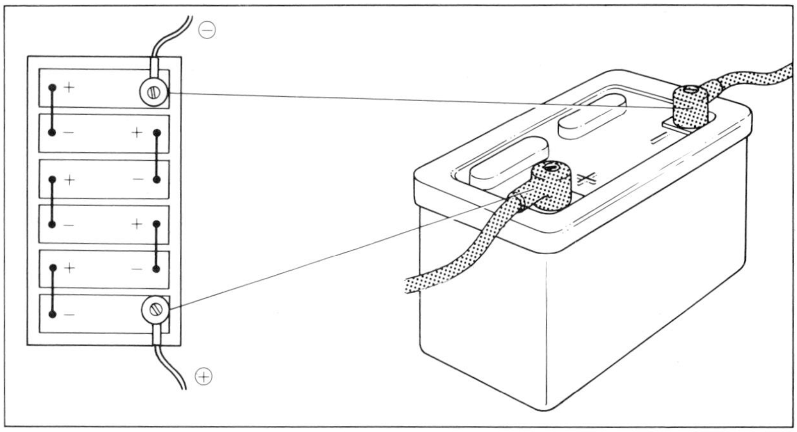

Figure 9.18 (Above) A six-cell car battery.

- Most car batteries consist of six lead–acid cells connected as shown in figure 9.18. What total voltage will this give?
- Milk floats are powered by lead–acid accumulators rather than a petrol engine. Why are other vehicles not run on lead–acid cells?
- What problems face manufacturers and scientists in their attempts to make a marketable battery-powered car?
- Why are battery-powered vehicles likely to become more common in the future?

When the lead–acid accumulator produces electricity (discharges), lead atoms on the negative terminal give up electrons to form lead ions.

$$Pb(s) \xrightarrow{\text{discharge}} Pb^{2+}(aq) + 2e^-$$

Lead(IV) oxide on the positive terminal takes electrons and reacts with H^+ ions in the electrolyte to form lead ions and water.

$$PbO_2(s) + 4H^+(aq) + 2e^- \xrightarrow{\text{discharge}} Pb^{2+}(aq) + 2H_2O(l)$$

Notice that lead ions form at both plates during discharge. These Pb^{2+} ions react with sulphate ions in the sulphuric acid and insoluble lead sulphate forms

$$Pb^{2+}(aq) + SO_4^{2-}(aq) \rightarrow PbSO_4(s)$$

Any lead–acid cell must be recharged before it gets 'flat' (fully discharged). When the battery is recharged, electrons are forced through the cell in the opposite direction and the reactions at the terminals are reversed.

As the battery discharges, H^+ ions are used up and this causes the acid concentration and the density of the electrolyte to fall. Thus, the state of charge in each cell of a battery can be checked by measuring the density of the acid solution using a hydrometer.

If the battery is discharged for too long, the soft lead sulphate on the plates changes to a hard inactive form which cannot be converted back to lead and lead(IV) oxide. The battery is said to be *sulphated* and cannot be recharged.

Summary

1 Particles and materials can be charged in two ways: positively and negatively.

2 The building blocks for atoms are protons, neutrons and electrons.

3 Particles and materials become negatively charged by gaining electrons. Particles and materials become positively charged by losing electrons.

4 An electric current is a flow of electrons.

5 Conductors conduct electricity, insulators do not allow electricity to pass through them.

6 A battery consists of two or more cells.

7 The only common solids which conduct electricity well are metals and graphite.

8 Metal/non-metal compounds conduct electricity when they are molten and when they are in aqueous solution.

9 The electrode connected to the positive side of the battery is called the anode, the electrode connected to the negative side of the battery is called the cathode.

10 Decomposition of molten or aqueous compounds by electricity is called electrolysis. The compounds decomposed are called electrolytes.

11 Charged particles like Na^+ and Cl^- are called ions.

12 Metals and hydrogen have positive ions.

13 Non metals (except hydrogen) have negative ions.

14 Most metal ions have a charge of 2^+. The only common metal ions without a charge of 2^+ are Na^+, K^+, Ag^+, Al^{3+}, Fe^{3+} and Cr^{3+}.

15 Metal/non-metal compounds are composed of ions. In these compounds the ions are held together by the attraction of positive ions for negative ions. This is called ionic bonding.

16 Non-metal compounds contain molecules. In these molecules, atoms of the non-metals are held together by covalent bonds. The bonds between separate molecules are known as intermolecular bonds.

17 When primary cells produce electricity, they are used up and cannot be recharged.

18 Secondary cells (accumulators) can be recharged and used again.

Study questions

1 Explain the following:
  a) Dust clings to a record much more just after it has been played.
  b) Tiny crackles are sometimes heard on removing a nylon shirt or blouse.
  c) Your hair will stand on end if it is combed vigorously on a dry day.
  d) A balloon, if rubbed against a woollen sweater will 'cling' to the wall after it has been rubbed.

2 a) Explain in terms of electrons why a polythene rod becomes negative when it is held by hand and rubbed with a woollen cloth.
  b) Why does a metal rod not become charged when it is rubbed in the same way?
  c) What important use of metals and polythene does this simple experiment illustrate?

3 Two small, light, conducting balls are suspended from the same point on insulating threads. A charge is then shared between them by touching them both with the same rod.
  a) Sketch what you would see.
  b) Describe and explain what will now happen if one of the balls is touched by hand.

4 A current of 0.5 A flowed for six minutes and twenty-six seconds through two electrolytic cells in series. 0.216 g of silver deposited on the cathode of the first cell and 0.059 g of metal X on the cathode of the second cell (Ag = 108, X = 59).
  a) What quantity of charge passed through the two cells?
  b) Calculate the quantity of charge needed to deposit one mole of (i) silver and (ii) X.
  c) What is the charge on the ions of X? (The Faraday constant is 96 500 coulombs)

5 The electrolysis of a molten pure substance produced three moles of chlorine (Cl_2) at the anode and two moles of metal X at the cathode in a certain period of time.
  a) How many moles of atomic chlorine, Cl, are contained in three moles of Cl_2?
  b) How many moles of atomic chlorine, Cl, are produced in the same time as one mole of X?
  c) If the formula of the substance being electrolysed is XCl_n, what is the value of n?
  d) Give the symbols, with charges, for the ions present in the molten substance being electrolysed.
  e) What metal could X be?

6 The following passage is entitled 'Anodising aluminium'. Read it carefully.

Aluminium is widely used as a material for decoration and constructional purposes. When the surface is untreated it changes slowly from a shiny to a dull grey colour due to the formation of an extremely thin layer of aluminium oxide. This layer is non-porous and stops further corrosion. If the layer is made thicker by anodising, it becomes porous and can easily be dyed different colours giving the finished product an attractive appearance.

The aluminium is first degreased by washing with tetrachloromethane (carbon tetrachloride). Then it is anodised by using it as the anode of an electrolytic cell, after which it is rinsed and heated in the dye. Finally it is cold-rinsed and dipped in boiling water to seal in the colour.

  a) State briefly the effect of anodising a piece of aluminium.
  b) Why is aluminium anodised?
  c) A new aluminium ornament which has not been anodised changes in weight. Explain why this is so.
  d) Why is tetrachloromethane and not water used to degrease aluminium?
  e) Which other liquid would be a suitable degreasing agent?
  f) Why is anodising necessary before aluminium can be dyed?
  g) Is anodised aluminium likely to be used for constructional purposes? Explain your answer.
  h) State *two* properties of aluminium which make it especially useful for constructional purposes.
  i) (*Hard*) How would aluminium oxide on the surface of anodised aluminium be affected by fumes of hydrogen chloride? Write an equation for any reaction which occurs.

7 a) Describe briefly the process of nickel plating.
  b) Why is it useful to nickel-plate articles?
  c) Which electrode is the article to be plated?
  d) During nickel plating
    i) what is the other electrode made of?
    ii) what is the electrolyte?
    iii) write equations for the processes which take place at the electrodes.

8 Na^+, Mg^{2+}, Al^{3+}, NO_3^-, S^{2-}.
Using only the ions listed above, write the names and formulae of
  a) three nitrates
  b) three sulphides
  c) two magnesium salts
  d) two ions each with a single charge
  e) an ion containing more than one element.
  f) an ion which would need 193 000 coulombs to deposit one mole at the cathode in electrolysis.

10 Currents and electricity

Blackpool illuminations.

It is hard to imagine life without electricity – electric fires, electric lights and electricity bills.

10.1 Electricity in everyday life

Every day, we depend on electricity for cooking, for lighting and for heating. At the flick of a switch or the press of a button, we use electric currents to operate power tools and electrical appliances. In addition to devices which use mains electricity, there are many others, like torches, radios and calculators, that rely on the electric currents from cells and batteries.

There are two major reasons why electricity is so useful to our modern civilisation.

- *It can be used to transfer energy easily and conveniently from one place to another.* This energy consists of a flow of electrons, i.e. moving charge (section 9.2).
- *It can be converted readily into other forms of energy* and used to heat a room, cook a meal, drive an electric motor or provide light.

- Make a list of five important jobs which electricity does in your home.
- Would any of these jobs be impossible without electricity?
- Electricity is used more widely than gas for our energy supplies. Why is this?

10.2 Currents in electrical circuits

In chapter 9 we learnt that the current in a circuit consisted of a flow of electrons, which have negative charge. These electrons flow from the negative terminal of the battery through the circuit to the positive terminal. The current (electrons) must have a complete circuit (path) of conductors before it can flow through the equipment.

All the circuits that we have looked at so far have been connected **in series**. In a

(*Above*) Each of these appliances depends on electricity for its use. How were these jobs done before electricity was available in our homes?

series circuit, there is only one route for the current, because there are no junctions. Look closely at the circuit diagram in figure 10.1 which contains two bulbs and three ammeters in series. When the circuit is complete, all three ammeters show the same reading, 0.2 amperes. This is because *the current is the same at all points in a series circuit*. Electrons leaving the negative side of the battery pass through each section of the circuit at the same rate, so the current is the same at all points.

Figure 10.2 shows a circuit in which the bulbs are not connected in series. In this case, each bulb is connected singly across the battery. There are junctions in the circuit and more than one way for the current to flow round it. This time the bulbs are said to be connected **in parallel**.

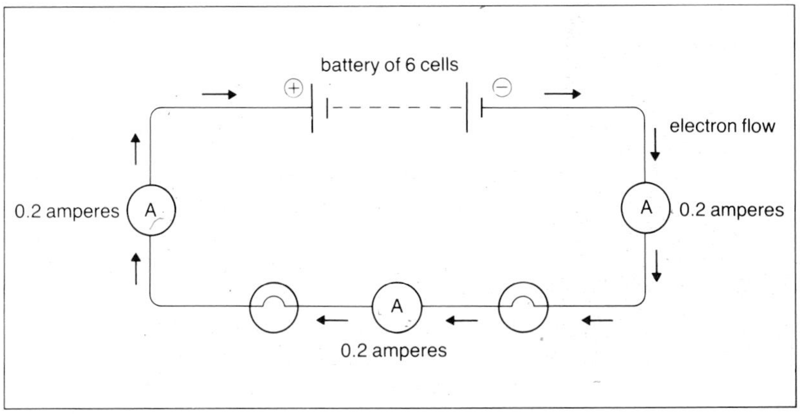

Figure 10.1 Two bulbs and three ammeters connected in series.

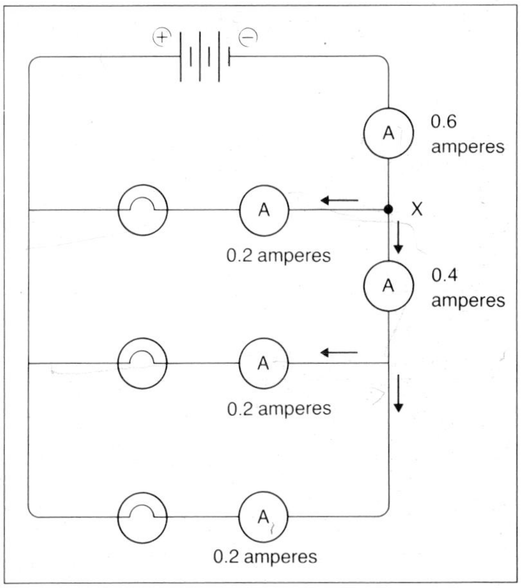

Figure 10.2 Three bulbs connected in parallel.

Suppose in figure 10.2 the bulbs are identical and the ammeters are identical.

- What can you say about the brightness of the three bulbs?
- What is the current arriving at junction X?
- What is the sum of currents going away from junction X?

This experiment should help you to see that:

In a parallel circuit, the sum of the currents approaching a junction is the same as the sum of the currents leaving the junction.

10.3 The effects of an electric current

An electric current can have several effects. Some of these effects can be used to measure the size of electric currents.

- **The lighting effect** Torches and electric lights are an obvious example of this effect. Energy in the moving electrons in the current is being converted into light energy. When an electric current flows through the bulb, the filament glows brightly and gives out light. It is possible to measure currents by comparing the brightness of bulbs, but the method is inaccurate and unreliable.
- **The heating effect** In an electric light, energy is given out as heat as well as light.

- Make a list of five different electrical appliances which use the heating effect of electricity.
- Design a meter to measure current using its heating effect. Say briefly how your meter works.

■ **The chemical effect** When an electric current passes through an electrolyte, changes take place at the electrodes and new materials are produced. This is called electrolysis. Electrical energy is being changed into chemical energy in the products at the electrodes. In section 9.5 we learnt that this chemical effect of an electric current (i.e. electrolysis) can be used to extract metals like aluminium from their ores, and to electroplate articles with copper, nickel and silver.

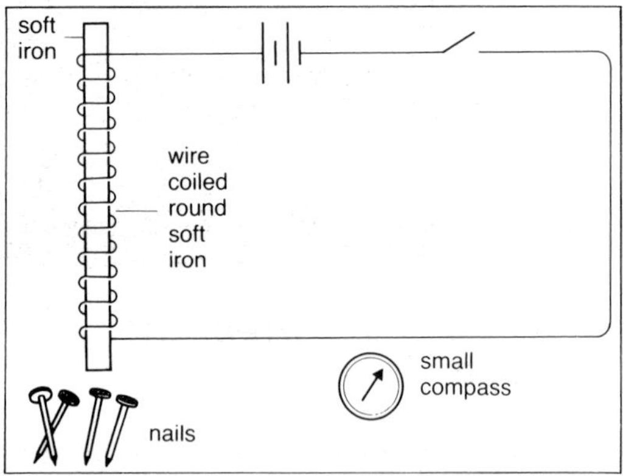

Figure 10.3 The magnetic effects of an electric current.

■ **The magnetic effect** Figure 10.3 shows two ways of demonstrating the magnetic effects of an electric current. When the switch is closed, the soft iron becomes magnetised and attracts the nails. At the same time, the compass needle is deflected. The properties of magnets and the magnetic effects of an electric current are discussed more fully in chapter 11.

Using the magnetic effect to measure currents

The current balance

We can use the magnetic effect of an electric current to make a current measuring meter (figure 10.4). Fix a magnet to a straw with tape. Then push a needle through the straw so that the straw balances horizontally when the needle is laid across the metal channel. The straw can be balanced exactly by moving a wire loop along the straw until it balances.

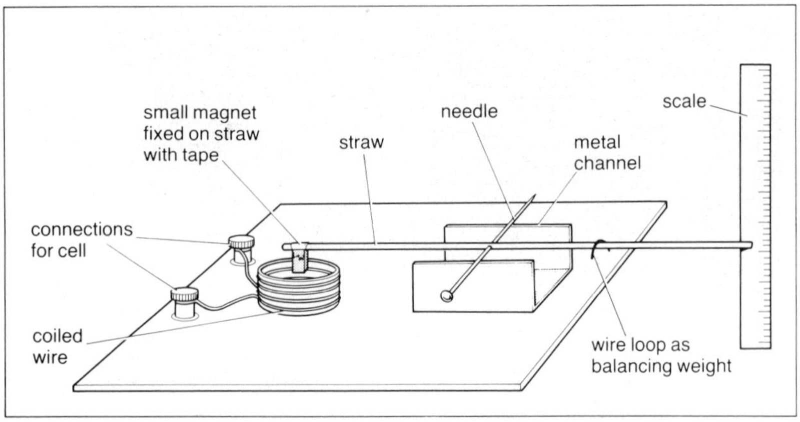

Figure 10.4 A current balance.

Connect the coil of wire to a cell and measure how far the straw pointer moves up when a current flows. When you connect a cell to the balance, the straw might move the wrong way because the magnet is pushed out of the coil rather than being pulled into it. If this happens, just reverse the connections from the cell to the current balance.

If the one cell is replaced by two and then three and then four, the pointer is deflected further and further up the scale. This is because the current through the coil is increasing, producing a greater magnetic effect.

The disadvantage of a current balance like this is that it is easily disturbed and awkward to use. Scientists normally use more permanent and robust instruments. Our current balance has a small *moving magnet* and a *fixed coil* of wire. However, we could have used the opposite arrangement, i.e. a *moving coil* of wire with a *fixed magnet*. Most accurate meters, like the one described in the next paragraph, work in this way, and can be modified for use as ammeters or voltmeters.

Figure 10.5 A moving-coil ammeter (part of the magnet's south pole has been 'cut away' to give a clearer view of the working parts).

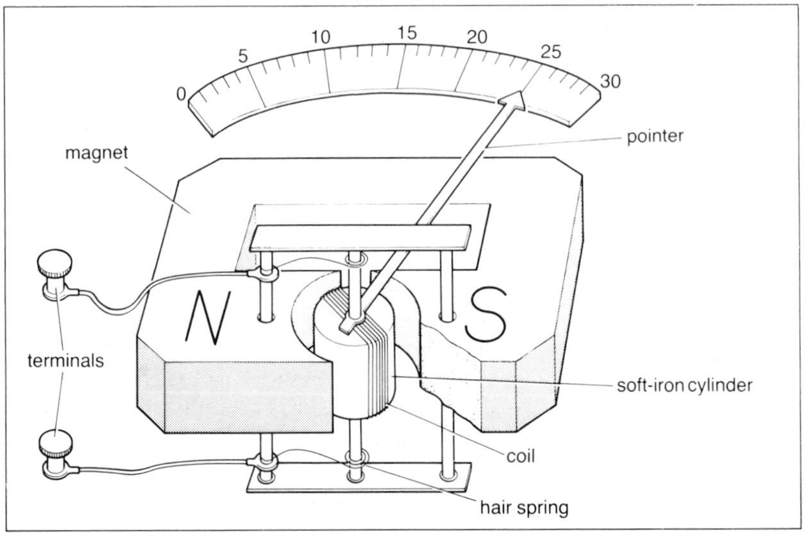

Most of the meters in the cockpit of this aeroplane are modified moving-coil meters.

The moving-coil ammeter

The moving-coil ammeter has a coil pivoted between the poles of a magnet (figure 10.5). Current enters and leaves the coil via hair springs. When a current flows through the coil, magnetic forces act on it (section 11.3) causing it to rotate until it is stopped by the hair springs. The greater the current, the greater the forces on the coil and the further it twists before it is stopped by the springs. Thus, the angle through which the pointer moves depends on the size of the current. An ammeter can be made more sensitive (i.e. able to detect smaller and smaller currents) by having

- more turns in the coil,
- a stronger magnet,
- a small gap between the magnet and the soft-iron cylinder,
- a lighter coil and pointer,
- weaker hair springs.

The most sensitive ammeters are capable of detecting currents of only a few microamperes. One microampere ($1\,\mu A$) is one millionth of an ampere.

$$1\,\mu A = \frac{1}{1000000} A = 10^{-6} A$$

10.4 Electric current and voltage

An electric current consists of a flow of tiny negative electrons from the negative terminal of the battery to the positive terminal. Each electron carries a charge of 1.6×10^{-19} coulombs, so about 6 million million million electrons have a total charge of one coulomb.

Electric currents are measured in **amperes** (A). When the current is one ampere, the rate of flow of charge is one coulomb per second, i.e. 6 million million million electrons pass each point in the circuit every second.

One ampere = one coulomb per second.

And one coulomb is one ampere flowing for one second.

- How many coulombs of electric charge pass if
  a) 2 A flow for 1 s,
  b) 2 A flow for 2 s.
- The current in a torch bulb is 0.5 A. How many coulombs pass through the bulb when it is used for one hour?

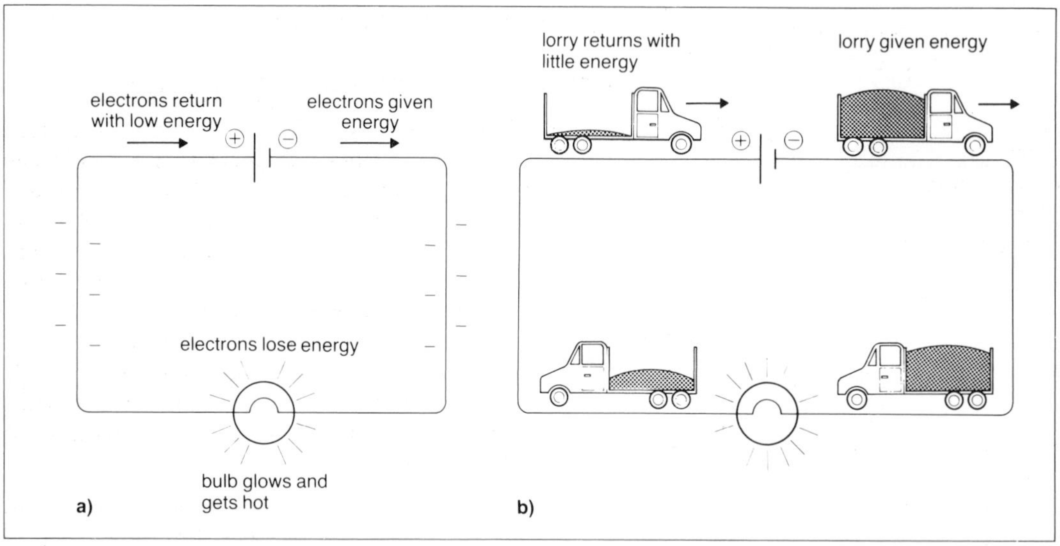

Figure 10.6 Comparing an electric current to a fleet of lorries and their cargoes.

In an electrical circuit, the battery acts as an electron pump. It provides the electrons with energy and forces them out of the negative terminal, through the circuit and round to the positive terminal (figure 10.6a). As the electrons move through the wires and the bulbs in the circuit, they lose energy which becomes heat and light. Some batteries give electrons more energy than others. They push electrons out more energetically. We say that these batteries have a greater **potential difference (p.d.)** or **voltage**. Potential difference is measured in **volts** (V). The greater the voltage, the more energy (in joules) is given to each electron (or each coulomb of charge) driven round the circuit.

It might help you to understand the ideas of current and voltage if you imagine the current to be a fleet of lorries moving round the circuit (figure 10.6b). Each lorry represents one coulomb of charge which is given a lorry load of energy on leaving the battery. As the lorry moves round the circuit, its cargo of electrical energy is transformed into heat and light energy in getting it through lamps and resistors. Every time the lorry (coulomb) passes through the battery, it receives a fresh cargo of energy.

The voltage of the electricity supply in your home is 240 volts (240 V). The voltage of a car battery is 12 V and that of a dry cell is about 1.5 V.

A battery with a voltage of one volt (1 V) gives one joule of energy to each coulomb of charge which passes round the circuit.

One volt = one joule per coulomb.

If two joules (2 J) are given to each coulomb, the voltage is 2 V. If 3 joules are given to 2 coulombs, the number of joules per coulomb is 1.5 and so the voltage is 1.5 V. In other words:

$$\underset{(V)}{\text{voltage}} = \frac{\text{energy supplied by battery } (E)}{\text{charge flowing through circuit } (Q)}$$

$$\Rightarrow E = V \times Q$$

If the charge (Q) flowing in the circuit takes the form of a current I flowing for a time t then:

$$Q = I \times t$$

Substituting for Q in $E = V \times Q$ we get:

$$\underset{\text{joules}}{E} = \underset{\text{volts}}{V} \times \underset{\text{amperes}}{I} \times \underset{\text{seconds}}{t}$$

The energy (E) starts as chemical energy in the materials of the battery and then becomes electrical energy in the circuit. As it passes through the wires and the bulb, it is transformed into heat and light.

The voltage (potential difference) between two points in a circuit can be measured using an instrument called a **voltmeter**. A voltmeter looks very much like an ammeter but the scale is marked in volts. The voltmeter is connected across (in parallel with) the part where we want to measure the voltage (figure 10.7).

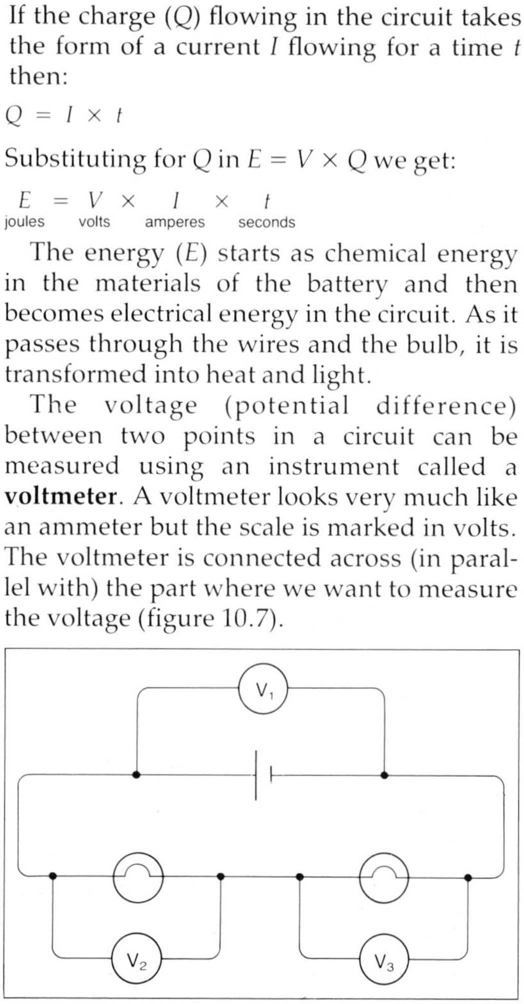

Figure 10.7 Voltmeter V_1 measures the potential difference (voltage) across the cell. What do voltmeters V_2 and V_3 measure?

- Is an ammeter connected in series or in parallel to measure the current in a circuit?
- A set of twelve identical 'fairy' lamps on a Christmas tree were connected in series to the 240 V mains supply. What is the voltage across (a) the whole set of twelve lamps and (b) one lamp in the set?

10.5 Resistance and resistors

When an electric current passes through a circuit, electrons move from the negative terminal of the battery to the positive terminal. As the electrons move round the circuit, they are often held up by atoms in the wires through which they pass. Electrons pass easily through copper wire, but much less readily through nichrome wire of the same length and thickness. We say that the copper wire has a lower **resistance** than nichrome (an alloy of nickel and chromium). Because of this, copper is normally used for the connecting wires and cables in electric circuits.

When an electric current is passed through thin nichrome wire, electrons cannot flow along easily. They bump into atoms in the wire and make them vibrate more rapidly. The wire gets warm and may even become red hot if it has a high resistance and the current is high.

Conductors which are specially made to provide a high resistance and reduce the flow of electricity are called **resistors**. The symbol for a resistor in a circuit is shown in figure 10.8.

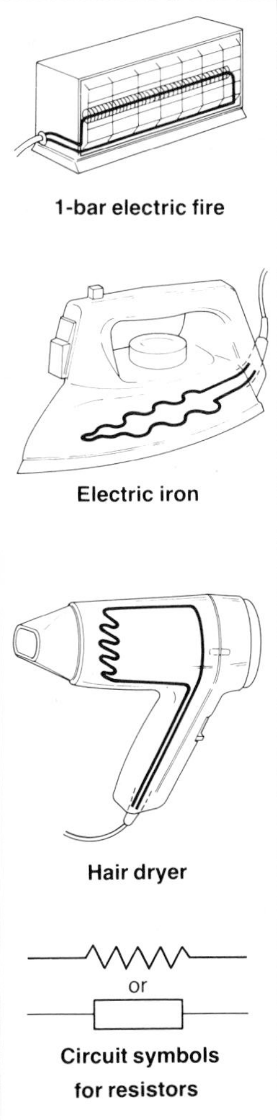

Figure 10.8 (Above) Important resistors.

Figure 10.10 (Lower right) Variable resistors.

Important resistors

Heating elements and light bulbs

The heating elements in electrical appliances such as electric fires, electric kettles, hot plates and hair dryers are usually made from nichrome or other nickel alloys (figure 10.8). These alloys will stay red hot for long periods without melting or reacting with oxygen in the air.

In light bulbs, the thin filament wire is made of tungsten, which has a very high melting point (3380 °C). When current flows through the filament, it glows white hot (figure 10.9).

- Silver is a better conductor than copper. Why, then, is copper used for connecting wires rather than silver?
- Which has the greater resistance;
  a) a long piece or a short piece of the same wire,
  b) a thick piece of wire or a thin piece of the same length?
- Most light bulbs contain nitrogen or argon rather than air. The gas inside prevents the white hot tungsten from vaporising and then condensing as a dark grey layer on the inside of the bulb. Why must the gas inside the bulb not be air?

Sometimes it is necessary to vary the resistance in a circuit. This can be done using a variable resistor. Figure 10.10 shows a laboratory variable resistor and a simple variable resistor used in radios, together with the circuit symbol.

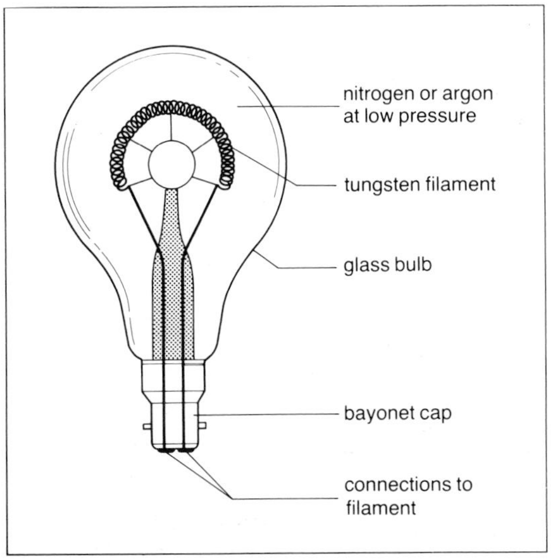

Figure 10.9 A light bulb.

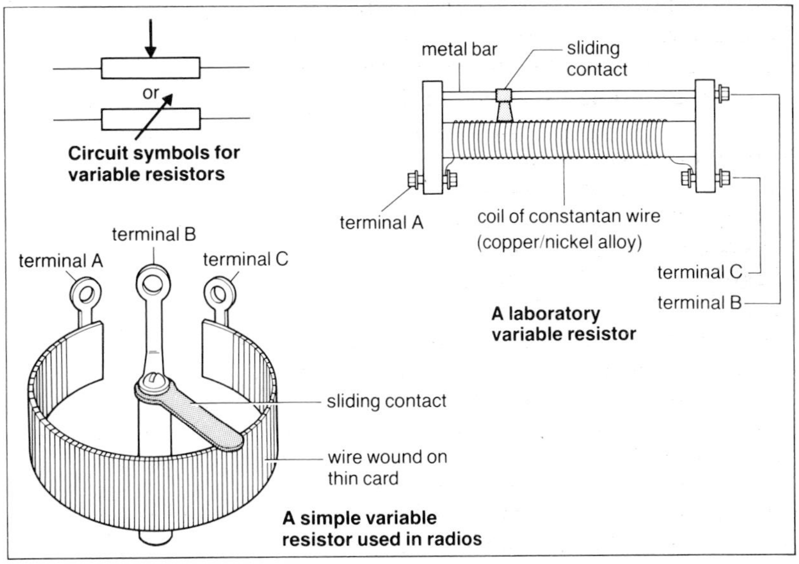

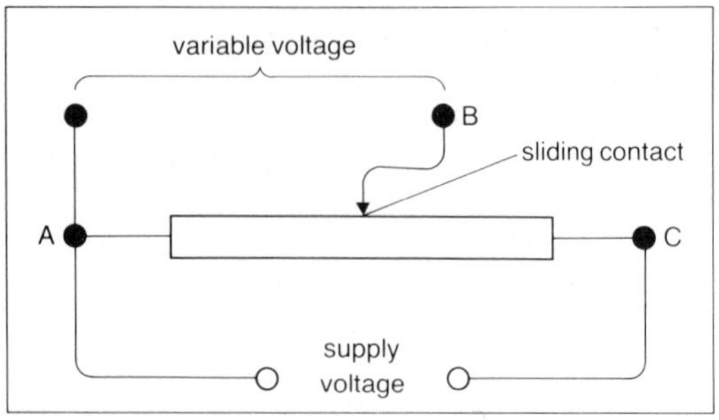

Figure 10.11 Using a variable resistor as a potential divider.

Variable resistors can be used in electric and electronic circuits in two ways:

- As **rheostats** for changing the resistance in a circuit and hence the current. Connect terminals A and B in figure 10.10 into the circuit. If the sliding contact is now moved to the right, the circuit includes more turns of the coil. This increases the resistance and reduces the current. Devices like this can be used in dimmer switches to control the current and hence the brightness, of an electric light.
- As **potential dividers** for changing the voltage supplied to a circuit. A large voltage is applied across the whole coil using terminals A and C. Varying smaller voltages (potential differences) can now be 'tapped off' between terminals A and B by moving the sliding contact along the bar (figure 10.11). Variable resistors are used in this way to control the volume and brightness in television and radio sets.

Figure 10.12 (Below) Investigating Ohm's law.

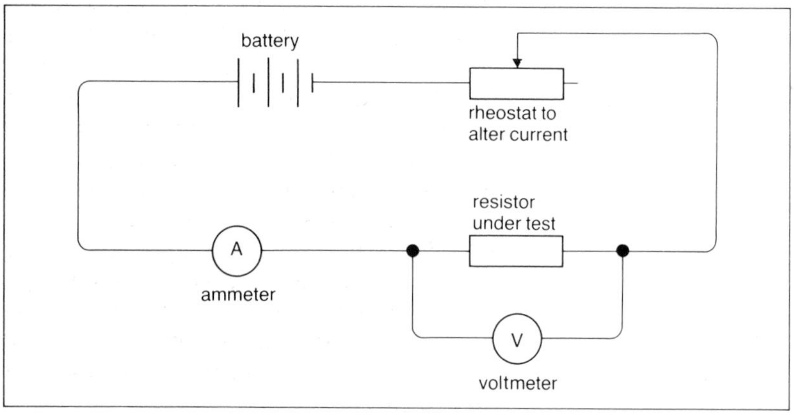

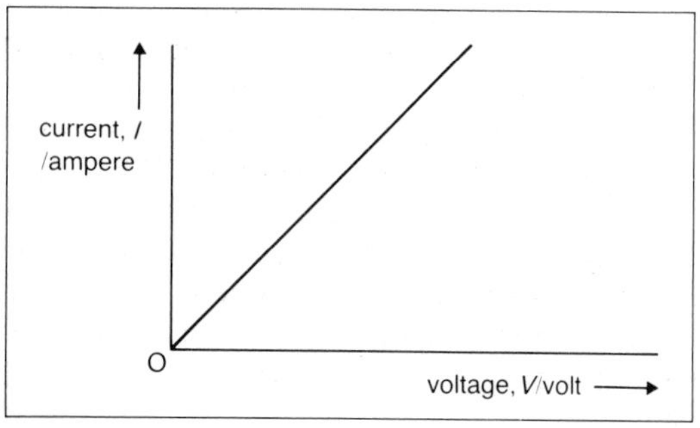

Figure 10.13 (Left) A graph of *I* against *V* for a metal (ohmic conductor).

10.6 Measuring resistance

One of the first people to investigate the resistance of conductors was the German scientist, Georg Ohm (1787 – 1854). The unit of resistance is called the **ohm** in honour of him. During the 1820s, Ohm used a circuit similar to that in figure 10.12 to measure the current (I) in a resistor when the voltage (V) across it changed. The current in the resistor in figure 10.12 and the voltage across it can be varied by altering the setting on the rheostat. For metal conductors Ohm discovered that a graph of current (I), against voltage (V), is a straight line though the origin (O) (figure 10.13). These results show that *the current in a metal conductor is directly proportional to the voltage across it, provided its temperature does not change.* This is known as **Ohm's law**, which can be written in symbols as

$$I \propto V \qquad \text{or} \qquad \frac{V}{I} = \text{constant}$$

From these results, we can see that doubling the voltage will double the current, trebling the voltage will treble the current and so on. If a resistor has a large resistance, then a large voltage is required to drive a current through it. The larger the resistance, the greater the voltage needed to push each ampere of current through. Scientists say that:

A resistor has a resistance of one ohm (1 Ω) if a voltage of one volt will drive a current of one ampere through it.

If a voltage of 5V is required to drive a current of 1A through a resistor, then its resistance is 5 ohms (5Ω). The resistance is simply the number of volts required per ampere of current.

$$\text{resistance (ohms)} = \frac{\text{voltage (volts)}}{\text{current (amperes)}}$$

$$R = \frac{V}{I}$$

Using this equation, it is possible to calculate any one of R, V or I provided the other two values are known.

- What is the resistance of a wire, in which a current of 3A flows when the voltage across it is 12V?
- A resistor of 2Ω carries a current of 3A. What is the voltage across it?

Conductors which obey Ohm's law, by giving a straight line graph of V against I, as in figure 10.13, are sometimes called *ohmic conductors*. Metals and alloys are ohmic conductors. Semiconductors like silicon and germanium are non-ohmic: they do not obey Ohm's law (table 10.1).

Table 10.1
Comparing ohmic and non-ohmic conductors

Ohmic conductors	*Non-ohmic conductors*
obey Ohm's law	do not obey Ohm's law
metals and alloys	semiconductors: germanium, silicon

If the circuit in figure 10.12 is used to test a torch bulb instead of a resistor, the results are different from those in figure 10.13. In this case, the graph of I against V flattens off as V increases (figure 10.14).

As the current through the bulb increases, the filament gets hotter and hotter and the current is less than expected for a given voltage. This shows that the resistance of the torch bulb increases as the filament gets hotter. Why does the resistance of the filament increase when it gets hot? As the filament gets hotter, atoms in it will be vibrating more and more and this obstructs the steady flow of electrons in the electric current. This makes the passage of the current more difficult and so the filament's resistance is greater. On the other hand, when a metal conductor is cooled, its resistance gets less. At very low temperatures, the atoms hardly vibrate at all, the resistance becomes very low, and some metals become **superconductors**.

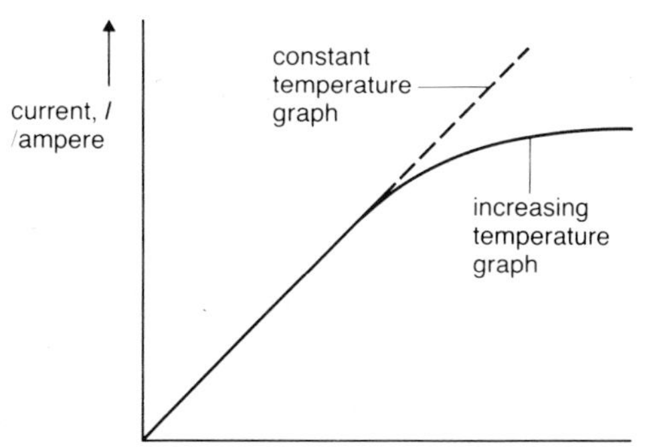

Figure 10.14 A graph of I against V for a torch bulb.

10.7 Using electricity: household circuits

Electricity is transmitted across the country from power stations to our homes, schools and factories by the National Grid system. The current is carried in thick cables supported by huge pylons. Thick cables have a lower resistance than thinner ones and thus do not get so hot during transmission. This means that a smaller proportion of the electrical energy is lost as heat.

- What would be the advantage of using even thicker cables in the grid system?
- What are the disadvantages in using even thicker cables?

The current supplied by the National Grid to the mains sockets in buildings is *not* a one-way flow of electrons like the current from a battery. Electrons in the current from the mains flow alternately forwards and backwards. The direction of the current changes fifty times per second. This type of current is called **alternating current (a.c.)** as opposed to the one-way **direct current (d.c.)** from a battery. Power stations supply alternating current to our homes, schools and industry because it is easier to generate than d.c. and its voltage can be changed more readily (section 11.7).

Wires and cables provide a resistance to the movement of electrons in both alternating currents and direct currents. Because of this, both a.c. and d.c. can be used for heating and lighting. Alternating currents, however, unlike direct currents, do not cause any chemical (elecrolytic) effects. The reason for this is that when mains a.c. is passed through an electrolyte, each electrode is alternately positive and then negative fifty times in each second. This is too fast for any changes to occur at the electrodes and this means that electrolysis cannot take place.

The electricity supply cable into each house includes a **live wire** and a **neutral wire**. The neutral wire is kept at zero potential by connecting it to a large metal plate in the earth at the local substation. When electric charge flows to the earth, it loses all its energy, so, we say the earthed metal plate is at zero potential. The live wire is alternately positive and negative with a potential difference (p.d.) of 240 V relative to the neutral wire.

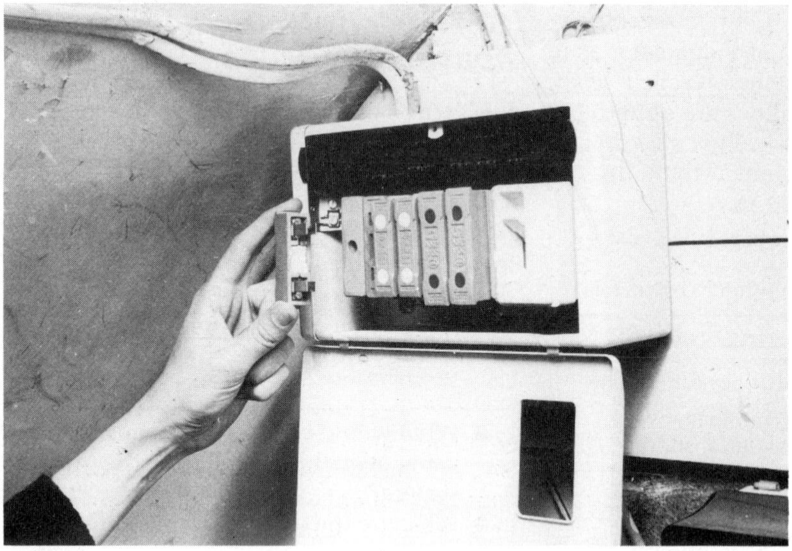

(*Above*) Each circuit in a house has a protective fuse in the fuse box. This photograph shows one of the fuses removed.

At each house, the electricity supply cable passes through the Electricity Board's main fuse and then via the meter to the *fuse box* (figure 10.15). From the fuse box, various parallel circuits branch out to different parts of the house. Most houses have a **ring main** circuit for the *power points*. There are usually two or three separate lighting circuits. As well as these, the electric cooker and the immersion heater usually have their own circuits. The cable for each circuit includes a live wire, a neutral wire and also an **earth wire**.

Each circuit also contains a **fuse** in series with the live wire. This is in the fuse box. A fuse is simply a thin wire which overheats and then melts ('blows') if the current flowing through it is too large. This protects the electrical appliances and prevents fires, which might occur if a large current caused part of the wiring to overheat.

- Look closely at figure 10.15. What size of fuse is used in the fuse box for (a) lighting circuits, (b) the ring main circuit and (c) the immersion heater circuit?
- Why are fuses always placed in the live wire? (Hint: would a power point be 'live' or 'dead' if a fuse in its neutral wire had blown?)
- Are switches placed in the live wire or the neutral wire?
- Suppose the switch to an electric kettle were placed in the neutral wire. Would the element be 'live' or 'dead' when the switch was 'off'? What would happen if you touched the element in this case?
- Several bulbs are wired in parallel in a lighting circuit. Suppose all the lights in a circuit are on when one light shorts and the 5 A fuse 'blows'. What happens?

Figure 10.15 (Below) A household electricity circuit.

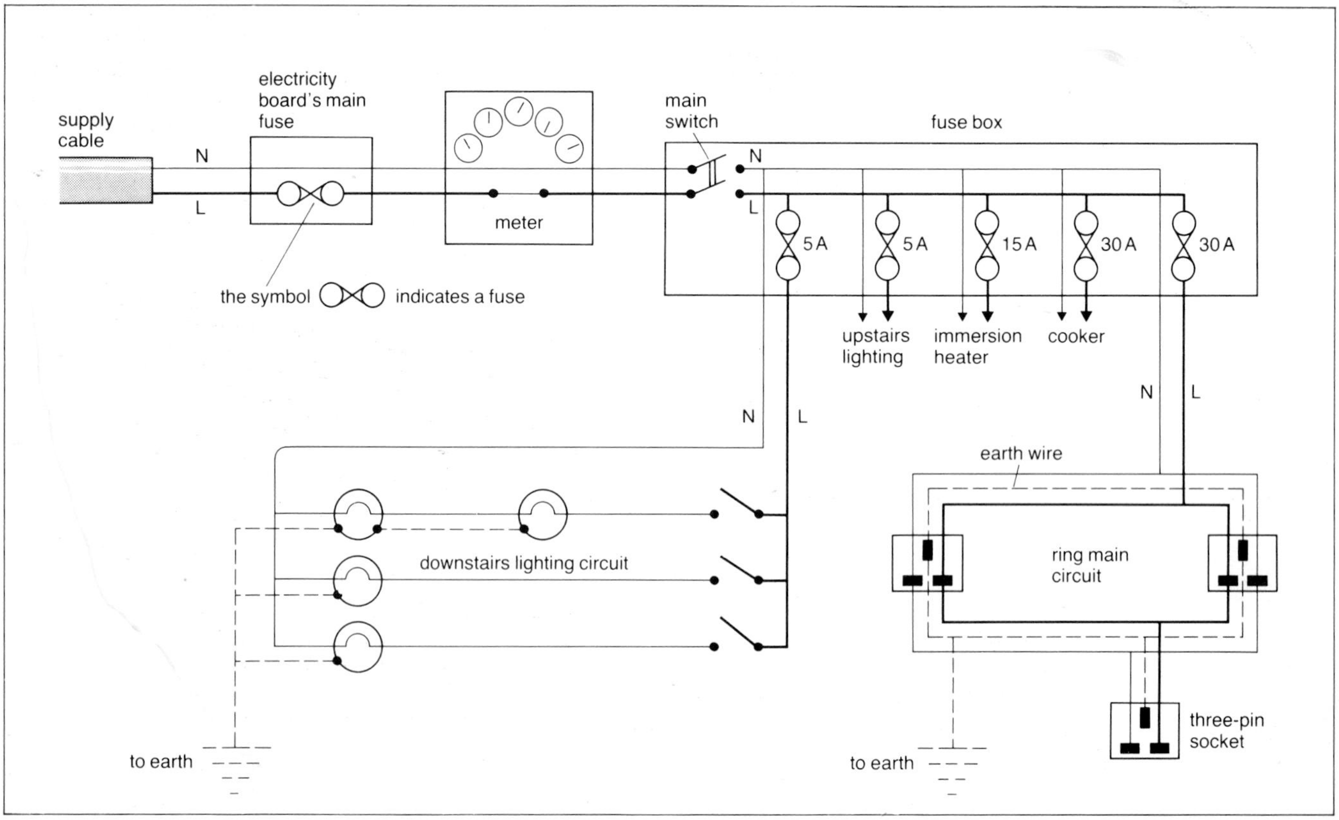

The ring main circuit

The ring main circuit connects all the mains sockets in a house. The long loop or 'ring' of cable which joins the sockets contains three wires – the live wire, the neutral wire and the earth wire. The ring main is protected by a 30 A fuse in the fuse box. This means that every one of the sockets can be used at the same time so long as the total current is not greater than 30 A.

Three-pin plugs

Most buildings in the United Kingdom have sockets on their ring main circuit which take fused three-pin plugs similar to that in figure 10.16. The two lower pins on the plug will connect an appliance, such as an electric fire, to the live wire and neutral wire of the 240 V mains supply (figure 10.17). Appliances connected in this way are therefore connected in parallel across the mains. The sockets are wired in parallel because appliances are normally designed to work off a supply of 240 volts.

The third pin on the plug is used to connect the metal parts of the appliance to the earth wire. This earth wire is connected to a metal water pipe in the house or to an earth connection on the Electricity Board's supply cable. The earth wire is an important safety device. Suppose the element of the electric fire touched the metal body of the fire. Without the earthed connection, anyone touching the fire would get an electric shock. Earthing the body of the fire provides a path of very low resistance to earth. If the element touches the bodywork of the fire, a very large current starts to flow which blows the fuse and cuts off the electricity.

Look carefully at figure 10.16. Notice that the three wires in the cable must be connected to the correct terminals of the plug:

- **brown wire to the live terminal, L,**
- **blue wire to the neutral terminal, N,**
- **green/yellow wire to the earth terminal, E.**

It is also important to use a fuse of the right value in each three-pin plug. This fuse protects the appliance from taking a current which might damage it or cause its wiring to overheat and start a fire.

Appliances like table lamps, radios, television sets and fridges take small currents (less than three amperes). They should have plugs fitted with 3 A fuses. Kettles, irons and electric fires, all of which take greater currents, should have plugs fitted with 13 A fuses.

Figure 10.16

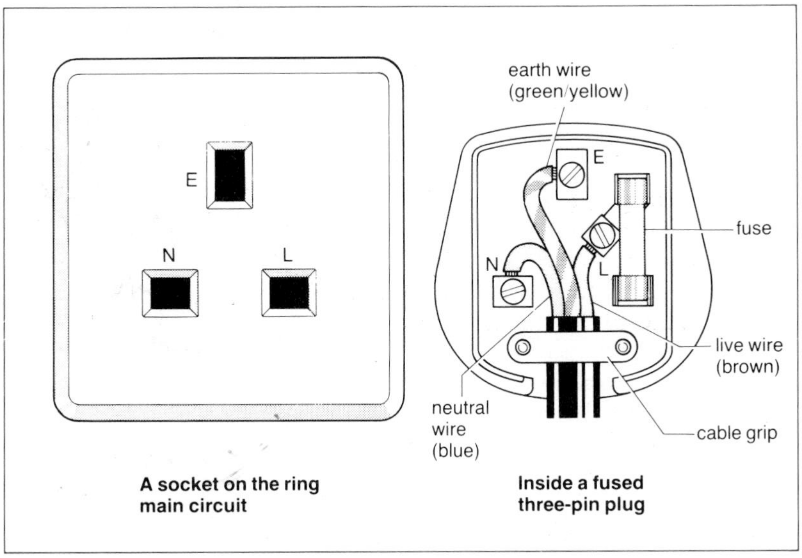

Figure 10.17 (Below) The circuit formed when an electric fire is plugged into a mains socket.

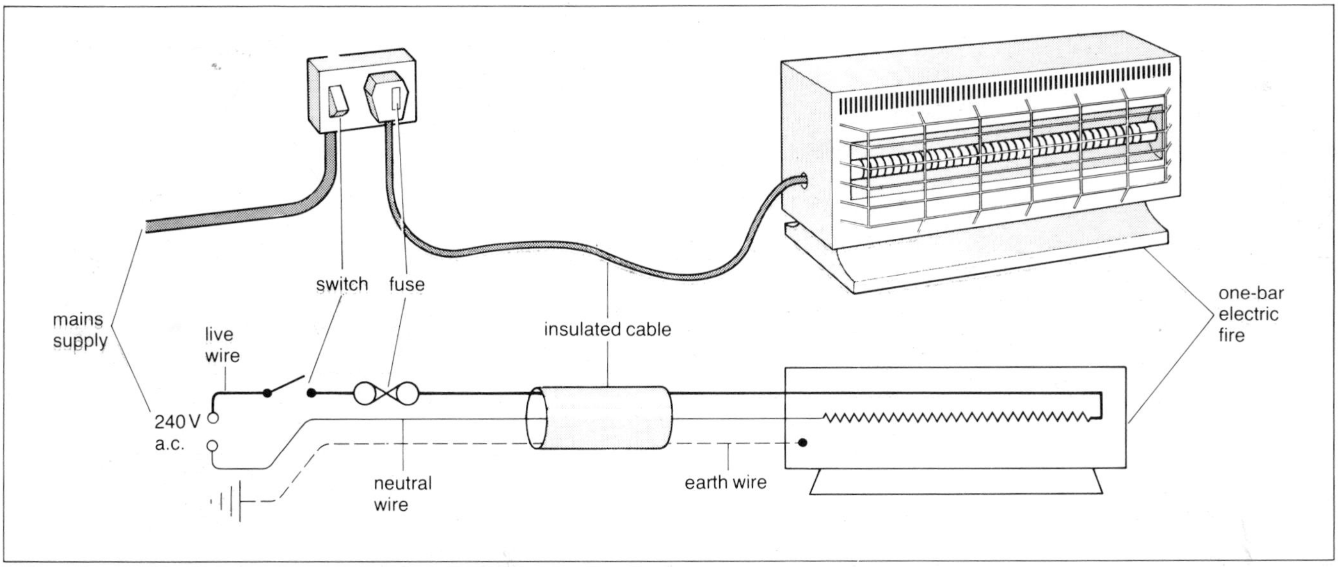

10.8 Power rating and electricity bills

In section 10.4, we found that the electrical energy (E) supplied by a current, I, flowing for time, t, through a voltage, V, is given by

$$\underset{\text{joules}}{E} = \underset{\text{volts}}{V} \times \underset{\text{amperes}}{I} \times \underset{\text{seconds}}{t}$$

For example, suppose a table lamp connected to the 240 V mains supply requires a current of 0.25 A. If the lamp is used for one hour, the electrical energy transformed into heat and light energy in the lamp is given by:

$$E = 240 \times 0.25 \times 3600$$
$$= 216000\,\text{J} = 216\,\text{kJ}$$

Now, we know from chapter 8 that power is the rate of doing work, that is, the rate at which energy is changed from one form to another. The unit of power is the watt (W). One watt is a rate of working of one joule per second. (1 W = 1 J/s).

The power (P) of the table lamp is given by,

$$P = \frac{\text{energy supplied}}{\text{time taken}}$$

$$= \frac{V \times I \times \cancel{t}}{\cancel{t}}$$

$$= V \times I$$

This means that:

Power is voltage × current.

In the case of the table lamp:

$$P = V \times I$$
$$= 240 \times 0.25$$
$$= 60\,\text{W}$$

This means that the lamp is turning 60 J of electrical energy into heat and light energy every second. The lamp is said to have a power or 'wattage' of 60 W. You may have noticed the power rating printed on electric light bulbs.

Table 10.2 shows the appropriate power ratings of some common domestic appliances. The power rating of an appliance tells us how much energy it uses per second. Thus, the hair dryer in table 10.2 uses 360 joules each second, whereas the radio requires only 6 joules each second. If both appliances are connected to the 240 V mains supply, we can calculate the current using $P = V \times I$. The current through the hair dryer, I_h, is

$$I_h = \frac{P}{V} = \frac{360\,\text{W}}{240\,\text{V}} = 1.5\,\text{A}$$

and the current through the radio, I_r, is

$$I_r = \frac{P}{V} = \frac{6\,\text{W}}{240\,\text{V}} = 0.025\,\text{A}$$

Notice that the hair dryer, with the larger power, draws a greater current from the mains because it requires more energy per second.

- How much electrical energy does the hand mixer in table 10.2 require per second?
- What becomes of this electrical energy?
- What current does the mixer take when it is connected to the 240 V mains?
- What current does the iron in table 10.2 take when it is connected to the 240 V mains?
- What size of fuse (3 A or 13 A) would you use with (a) the mixer and (b) the iron?
- Why is it more important to remember to turn off an electric iron than to turn off a light?

Table 10.2
The approximate powers of some common domestic appliances

Appliance	*Power*
radio	6 W
liquidiser	300 W
hand mixer	120 W
kettle	2000 W (2 kW)
sewing machine	50 W
iron	750 W
hair dryer	360 W
colour TV	250 W
electric fire	2600 W (2.6 kW)

Paying for electricity

Electricity Boards charge for the electrical energy which they supply. The amount of energy supplied to each house is measured on the meter, which is near to the fuse box. The meter measures energy in **kilowatt hours** (kWh) rather than joules, because one joule would be too small a unit in this case.

One kilowatt hour is the electrical energy taken by a one kilowatt appliance in one hour.

$1\,kWh = 1000\,W \times 3600\,s = 3600000\,J$

If a 2.6kW electric fire is used for four hours, it takes $2.6 \times 4 = 10.4$kWh of electrical energy. Note: the kilowatt hour is often referred to as a 'unit'.

- An 8kW cooker takes two hours to roast a chicken. How many kilowatt hours (units) of electrical energy is this?
- How much does this cost if the price per unit of electricity is 5p?
- Ask to see the electricity bills for where you live. Work out how many joules of electrical energy your home uses in a year.

Summary

1 Our lives are very dependent on electricity for heating, lighting and cooking.

2 The electric current is the same at all points in a series circuit.

3 The total current approaching a junction is the same as the total current leaving a junction in a parallel circuit.

4 There are four major effects of an electric current – a lighting effect, a heating effect, a chemical effect and a magnetic effect.

5 An ammeter is an instrument for measuring the size of an electric current.

6 A voltmeter is an instrument for measuring the voltage (potential difference) across two points in a circuit.

7 When a current of one ampere flows for one second, one coulomb of charge passes. Therefore,
1 ampere = 1 coulomb per second.

8 A battery with a voltage of 1 V gives 1 J of energy to each coulomb of charge which passes through it. 1 volt = 1 joule per coulomb.

9 If a current, I, flows for time, t, the charge, Q, which passes is given by: $Q = I \times t$.

10 When a current, I, flows for time t through a voltage, V, the electrical energy, E, transformed into other forms of energy is given by: $E = V \times I \times t$.

11 Ohm's law states that: The current in a metal conductor is proportional to the potential difference (voltage) across it, provided its temperature does not change.

12 The resistance of a conductor is the opposition which it offers to the flow of electrons.

13 $$\text{Resistance (ohms)} = \frac{\text{voltage (volts)}}{\text{current (amperes)}}$$

or

$$R = \frac{V}{I}$$

14 The electricity supplied by the National Grid system to our homes and factories is alternating current.

15 Many cables to electrical appliances contain three wires, which must be connected to the correct terminals in the three-pin plug:
the brown wire to the live terminal, L,
the blue wire to the neutral terminal, N,
the green/yellow wire to the earth terminal, E.

16 Power (watts) = voltage (volts) × current (amperes), or $P = V \times I$.

17 Electricity Boards measure the energy they supply to consumers in kilowatt hours (kWh). One kWh is the electrical energy taken by a one kilowatt appliance in one hour.

18 We have now met two definitions of the joule – a mechanical one and an electrical one. One joule is the energy required to
a) move a force of 1 N through 1 m, (i.e. 1 J = 1 Nm);
b) move a charge of 1 C through 1 V, (i.e. 1 J = 1 CV).

Study questions

1 Two identical bulbs are wired in parallel to a battery and a current of 1 A flows through one bulb.
   a) Draw a circuit diagram for this arrangement.
   b) What is the current through the second bulb?
   c) What is the total current drawn from the battery?
   d) If the two bulbs were wired in series with the same battery, would the current be more, less or the same as the total current drawn from the battery when the bulbs were connected in parallel? Explain your answer.
   e) Will the bulbs be brighter when they are connected in series or when they are connected in parallel? Explain your answer.

2 Suppose you have three identical bulbs and a single cell. Draw diagrams showing how you would connect the bulbs and the cell so that
   a) all three bulbs were equally lit and bright,
   b) all three bulbs were equally lit and dim,
   c) two bulbs were lit equally dimly and the other was bright.

3 In figure 10.18, all three lamps are identical. If ammeter A_1 reads 0.3 A, what do ammeters A_2, A_3, A_4 and A_5 read?

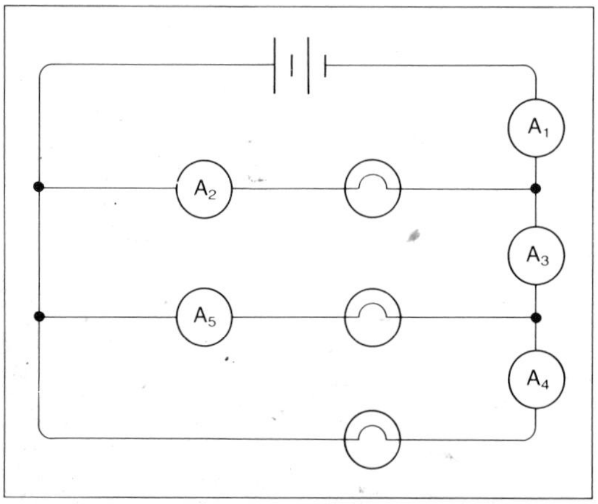

Figure 10.18

4 If all the cells in figure 10.19 give a voltage of 2 V, what voltages are produced by each arrangement.

5 A 12 V battery with a resistance of 1 ohm is connected to a bulb with a resistance of 2 ohms.
   a) What is the total resistance in the circuit?
   b) What is the current in the circuit?
   c) What is the voltage across the 2 ohm bulb?

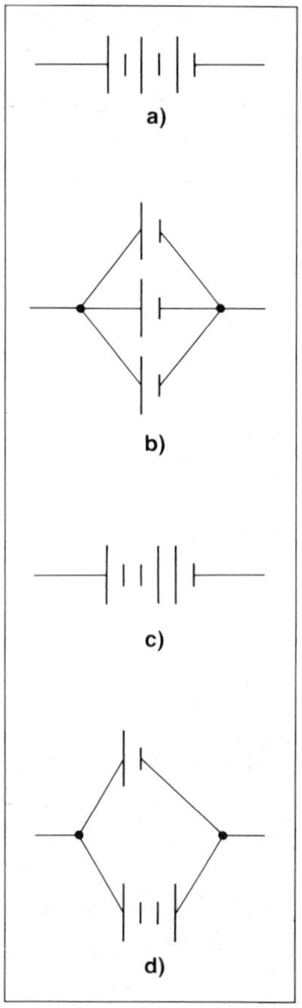

Figure 10.19 (Above)

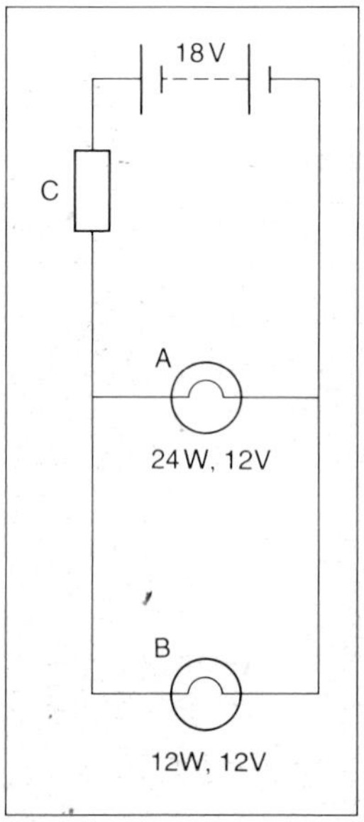

Figure 10.20

6 Figure 10.20 shows two lamps which are lit from an 18 V battery. The lamps are wired correctly.
   a) What is the current through lamp A?
   b) What is the current through lamp B?
   c) What is the total current from the battery?
   d) What is the resistance of C?
   e) What is the resistance of lamp A?
   f) What difference would you see in the two lamps while they are working?

7 During a ten-week Autumn term, a student estimated that, each day, she had used
   a 3 kW kettle for ten minutes,
   a 100 W table lamp for five hours,
   a 2 kW fire for three hours.
   a) How many 'units' (kilowatt hours) of electrical energy has she used during the ten week period?
   b) What will her electricity bill amount to if one 'unit' costs 5p?
   c) Why does the cable from the mains sockets to her 2 kW fire consist of three separate wires?

8 An aluminium block has an electrical heating coil embedded in it.
   a) Draw a well-labelled circuit diagram showing how you could measure the electrical energy supplied to the block via the coil in a given time.
   b) State how you would calculate the electrical energy supplied to the block in a given time.

9 Electric light bulbs consist of a coiled metal filament inside a thin gas-filled glass bulb.
   a) What metal is used for the filament?
   b) Why is this metal chosen?
   c) What gas is used inside light bulbs?
   d) Why must light bulbs not contain air?
   e) Why is a gas-filled bulb preferable to one with a vacuum?
   f) Why is the metal filament coiled?
   g) An electric light bulb is marked '80 W, 240 V'. What current does it take and what is its resistance?

10 a) Describe the construction of a moving-coil ammeter.
   b) State two features which an ammeter should have in order to be accurate and sensitive.
   c) The coil of an ammeter is replaced by one which is identical, except that it has a lower resistance. How will this affect the deflection for a given voltage across the meter?

11 Motors and generators: magnetism and electricity

From 2500 BC to the present, sailors have used magnetic compasses to navigate.

As long ago as 2500 BC, Chinese travellers used a magnetic ore called magnetite as a primitive compass. Since then magnets have been used in hundreds of other machines like motors, dynamos, electric bells and telephones.

11.1 Experiments with magnets

Magnetic poles

When a magnet is dipped into a box of pins, they cling to it (figure 11.1). A similar thing happens if the magnet is dipped into steel nails or tacks, but nothing happens when the magnet is dipped into small brass screws.

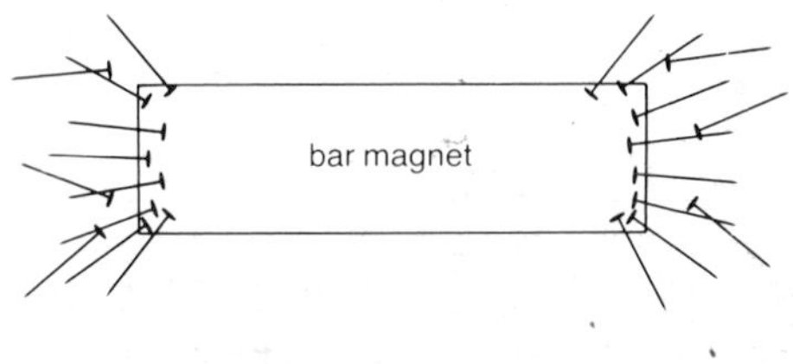

Figure 11.1 (Above) Pins cling to a bar magnet.

- Where is the strength of the magnet concentrated?
- Would the magnet attract (a) paper clips, (b) a gold ring?
- Are all metals magnetic?

Magnets will only attract metals and alloys which contain iron, cobalt or nickel. Thus, steel, which is an alloy of iron, is strongly attracted by magnets, but brass, an alloy of copper and zinc, is unaffected. The ends of the magnet where the pins cling most firmly are called **poles**.

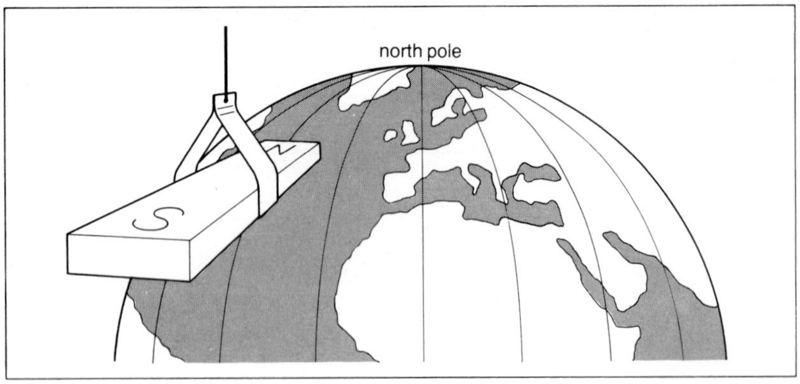

Figure 11.2 (Above) A small magnet can be used as a simple compass.

North poles and south poles

If a bar magnet is hung horizontally so that it can turn freely (figure 11.2), it always comes to rest in a north–south direction. What is more, one end of the magnet will always point north and the other end always points south. The pole of the magnet which points north is called the **north pole** or, more accurately, the north-seeking pole. The pole of the magnet which points south is called the **south pole**, or the south-seeking pole. Because of this behaviour, a small magnet can be used as a simple compass. Every magnet has a north pole and a south pole.

Forces between poles

When a magnet is suspended horizontally and a second magnet is brought near it, the two magnets exert forces on one another, and the suspended magnet moves (figure 11.3).

Like poles (i.e. two N-poles or two S-poles) repel each other, but unlike poles attract.

This behaviour is similar to that of positive and negative charges (section 9.1).

Figure 11.3 Unlike poles attract and like poles repel each other.

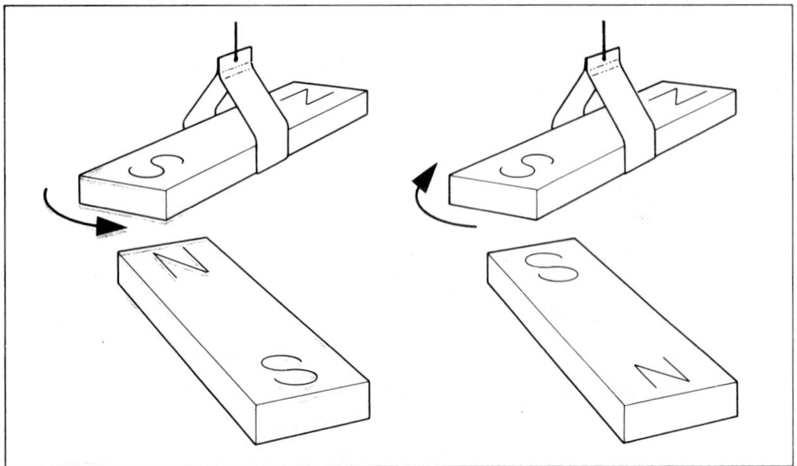

Induced poles

When a steel pin is brought near a strong magnet, it becomes a magnet itself. The magnet **induces** an opposite pole in the end of the pin nearest to itself (figure 11.4a). We can check this by attaching two pins to the N-pole of a magnet (figure 11.4b). The pins tend to repel each other. They move even further apart when the N-pole of another magnet is brought close to them (figure 11.4c).

- When two pins are attached to the opposite ends of a bar magnet they lean towards each other (figure 11.4d). Why is this?
- Why must a compass not be used close to a strong magnet?

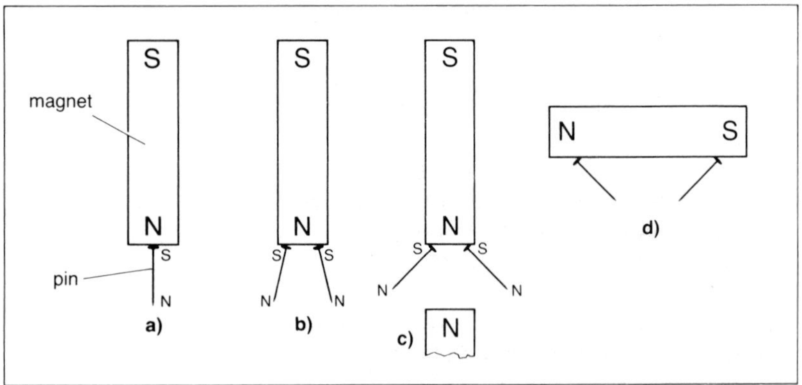

Figure 11.4 (Above) Investigating induced poles.

With a little care, it is possible to attach a chain of steel pins or iron paper clips to a magnet. Each pin or nail induces magnetism in the next one below it and the unlike poles formed in this way attract each other (figure 11.5).

Using a small magnet, a student formed one chain of four paper clips and a second chain of three pins. When the chains were taken off the magnet, the chain of iron paper clips collapsed completely, but the chain of steel pins did not break.
- Which are easier to magnetise, iron clips or steel pins?
- Which stay magnetised longer, iron clips or steel pins?

These experiments show that iron is easy to magnetise, but it tends to form **temporary magnets** which quickly lose their magnetism. As a result of this, iron is used in electromagnets (section 11.4) in which its magnetism can be 'switched' on or off very easily. Scientists sometimes describe this iron as **soft iron** because it is so easy to

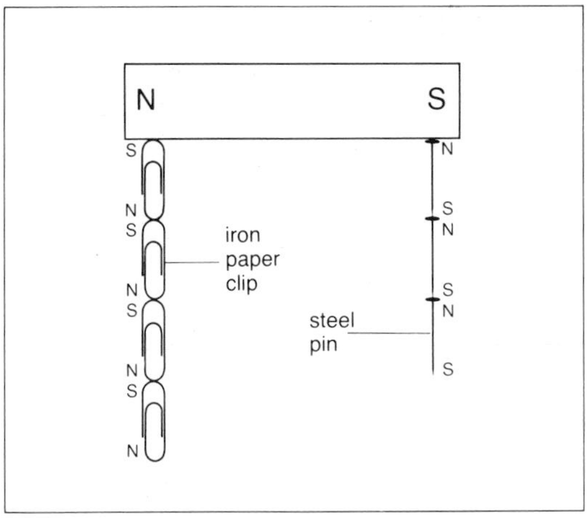

Figure 11.5 Which chain, paper clips or pins, can be taken off the magnet without collapsing?

magnetise and demagnetise. On the other hand, steel keeps its magnetism much better and is therefore used to make **permanent magnets**.

At one time, all permanent magnets were made of steel. Nowadays, they are either alloys of iron, cobalt and nickel, or compounds of iron such as barium ferrite. Powdered ferrites can be mixed with plastics and used to coat recording tape or the surface of floppy disks used in computers. The mixture of powdered ferrite and plastic can also be moulded into specially shaped magnets.

- One of the alloys used for strong permanent magnets has the trade name *Alnico*. What three elements does it contain?
- What advantage do ferrite magnets have over alloy magnets?

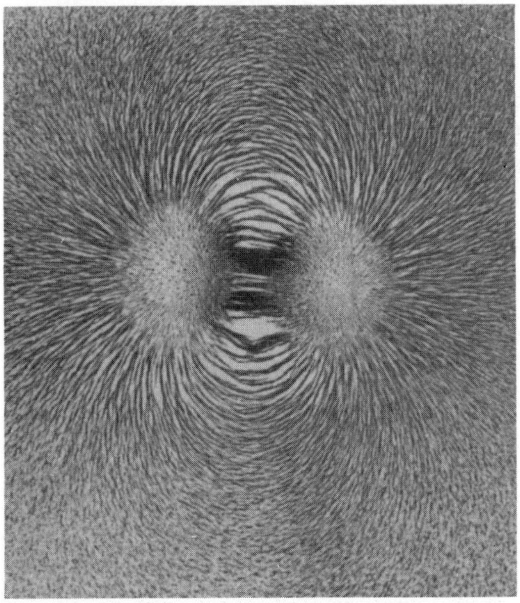

Investigating the magnetic field around a bar magnet using iron filings.

11.2 Magnetic fields

A magnet can attract iron clips and other magnetic materials even when they are some distance away. Strong magnets can also act through other materials, like paper and wood, and they can exert their magnetic forces through a vacuum. The region around a magnet in which its magnetic force can be felt is called a **magnetic field**.

One way to detect a magnetic field and find its direction is to use a compass. Thus, the field around a bar magnet can be investigated using a small plotting compass (figure 11.6a). Put the bar magnet on a sheet of paper and place the plotting compass near one of its poles. See which way the compass points and mark the position of the poles of the compass with dots on the paper. Use the second dot as the starting point for the next position of the plotting compass (figure 11.6b). Continue in this way until the other pole of the magnet is reached or the field becomes too weak to detect.

A quicker way to investigate the magnetic field around a bar magnet is to use iron filings. The iron filings are sprinkled on to a sheet of paper placed on top of the magnet. The iron filings are magnetised and line up in the direction of the magnetic field when the paper is tapped gently.

The field around a magnet can be shown as series of lines called **lines of force** running from the N-pole to the S-pole. The direction of the lines at a particular point shows the direction in which a compass needle would set if placed at that point. Arrows are usually drawn on the lines to show the direction in which the N-pole of the needle will set. These arrows always point away from the magnet's north pole and towards the magnet's south pole.

Figure 11.6

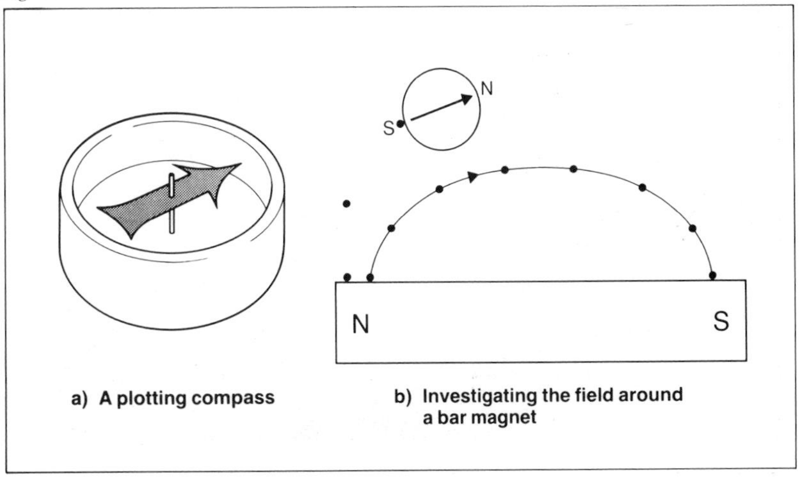

Figure 11.7 shows the magnetic fields around
a) a single bar magnet,
b) bar magnets with unlike poles together,
c) bar magnets with like poles together.

Notice the following points.

- The direction of a magnetic field is always away from a north pole and towards a south pole.
- Lines of force can never cross because they show the direction of the magnetic field at that point and the magnetic field can only have one direction at one point.
- At the point marked X in figure 11.7c, the field from one N-pole is equal but opposite in direction to the field from the other N-pole. The field from one magnet is cancelled by that from the other. X is therefore called a **neutral point**. The magnetic field there is zero.

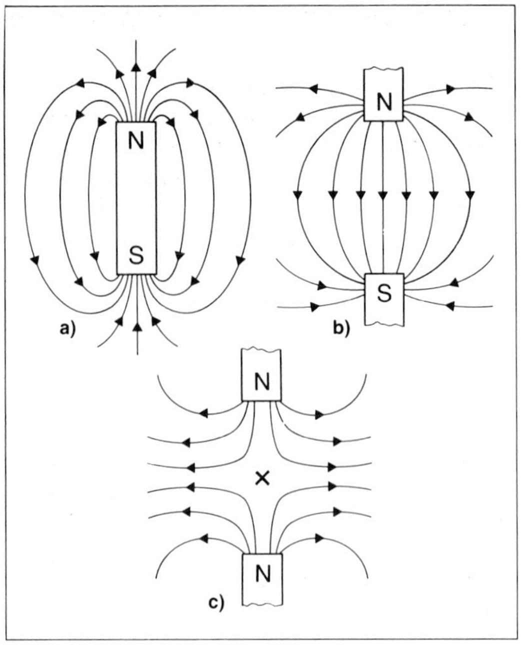

Figure 11.7 (Left) Magnetic fields.

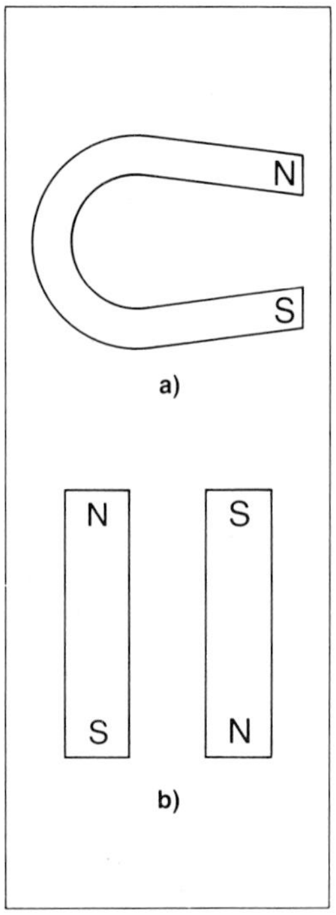

Figure 11.8 (Above).

- Copy the diagrams in figure 11.8 and draw in the magnetic lines of force. Show the direction of the magnetic fields with arrows on the lines of force.

The Earth's magnetic field

Travellers and navigators have known for centuries that a compass needle will set itself in a north–south direction. This led the English scientist, William Gilbert (1544–1603) to suggest that the Earth behaved as if a gigantic bar magnet was buried at its centre and along its north–south axis (figure 11.9).

Notice that the Earth's geographical north pole *attracts* the north poles of magnets, so it must be a south-seeking magnetic pole (remember: unlike poles attract). Similarly, the Earth's geographical south pole must be a north-seeking magnetic pole.

Since Gilbert's time, scientists have found that a compass does not point exactly north–south but to a point slightly away from true north. This means that the Earth's geographical north pole does not coincide with its magnetic north pole (figure 11.9).

(Below) The Northern Lights can be seen when charged particles from space become trapped in the Earth's magnetic field. They interact with the atmosphere at the poles to produce this spectacular display.

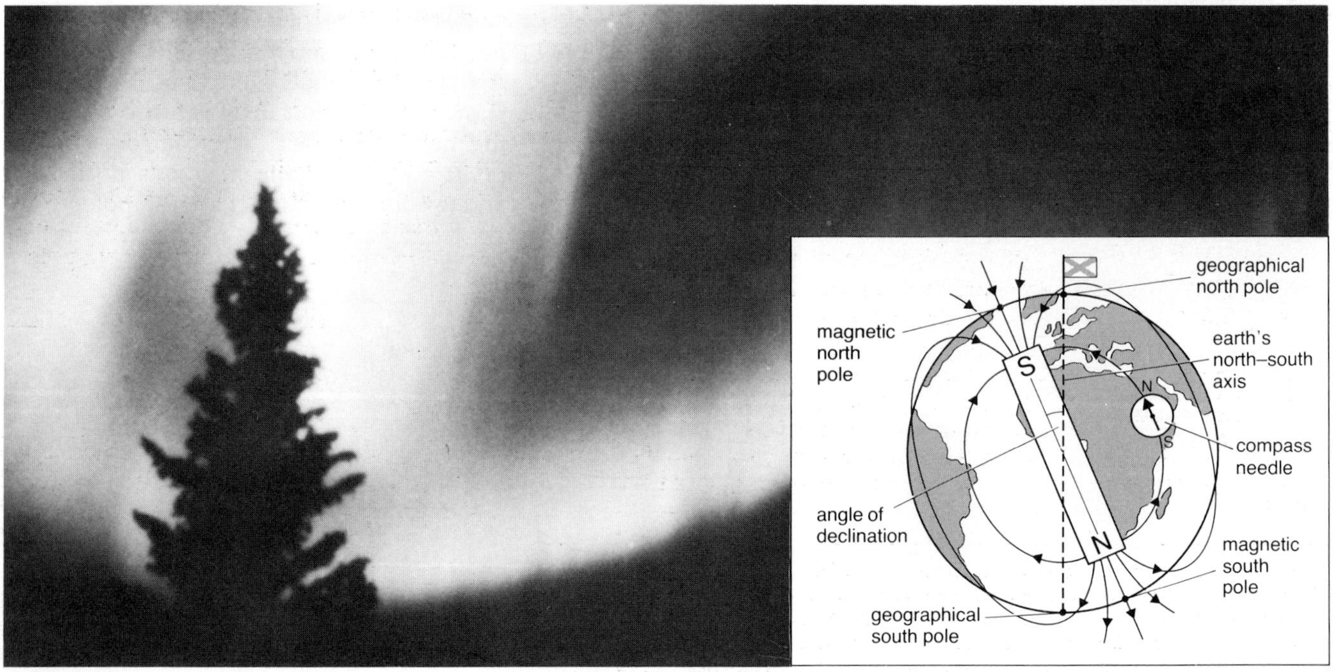

11.3 Magnetism from electricity

We have already seen that there is a magnetic field around a wire carrying an electric current (figure 10.3). In terms of electrons, this means that a magnetic field is produced when electrons are in motion. In other words, magnetism can be generated from electricity.

Figure 11.10 The magnetic field around a straight wire.

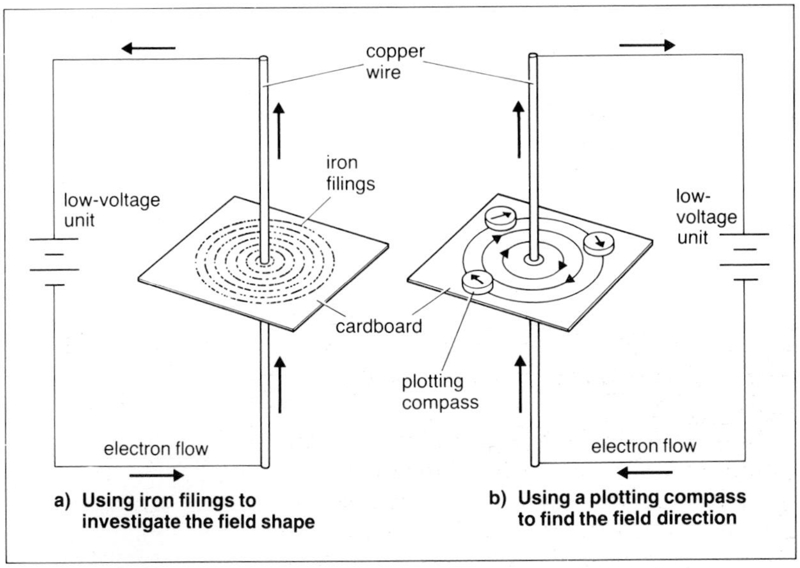

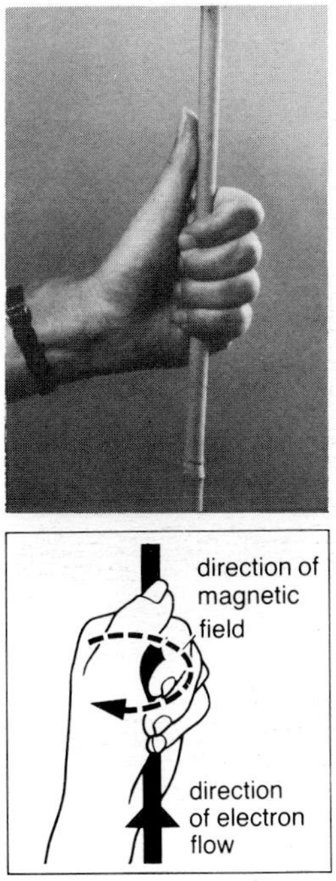

Figure 11.11 The left-hand grip rule.

The magnetic field around a straight wire carrying a current

The magnetic field around a straight wire can be investigated using the apparatus shown in figure 11.10. When the card is tapped, the iron filings set in concentric circles around the wire. Using a plotting compass, it is possible to find the direction of the field.

When the direction of the current is reversed, the compass points in the opposite direction. This shows that the direction of the field depends on the direction of the current.

If the direction of the current is known, the direction of the field around the wire can be predicted from the **left-hand grip rule*** (figure 11.11).

> If the wire is gripped with the left hand so that the thumb points in the direction of the electron flow, then the fingers point around the wire in the direction of the magnetic field.

*Throughout this book, we have taken the direction of the electric current as the direction of electron flow, i.e. from the negative terminal of the battery through the external circuit to the positive terminal. Many textbooks assume the so-called 'conventional current' is flowing from positive to negative. If this is done, the left-hand grip rule becomes the right-hand grip rule. Furthermore, the right-hand motor rule (section 11.5) and the left-hand dynamo rule (section 11.6) also change hands.

The magnetic field around a loop of wire carrying a current

Figure 11.12 shows the magnetic field around a circular loop carrying a current. Notice that the field at X and Y can be predicted using the left-hand grip rule.

- Describe the shape of the magnetic field through the loop.
- Will the *shape* of the field change if the current is reversed?
- Will the *direction* of the field change if the current is reversed?
- What happens to the field when the current is switched off?

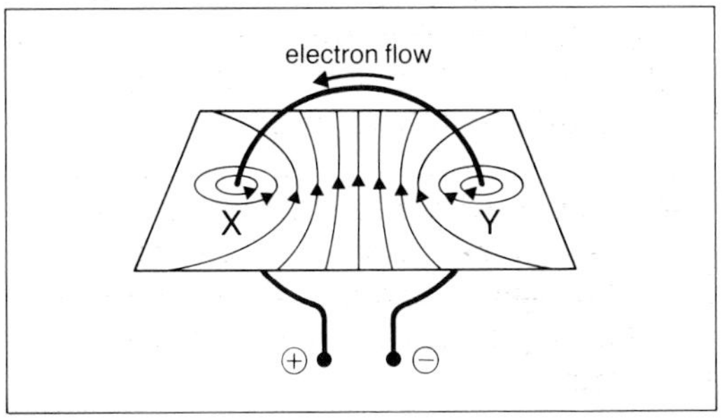

Figure 11.12 (Above) The magnetic field around a loop of wire carrying a current.

The magnetic field around a solenoid carrying a current

A solenoid is a cylindrical coil of wire. Figure 11.13 shows the magnetic field around a solenoid when a current flows through the coil. By using the left-hand grip rule (figure 11.11) at any point in the coils of the solenoid, it is possible to find the direction of the magnetic field. The magnetic field around the solenoid is similar to that around a bar magnet. The end of the solenoid marked N behaves like a north pole, and the end marked S behaves like a south pole. Inside the solenoid, the magnetic field goes from the south pole to the north pole.

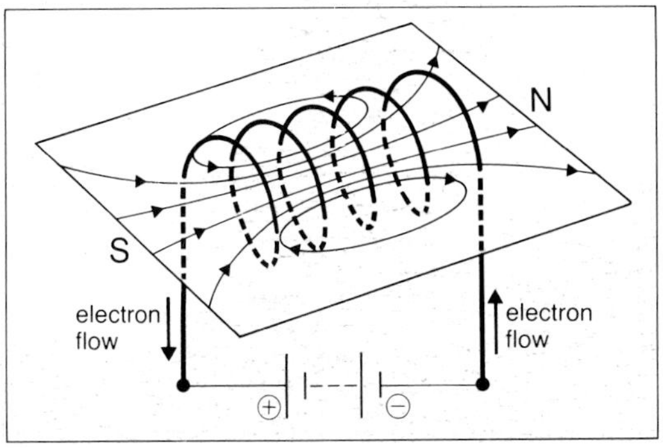

Figure 11.13 The magnetic field around a solenoid.

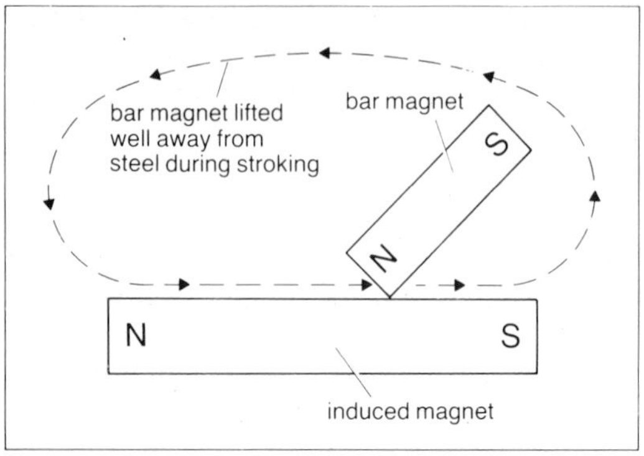

Figure 11.14 Magnetising a piece of steel by stroking.

Making magnets

Using a solenoid

Permanent magnets can be made by placing steel or some other magnetic material inside a solenoid with hundreds of turns and then passing a large *direct* current through the solenoid. The magnetic field inside the solenoid induces magnetism in the steel. A magnet can be demagnetised by removing it slowly from a solenoid through which an *alternating* current is flowing.

Stroking with a magnet

A convenient way to magnetise a piece of steel is to stroke it twenty or thirty times in one direction with one end of a bar magnet (figure 11.14). The pole induced in the steel at the end of a stroke is opposite to that of the stroking pole.

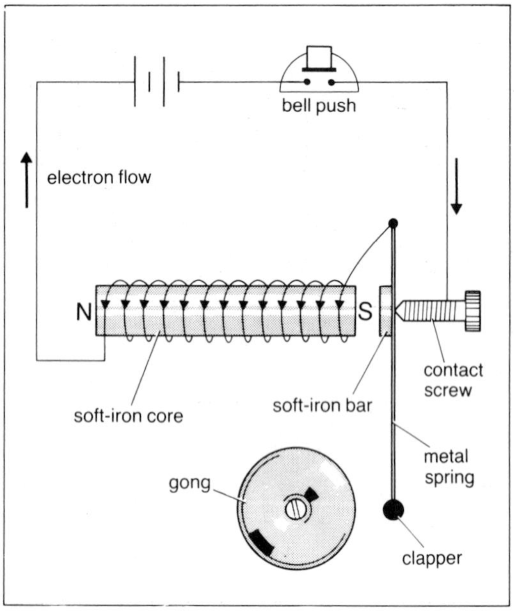

Figure 11.15 The electric bell.

11.4 Electromagnets

The solenoid in figure 11.13 is a simple electromagnet. When a current flows in the solenoid it acts like a magnet, but when the current is switched off, the magnetism disappears. It is possible to increase the strength of the electromagnet by having

- a larger current through the solenoid,
- more turns of wire in the solenoid,
- a soft-iron core through the solenoid.

Soft iron, not steel, must be used for the core because steel would remain magnetised even when the current was switched off.

Electromagnets are used in electric bells, door chimes, relays, telephones and electric motors.

Electromagnets have many uses. Here, heavy iron ingots are being moved.

The electric bell

When the bell push is pressed (figure 11.15), current flows through the solenoid. The soft-iron core is magnetised and attracts the soft-iron bar. This pulls the clapper onto the gong, but at the same time, the metal spring is pulled away from the contact screw and the circuit is broken. The electromagnet loses its magnetism and the metal

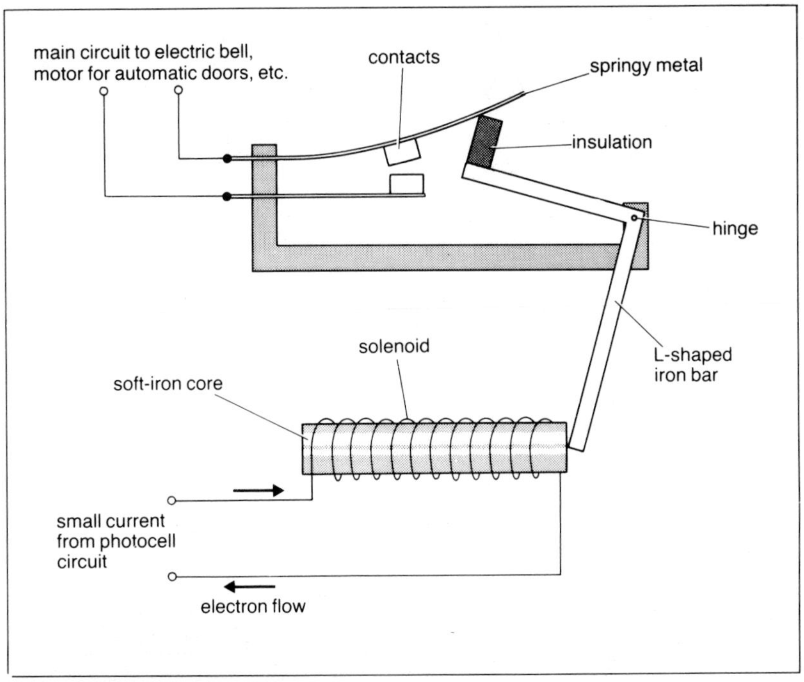

Figure 11.16 A relay system.

spring pulls the soft-iron bar back again. As soon as the metal spring touches the contact screw, the circuit is complete again, the electromagnet attracts the soft-iron bar and the cycle is repeated. As long as the bell push is pressed, the cycle continues and the bell rings continuously. Study question 7 looks at the working of door chimes.

The relay

Have you ever wondered how the automatic doors work in department stores, or how a burglar alarm works? The answer lies in the use of a *relay* which is a switch controlled by an electromagnet (figure 11.16). Electromagnetic relays can be compared with relay races. In a relay race, a baton is passed from one runner to another. In an electromagnetic relay, signals are passed from one circuit to another by stopping and starting electric currents.

In an automatic door relay (figure 11.16), a photocell circuit produces a small current in the solenoid as long as light falls on it. This magnetises the soft-iron core which attracts the L-shaped iron bar and holds the contacts open. As a trolley approaches the door, it breaks a beam of light which is directed onto the photocell. The current in the solenoid disappears (figure 11.16), the iron bar falls and the contacts close. A current will now flow in the main circuit, operating a motor for the automatic doors or an electric bell in the case of a burglar alarm.

Notice how a small current from the photocell can control a much larger current in the main circuit. This is an important reason for using relays.

Look at figure 11.16.
- Why must the solenoid around the soft-iron core be made of insulated wire?
- Why must the shaded parts of the hinge and the L-shaped bar not conduct electricity?
- Why is the top contact attached to springy metal?

11.5 Electric motors

Electric motors form an essential working part in many electrical appliances. Washing machines, vacuum cleaners, hair dryers, electric drills and refrigerators all depend on electric motors.

Figure 11.17 shows a simplified diagram of a cylinder vacuum cleaner. As the electric motor rotates, the fan draws air and dust into the cleaner. The dust bag traps the dust, but allows the air to pass through and then out at the other end.

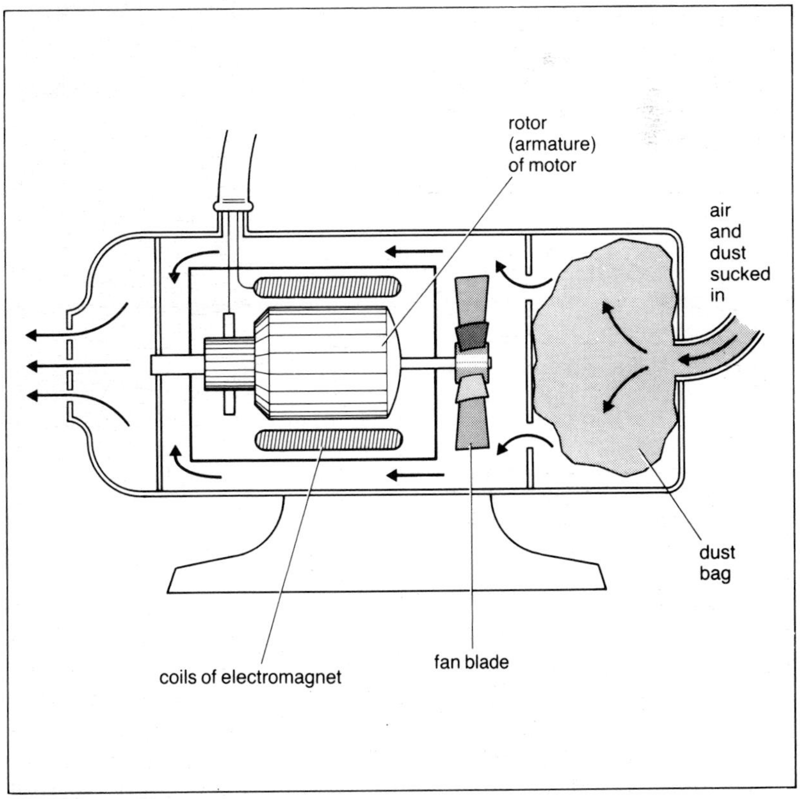

Figure 11.17 A cylinder vacuum cleaner.

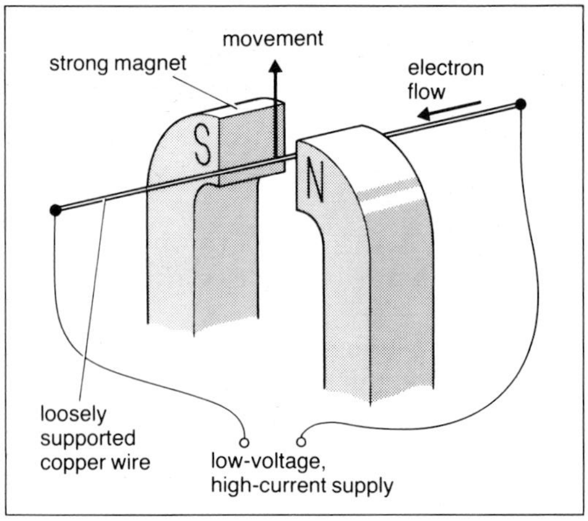

Figure 11.18

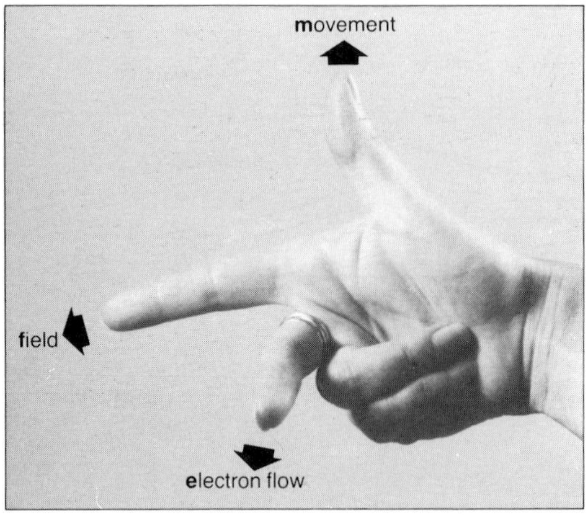

Figure 11.19 (Left) The right-hand motor rule.

How does the motor work?

An electric motor uses electricity and magnetism to produce movement. This movement (motor effect) can be demonstrated using the apparatus in figure 11.18. The copper wire is supported loosely between the poles of a strong magnet. When an electric current passes through the wire, the wire jumps upwards. If the current is reversed *or* the field is reversed, the wire tugs downwards. If *both* the field and the current are reversed, from the situation in figure 11.18, then the wire jumps upwards.

Notice that the wire always moves in a direction which is at right angles to the direction of both the field and the current. When a current passes through the wire, a force acts on the wire and makes it move. This force pulls the wire up or down depending upon

- the direction of the current,
- the direction of the field.

It is possible to predict the direction in which the wire will move using the **right-hand motor rule** (figure 11.19).

Hold the first finger, second finger and thumb of your right hand at right angles to each other. Now, turn your hand so the **F**irst finger points in the direction of the **F**ield (i.e. N to S) and the s**E**cond finger points in the direction of the **E**lectron flow. Your thu**M**b will now point in the direction of **M**ovement of the wire.

This motor effect is used in moving-coil ammeters (section 10.3) and in electric motors. Figure 11.20 shows a simple **direct current motor**. This consists of a coil which can rotate between the poles of a magnet. Each end of the coil is fixed to half of a split metal ring, called a **commutator**, which rotates with the coil. Two carbon contacts,

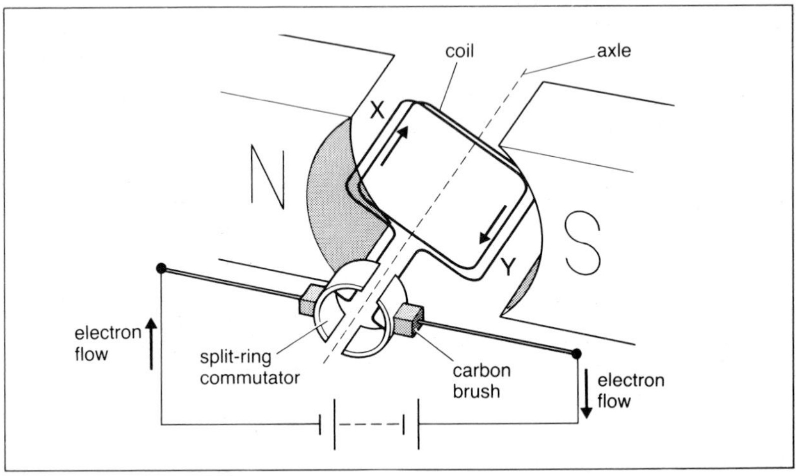

Figure 11.20 The d.c. electric motor.

known as **brushes**, press lightly against the commutator and connect it to the electrical supply.

Look closely at figure 11.20 and use the right-hand motor rule.

- Which way will side X of the coil try to move?
- Which way will side Y of the coil try to move?

The forces acting on the coil rotate it in a clockwise direction until it is vertical. In this position the gaps in the commutator are opposite the brushes so there is no current through the coil. The coil will slow down, but as it overshoots the vertical position, the two halves of the commutator change contact from one brush to the other (figure 11.20). Side X of the coil is now on the right, in the same position as side Y was at the instant shown in figure 11.20. Side X now feels a downward force, whilst side Y feels an upward force. This makes the coil continue its clockwise rotation. Without the commutator, the coil would just rotate until it was in the vertical position, then stop.

- Why do commercial motors use electromagnets rather than permanent magnets? (Hint: What happens to permanent magnets with age?)
- Why do commercial motors have coils of many turns?
- The coils are wound on a soft-iron core. Why is this?
- Why is the core not made of aluminium, which is lighter?

11.6 Generators, alternators and dynamos

When an electric current passes through a wire in a magnetic field, the wire tries to move (figure 11.18). This is the motor effect, which we can summarise as:

electric current + magnetic field → movement

In 1831, Michael Faraday showed that the effect could be worked 'backwards'. Faraday moved a wire in a magnetic field and produced an electric current in the wire.

movement + magnetic field → electric current

Faraday's original discovery has given us generators in power stations, alternators in motor cars and dynamos for bicycles. All of these machines use magnetism and movement to generate electrcity. Electric currents made in this way are called *induced* currents and the effect is sometimes called **electromagnetic induction**.

Figure 11.21 shows an easy way to generate electric currents and investigate electromagnetic induction. When the wire is held still between the poles of the magnet, there is no current in the ammeter. But what happens if the wire is moved in the six directions shown in the diagram?

- When the wire is moved in directions 1, 2, 3 and 4, there is no deflection on the ammeter and therefore no induced current.
- When the wire is moved up (direction 5) or down (direction 6), an induced current flows through the ammeter.
- When the wire moves up, the current flows one way. When the wire moves down, it flows in the opposite direction.
- The current only lasts while the wire is moving.

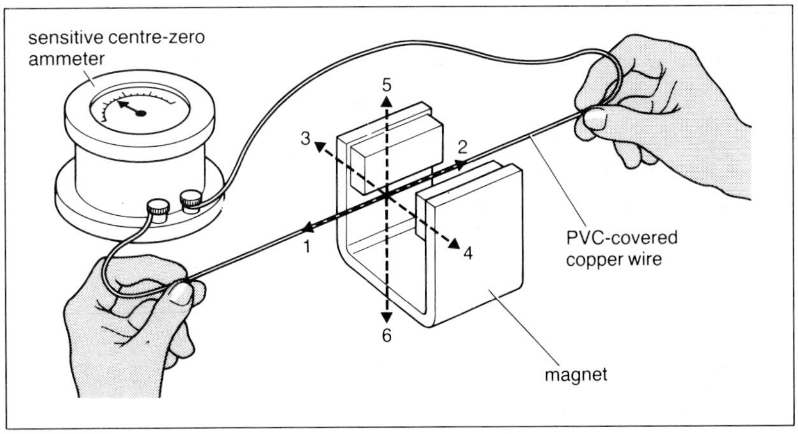

Figure 11.21 (Above) Making induced currents.

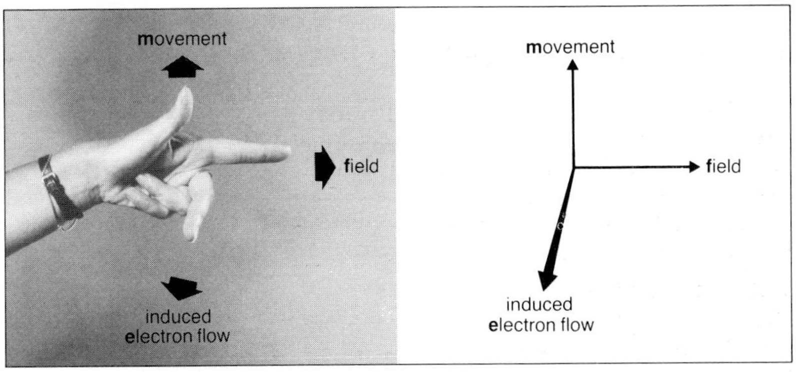

Figure 11.22 The left-hand dynamo rule.

- What will happen if the magnet is moved but the wire is held still?
- What happens if the magnet is moved
  a) parallel to the wire (directions 1 and 2),
  b) parallel to the field (directions 3 and 4),
  c) at right angles to the field and the wire (directions 5 and 6)?

These results show that *a current flows in the wire whenever it 'cuts through' the magnetic field, across the lines of force* but not when it moves along them. It is possible to predict the direction of the induced current in the wire using the **left-hand dynamo rule** (figure 11.22).

Hold the first finger, second finger and thumb of your left hand at right angles to each other.
Now turn your hand so that the **F**irst finger points in the direction of the **F**ield (i.e. N to S) and the thu**M**b points in the direction of **M**ovement of the wire.
Your s**E**cond finger now points in the direction of the induced **E**lectron flow.

Notice that the *left hand* is used for the *dynamo rule*, because this effect is opposite to the motor effect which uses the right-hand rule.

Figure 11.23 shows another way to investigate electromagnetic induction. As the magnet *moves* into the coil a current is induced.

- What would happen if
  a) the magnet moved into the coil faster,
  b) a stronger magnet were used,
  c) the coil had more turns?
- Would it matter whether the magnet were moved into the coil or the coil were moved towards the magnet?

These experiments show that the induced current *increases* if
- the magnet or the coil is moved faster,
- the magnet is stronger,
- the coil has more turns.

These results are summarised in **Faraday's law of electromagnetic induction** which says:

The size of the induced current is proportional to the rate at which the coil (conductor) cuts the magnetic lines of force.

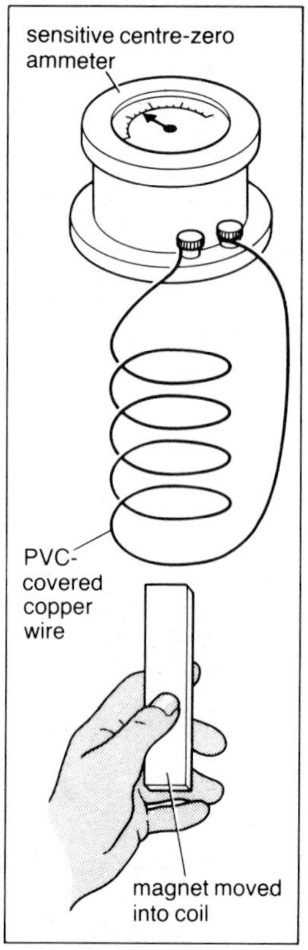

Figure 11.23 (Above) Investigating electromagnetic induction.

The a.c. generator (alternator)

Generators convert kinetic energy into electrical energy. They have a coil of wire which rotates between the poles of a magnet.

Figure 11.24 shows a very simple a.c. generator which uses the dynamo effect just described. The ends of the coil are connected to slip rings which are fixed to the axle and rotate with the coil. Carbon contacts connect the slip rings to the rest of the circuit, acting as pick-up points for the electric current generated. As the coil rotates, it cuts the magnetic lines of force and an induced current is generated.

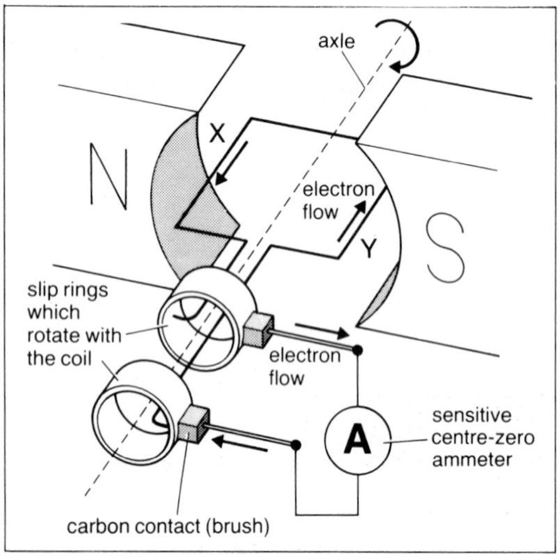

Figure 11.24 A simple a.c. generator.

- Use the left-hand rule to check that you agree with the direction of electron flow in the coil in figure 11.24.

Figure 11.25 shows how the induced current varies during one turn of the coil. As the coil moves through the horizontal position in figure 11.24, sides X and Y are cutting through the magnetic lines of force at the greatest rate. The current is therefore greatest at this time. As the coil moves towards the vertical position, the current falls. When the coil is moving through the vertical position sides X and Y are moving parallel to the lines of force and the current is zero. After the coil has passed the vertical, the induced current increases again, but its direction is reversed because side X is now moving down and side Y is moving up. The induced current reaches its greatest value as the coil passes through the horizontal and then decreases again.

Notice that an alternating current flows in the circuit to the ammeter. Because of this, the a.c. generator is sometimes called an **alternator**.

The huge a.c. generators in power stations normally have a rotating magnet rather than a rotating coil. The advantage of this is that the coil is stationary and brushes are not needed for contact between the slip rings and the circuit. This cuts out the wear caused by sparks and friction between the brushes and the slip rings. Generators in

Figure 11.25 (Below) Variation of the induced current during one turn of the coil.

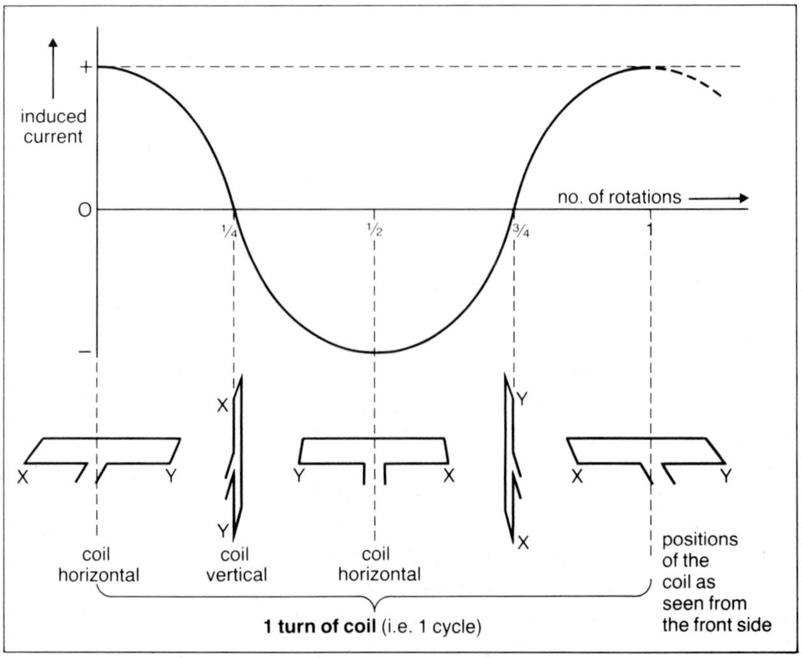

(*Above*) The huge a.c. generator at Didcot power station during construction. The spoked 'fans' are the blades of the steam turbines. You can see the large rotor (magnet) in the foreground. The ring of holes around it are for the stationary coils.

which the magnet moves rather than the coil are sometimes called **dynamos**. This arrangement is also used in car alternators. Stationary coils are placed around an electromagnet which is made to rotate by the engine. Alternating current is generated. It is then changed into direct current so that it can charge the batteries and power the car's electrical equipment.

An alternator (a.c. generator) can be modified to generate *direct* current by connecting the ends of the coil to a single split ring, called a commutator, rather than to separate rings. The split ring and the brushes are arranged in the same way as they are in a d.c. motor (figure 11.20). The brushes are carefully positioned so that their connections to the two halves of the split ring change just as the coil passes through the vertical position. This is the position where the direction of the induced current in the coil reverses. In this way the current in the external circuit always flows in the same direction (figure 11.26).

Notice that the d.c. motor and the d.c. generator use the same apparatus. If an electric current is passed through the coil, it will start to rotate and the apparatus acts as a motor. Electrical energy is being transformed into kinetic energy.

If the coil is made to rotate, an electric current is induced in it and the apparatus acts as a generator. In this case, kinetic energy is being transformed into electrical energy.

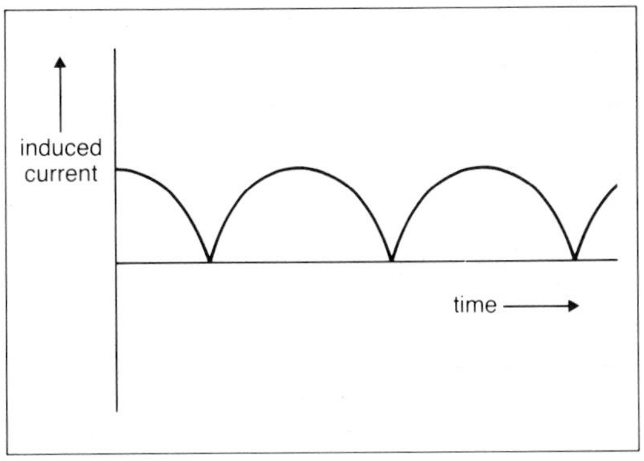

Figure 11.26 The current produced by a d.c. generator.

11.7 Transmitting electricity

Transformers

If a magnet is moved into a coil, a voltage is induced in the coil as long as the magnet is moving, and the lines of force from the magnet are cutting across the turns of the coil (figure 11.23). An induced current will flow through the coil if it is part of a closed circuit.

An induced current can also be obtained when the magnet is replaced in a coil and the current in this primary coil is switched on or off (figure 11.27). When the current in the primary circuit is switched on, the primary coil acts like an electromagnet and a magnetic field 'grows' around it. Lines of magnetic force cut across the secondary coil and a voltage and current are induced in the

Figure 11.27 (Below) Generating and transforming electricity.

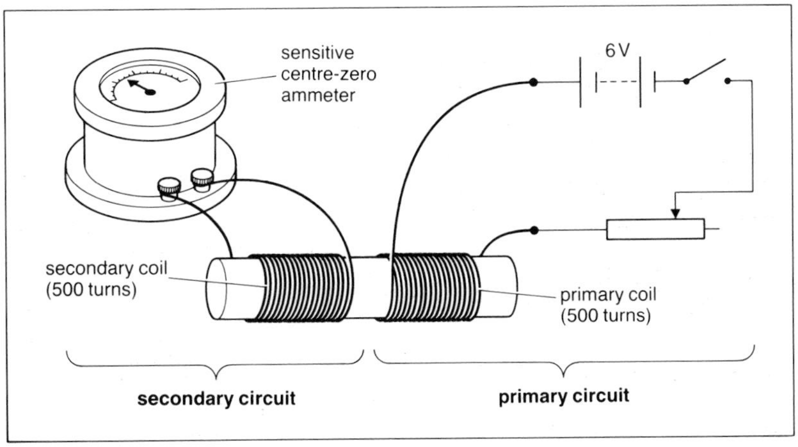

secondary circuit for *as long as the current in the primary is changing*. Once the current in the primary coil has reached a steady value, the voltage induced in the secondary coil is zero, because the magnetic field from the primary circuit is no longer changing.

A similar effect occurs as the magnetic field dies away, when the current in the primary coil is switched off. The lines of force cutting across the secondary coil change and an induced voltage again appears in it.

If we use an alternating current in the primary coil, the current will change and reverse all the time. This will induce a continuous alternating voltage in the secondary coil.

We can increase this induced voltage by having more turns in the secondary coil and by winding the two coils on the same iron ring, which concentrates the magnetic field through the secondary coil.

These simple experiments illustrate the principle behind **transformers**. A transformer changes (transforms) an alternating voltage to a higher or lower alternating voltage. Like our experiment in figure 11.27, it has a primary coil, a secondary coil and a core (figure 11.28).

The voltage, V, induced in a coil is proportional to the number of its turns, n;

$$V \propto n$$

This means that:

$$\frac{\text{voltage across secondary } (V_s)}{\text{voltage across primary } (V_p)} = \frac{\text{number of turns in secondary } (n_s)}{\text{number of turns in primary } (n_p)}$$

- **Step-up transformers** (figure 11.29a) have more turns in the secondary coil than the primary. The output voltage from the secondary is therefore greater than the voltage applied to the primary.
- **Step-down transformers** (figure 11.29b) have fewer turns in the secondary and this gives a lower voltage output from the secondary than that put into the primary.

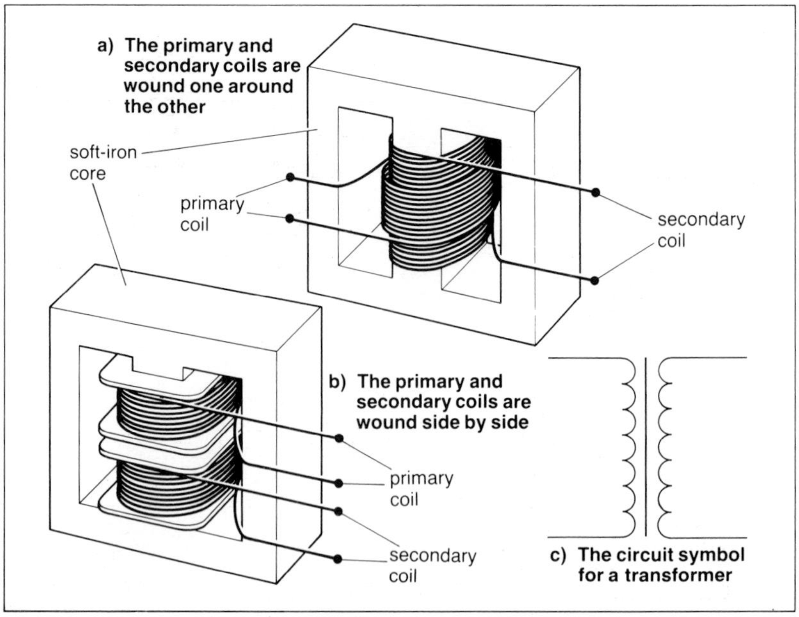

Figure 11.28 Types of transformer.

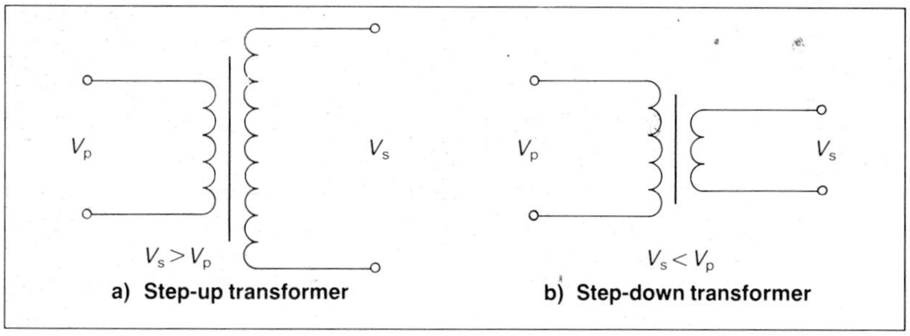

Figure 11.29

> Suppose a transformer is being used to operate a 12 V bulb from the 240 V mains supply.
> - Is it a step-up or a step-down transformer?
> - If there are 500 turns on the primary, calculate the number of turns on the secondary coil, using the formula above.
> - Why is a transformer needed?

Transmitting electricity

Transformers play a major part in the transmission of electricity from power stations to our homes and industries via the National Grid system. There are more than two hundred power stations in the UK. Most of these use coal as their fuel but others use oil, gas and uranium. Heat from the fuel is used to boil water and produce steam. The steam is then used to turn huge turbines and drive alternators.

Modern power stations generate electricity at 25 000 V and then step this up to 275 000 or 400 000 V using a transformer, before transmitting the electricity over long distances on the Supergrid (figure 11.30).

If we assume that the transformer is 100% efficient and all the electrical energy in the primary is transferred to the secondary,

$$\text{electrical energy taken from primary} = \text{electrical energy given to secondary}$$

$$\therefore V_p \times I_p \times t = V_s \times I_s \times t$$

where V_p and I_p represent the voltage and current in the primary, V_s and I_s are the

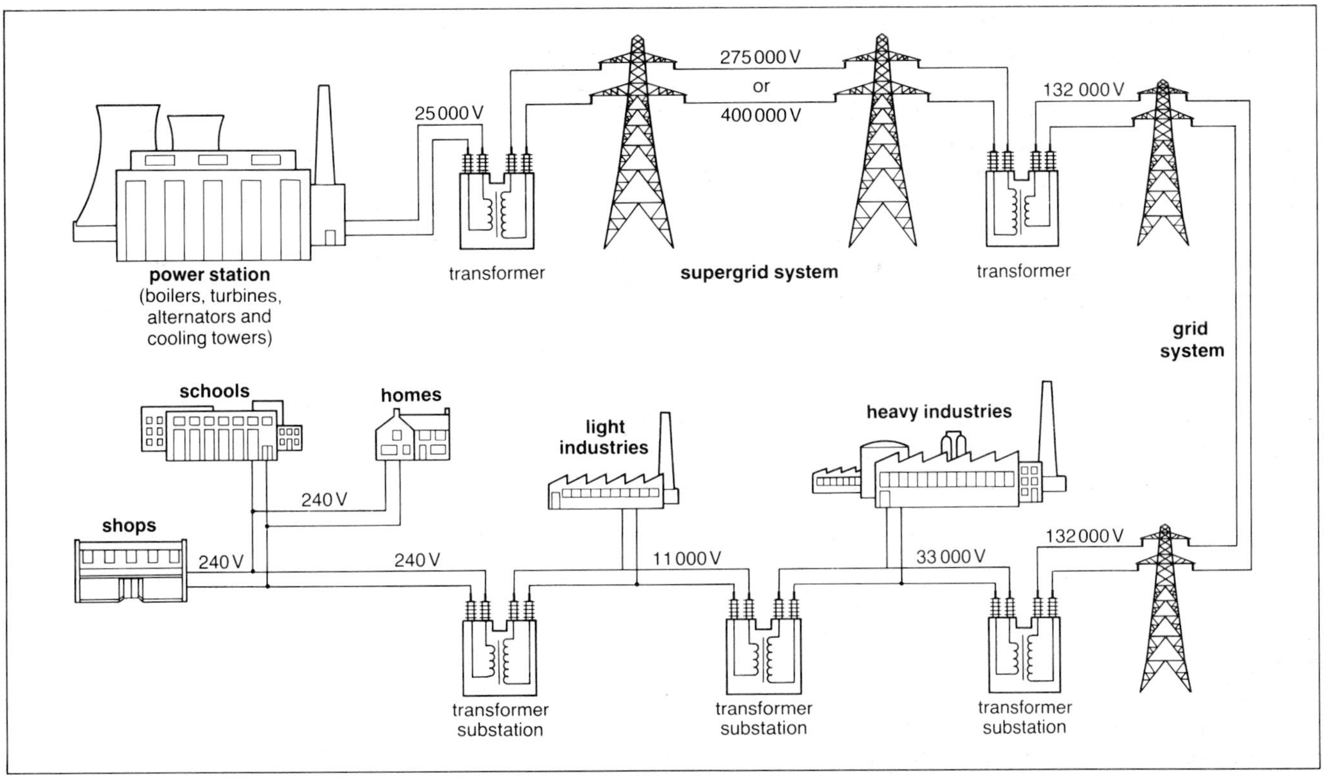

Figure 11.30 (Above) Transmitting electricity via the grid system. Notice how transformers are used to step up and then step down the voltage.

voltage and current in the secondary and t is the time for which the current flows.

$$\Rightarrow V_p \times I_p = V_s \times I_s$$

$$\Rightarrow \frac{V_s}{V_p} = \frac{I_p}{I_s}$$

From the last equation, we can see that if the voltage is stepped up from 25 000 V to 400 000 V, then the current is stepped down in the same proportion. This is the major advantage for the Supergrid system because a lower current has a much smaller heating effect in the cables. Less energy is therefore lost as unwanted heat. The lower current also requires thinner and lighter cables. On the other hand, transmission of the electricity at such high voltages requires greater insulation.

At a later stage, the voltage is reduced by step-down transformers in substations for use by consumers in factories, schools and homes. Industrial plants usually take electrical energy from the grid system at 33 000 V or 11 000 V. Transformers reduce the voltage further to 240 V for use in homes and schools.

(Right) A large 25 000 V to 400 000 V step-up transformer at the Hunterston power station, in the south of Scotland.

Summary

1 Magnets will only attract metals and alloys which contain iron, cobalt or nickel.

2 The pole of a magnet which points north is called the north pole or north-seeking pole. The pole which points south is called the south pole.

3 Like poles repel each other; unlike poles attract.

4 The region around a magnet in which its magnetic force can be detected is called a magnetic field.

5 The direction of the magnetic field around a wire carrying an electric current can be predicted by the left-hand grip rule.

6 A magnetic material can be magnetised by
a) placing it inside a solenoid carrying a *direct* current,
b) stroking it with a magnet.
A magnet can be demagnetised by withdrawing it slowly from a solenoid carrying an *alternating* current.

7 Electromagnets are used in electric bells, door chimes, relays, telephones and motors. These appliances turn electrical energy into kinetic energy.

8 An electric motor uses magnetism and electricity to produce movement. The direction of movement can be predicted from the right-hand motor rule.

9 The motor effect can be worked backwards in machines such as generators, alternators and dynamos, which use magnetism and movement to generate electricity. Electric currents made in this way are called induced currents and the effect is called electromagnetic induction.

10 A current will flow in a closed circuit whenever the wire cuts across lines of magnetic force.

11 The direction of an induced current can be predicted using the left-hand dynamo rule.

12 A transformer changes (transforms) an alternating voltage to a higher or lower alternating voltage.

13 In a transformer:

$$\frac{V_s}{V_p} = \frac{n_s}{n_p} = \frac{I_p}{I_s}$$

Study questions

1 Figure 11.31 shows the lines of force between the poles of two pairs of magnets. Which of the poles (A, B, C and D) are north poles and which are south poles?

2 Describe how an electric current can be used to
a) make a temporary magnet,
b) make a permanent magnet,
c) demagnetise a steel bar.

3 What effect does a magnetic field have on
a) a compass needle,
b) a moving copper wire,
c) a copper wire carrying an electric current?

Figure 11.31

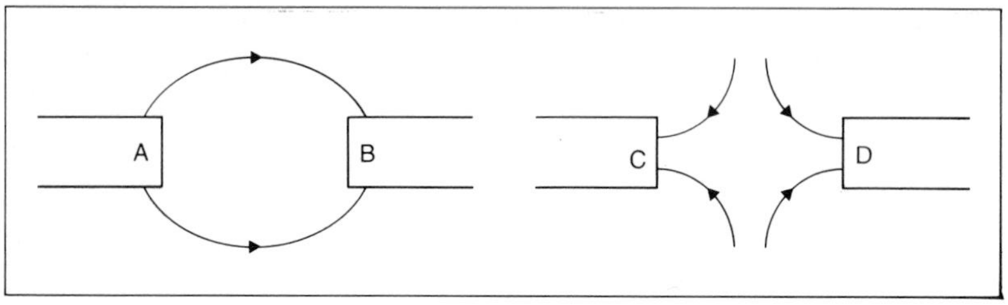

4 a) Describe the structure of an electromagnet.
b) How do the properties of an electromagnet differ from those of an ordinary magnet?
c) Make a drawing of an instrument which uses magnetism to measure electric currents. (You may like to refer back to chapter 10.)
d) Explain how the instrument in (c) works.
e) In what units is the instrument graduated?
f) How could the instrument be changed to measure larger currents?

5 Figure 11.32 shows an electromagnet which holds and then releases a small steel ball.
a) Will end A be a N-pole or a S-pole when the switch is closed?
b) Why is soft iron used for the core rather than steel?
c) How could the electromagnet be made stronger so that it will hold a larger ball?

6 a) Describe an experiment you could use to investigate the magnetic field around a solenoid carrying a current.

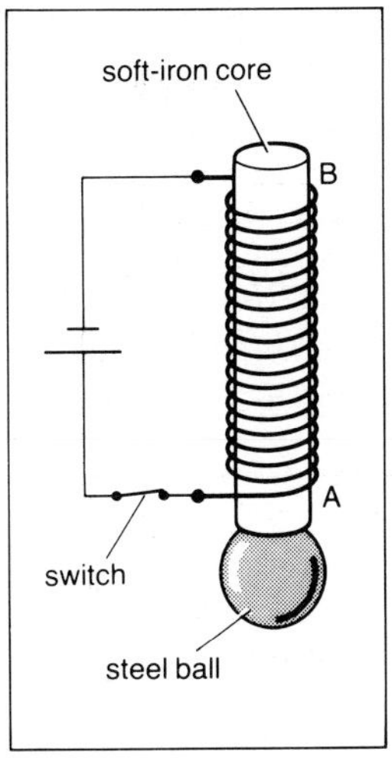

Figure 11.32 (Above)

b) Draw a diagram of a solenoid. Show the direction of the current in the solenoid, the N-pole and S-pole of the solenoid and the direction of the magnetic field.

c) Explain, with a diagram, how an electric relay works.

d) Describe briefly one everyday use of a relay as an electromagnetic switch.

7 Figure 11.33 shows the circuit for simple door chimes. The striker bar is supported through the centre of the plastic tube by the metal spring. Part of the striker bar is a soft-iron rod.

a) How is the circuit through the coil completed?

b) Which end of the coil becomes a north pole when a current flows through the coil?

c) What happens to the soft-iron rod as soon as a current flows through the coil?

d) Why do the chimes then make a sound?

e) What happens when the button is released and the circuit is broken?

Figure 11.33 (Below) The circuit for simple door chimes.

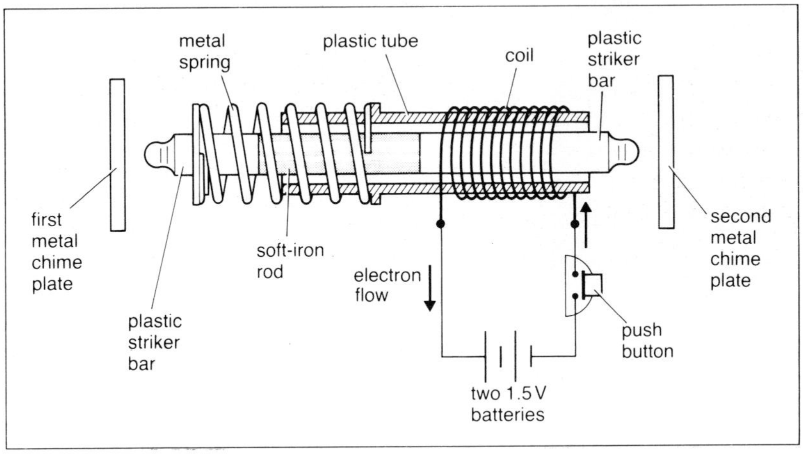

8 a) Explain what is meant by electromagnetic induction.

b) What is the function of a transformer?

c) What is a step-up transformer?

d) A transformer is used in a substation to change the voltage from 12 000 V to 240 V.

i) If the primary coil has 10 000 turns, how many turns does the secondary have?

ii) What current flows in the primary, if the output current from the secondary coil is 1 A?

e) In practice, the current in the primary coil is greater than you calculated in (d). Why is this?

f) Why is electricity transmitted via the grid system at very high voltages?

9 a) Describe the structure of an a.c. transformer suitable for lighting a 12 V lamp from a 240 V mains supply.

b) Explain how the transformer works.

c) Give one reason why the efficiency of the transformer is less than 100%.

d) Suppose the transformer is used to light a 12 V lamp 100 metres from the nearest mains point. The transformer can be installed either near the mains point or near the lamp. Explain why one of the two installations gives a higher efficiency for the transmission of power to the lamp and therefore a slightly brighter light from the lamp.

12 Energy all round

The Hoover Dam, USA. Hydroelectricity is generated as water from the reservoir falls under gravity and drives the turbines.

Without energy our vehicles, our machines, our home comforts and even our bodies would be useless.

12.1 What is energy?

In chapter 8 we met the terms work and energy. We already know that:

- Work is done whenever a force moves.
- Work done = force × distance.
- When a force of 1 N moves a distance 1 m, 1 joule of work is done.
- Energy is needed to do work. Energy is the ability to do work.

Look at figure 12.1. When the man uses the rope and pulley to lift the bricks, he applies a force to overcome the weight of the bricks. As the bricks are raised, the man exerts his force downwards and work is done. The man needs energy to do this work, and the energy comes from the food he has eaten. Food is the fuel that provides all animals with the energy they need to work, keep warm and stay alive.

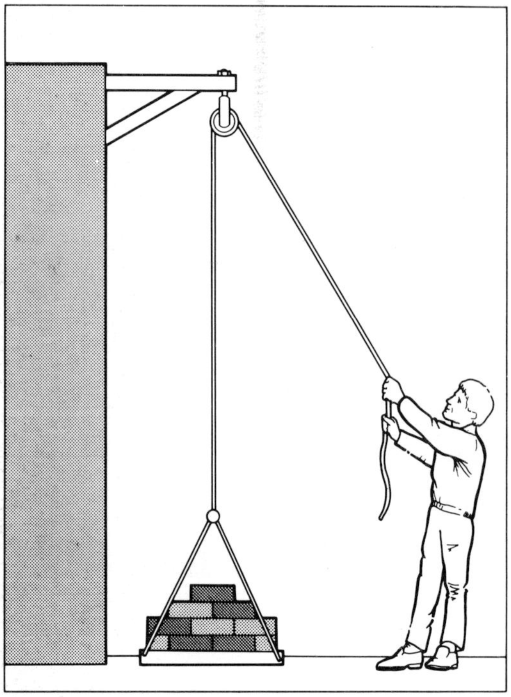

Figure 12.1 Using a rope and pulley to raise bricks.

Energy in different forms

Energy comes in different forms. These are listed in table 12.1. If you are unsure about any of them, look back to section 8.4.

Table 12.1
Forms of energy

potential energy
kinetic energy
heat
chemical energy
electrical energy
wave energy (sound, light, radio, etc.)
nuclear energy

Look at the man raising bricks in figure 12.1.

- What form of energy does the man himself use when he does work on the bricks?
- After the bricks have been raised, they now possess energy themselves. What form of energy is this?
- Suppose, after raising the bricks, the man loses his grip on the rope and the bricks fall, pulling the rope through the man's hands. What form of energy would the man feel with his hands?
- What form of energy do the bricks possess as they fall?
- What forms of energy appear as the bricks hit the ground?
- Suppose the man tires of pulling the rope, and uses a petrol-driven motor to raise the bricks. What is the source of energy in this arrangement? Is all this energy used to raise the bricks? If not, where does some of it go?
- Suppose, after raising the bricks, the man handed the end of the rope to a small child, (figure 12.2). What would happen? What would the potential energy of the bricks be converted to?

Figure 12.2 Suppose the man handed the end of the rope to a small child . . .

Converting energy from one form to another

Notice that energy is being converted from one form to another in all the events involving the bricks and the man. For example, the chemical energy of food in the man is converted to potential energy in the raised bricks, and this potential energy is converted to heat and sound energy when the bricks hit the ground.

Notice too how the original source of useful energy is often a fuel: food fuel if the man pulls the rope, petrol if he uses a motor. In both cases, not all the chemical energy in the fuel is converted to potential energy in the bricks. A great deal of it gets turned to heat. The man gets warm as he pulls the rope, and the petrol engine gets hot.

Even though the man and the petrol engine are not very efficient at turning chemical energy into useful work, they never lose energy for good. *All* of the chemical energy gets converted into some other form of energy; none is lost. This important point is summarised in the **law of conservation of energy** which says:

Energy cannot be destroyed. It only changes into different forms.

Only about 25% of the man's chemical energy is converted to potential energy in the bricks. The rest of the energy is converted to heat. The man's **efficiency** is only 25%; and this is about the same as the efficiency of the petrol engine. Even with low efficiencies, energy is never actually *lost*, it just gets converted to heat instead of useful work (figure 12.3). Some other energy conversions are shown in figure 8.7.

Figure 12.3 Energy conversion of a man.

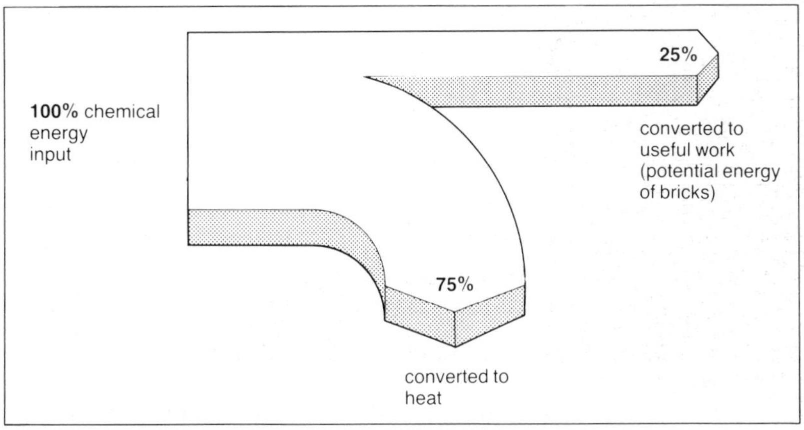

How efficient are energy conversions?

Look at figure 12.4, which shows a mouse on a treadmill generating electricity to light a lamp. We can trace the energy conversions using a flow diagram like this:

chemical energy of mouse's food
↓
kinetic energy of moving mouse and treadmill
↓
electrical energy of generator
↓
light energy of lamp

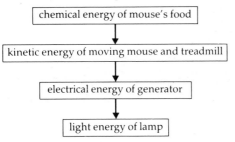

At each stage, though, some energy is lost as heat; the mouse, the generator and the lamp all get warm. We could show this on the flow diagram as

chemical energy of mouse's food
↓ → heat
kinetic energy of moving mouse and treadmill
↓ → heat
electrical energy of generator
↓ → heat
light energy and heat energy of lamp

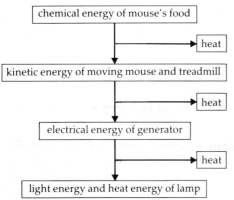

The efficiency of each energy conversion is shown in figure 12.5. If all the energy quantities are added together, it is found that the *total* energy output is the same as the total energy input. Energy is never lost, only transformed.

- Look at figure 12.6, then draw a flow diagram for the energy changes involved in the experiment.

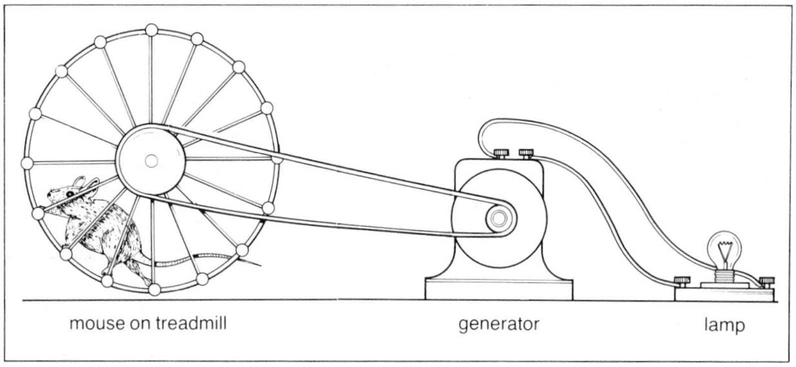

Figure 12.4 (Above) A mouse on a treadmill generates electricity to light a lamp.

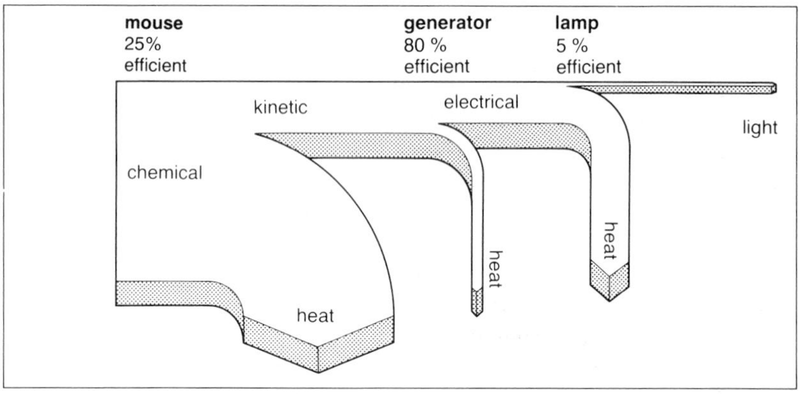

Figure 12.5 The efficiencies of the energy conversions shown in figure 12.4.

Figure 12.6 (Below) What are the energy changes here?

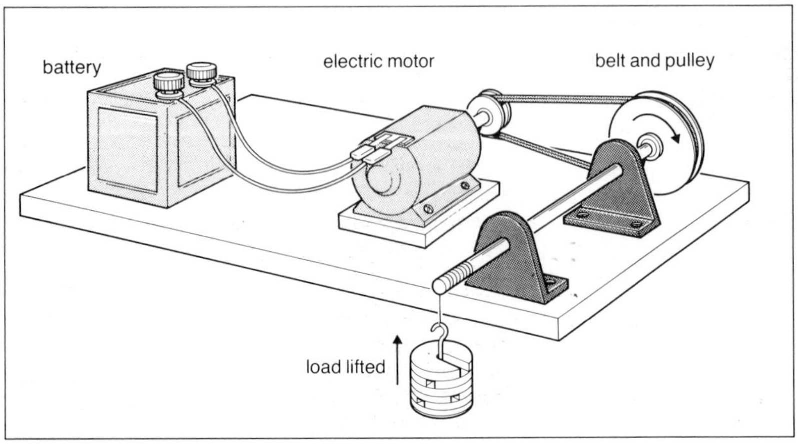

12.2 Our energy-dependent society

We need energy to make changes occur. Whether we are changing the temperature of a room, changing the position of bricks or changing food by cooking, energy is needed. In this section, we shall see that our modern society uses vast amounts of energy to provide all the changes we need and want.

A million years ago, primitive men and women relied on their own energy to make the changes they wanted. The food they ate was their only source of energy. About ten thousand years ago animals like horses and oxen were first used to increase the power of humans. Later still men and women learned to use wind and water power. In the last two hundred years we have used fossil fuels like coal and oil to increase enormously the power at our command from steam engines, petrol engines and the like.

How much energy does the human body supply?

It is quite easy to estimate the rate of working or **power** of your body. When you run upstairs, your potential energy increases.

Time how long it takes to run up a flight of stairs. Knowing the height of the stairs and the weight of your body, you can work out your own power.

Suppose a girl of mass 50 kg (weight 500 N) takes 5 s to run upstairs through a vertical height of 10 m.

work done = force × distance
= 500 N × 10 m = 5000 J

power = rate of working

$$= \frac{\text{work done}}{\text{time taken}}$$

$$= \frac{5000\,\text{J}}{5\,\text{s}} = 1000\,\text{W} = 1\,\text{kW}$$

Of course, it would not be possible to work at this rate for long. Running upstairs is very tiring. Spread over a whole day, you could perhaps only work at a tenth of this rate, so your *average* power might be 0.1 kW, or 100 W. Figure 12.7 shows the power required for different activities.

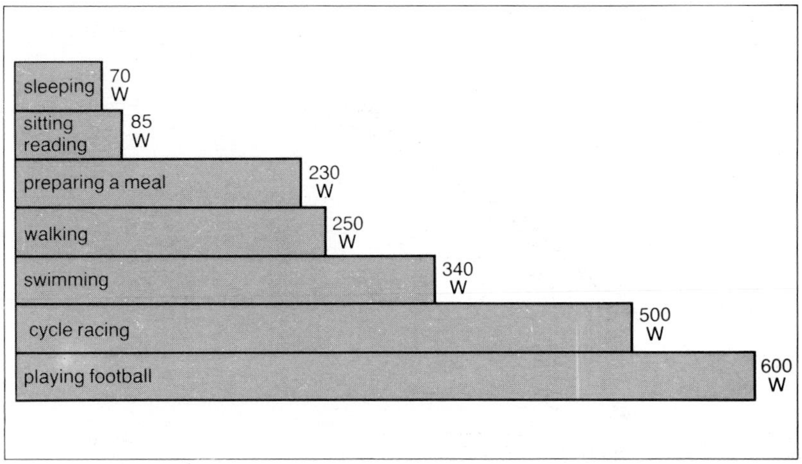

Figure 12.7 Power rating of different activities.

Suppose an average person works at a rate of 100 W through an eight-hour day.
- How many joules of energy does the person supply each second?
- How many seconds does the person work in an eight-hour day?
- How many joules of energy does the person supply in an eight-hour day?

How much food does the human body need?

The calculations you have just done show that in an eight-hour day our average worker supplies about 2900 kJ. But we have already seen that the human body is only 25% efficient. The average worker would therefore need much more than 2900 kJ of food energy to keep going.

The exact amount of food energy needed by a person depends on how active that person is, as figure 12.8 shows. Notice that 8000 kJ is needed even for a 'starvation diet'. This is the energy needed to keep up the basic body processes, like breathing and digestion.

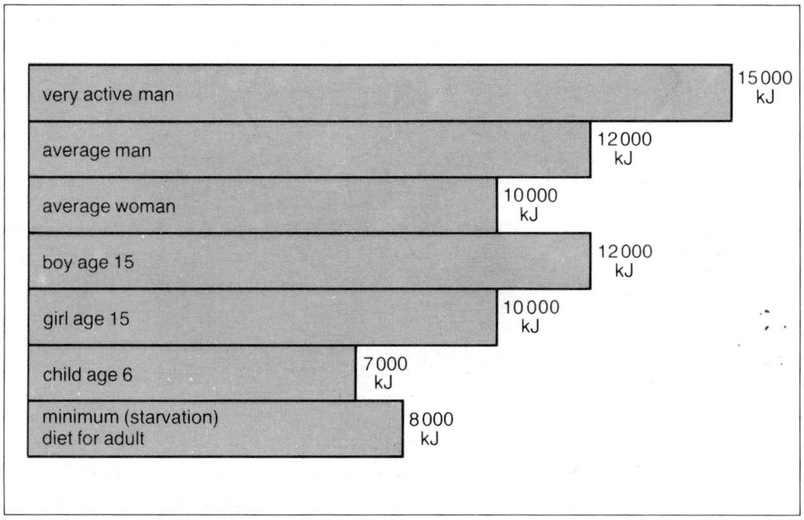

Figure 12.8 Approximate daily food energy intake for different people.

Machines – the slaves of modern society

Unlike early men and women, we have many machines and appliances to work for us and keep us warm and comfortable. Early people had only their own muscle power, and you will remember the average power of a person over any long period of time is only about 0.1 kW. Even animals, such as oxen and horses, only increase the available power to a little over 0.5 kW. (In fact the horsepower (hp) is still sometimes used as a unit of power. 1 hp = 0.75 kW.)

Today, thanks to fuels and electricity, we have much greater power available to use. Look at table 12.2, which shows the power ratings of various everyday machines and appliances.

Table 12.2
The power ratings of various machines and appliances

Appliance	*Power / kW*
refrigerator	0.1
electric light (100 watt)	0.1
colour television	0.3
vacuum cleaner	0.5
tumble drier	2.0
electric bar fire	2.0
washing machine	2.5
electric kettle	2.5
immersion heater	3.0
home central heating	6.0
small car travelling at 70 km/h	10.0

(Above) The average power of a person is 0.1 kW

- Assuming a human's power output is 0.1 kW, how many humans is a vacuum cleaner equivalent to?
- How many humans is a small car travelling at 70 km/h equivalent to?

It is clear from all this that the energy needs of each person in a country such as Britain are very large. In fact, every man, woman and child in Britain consumes about 1.6×10^{11} J of energy every year, in fuels and electricity. This huge number is difficult to appreciate. But remember, our requirement of energy *from food alone* is about 11 000 kJ per day or 4.38×10^{9} J per year. So we each use far more energy than we need simply in terms of food. This is because all our modern conveniences like cars and central heating need huge amounts of energy to manufacture and to run.

In other parts of the World the story is rather different. Table 12.3 shows the energy consumption of different countries.

Table 12.3
Energy consumption per person in various parts of the World (1983)

Country	*Energy consumed per person / J*
USA	3.3×10^{11}
USSR	2.1×10^{11}
West Germany	1.8×10^{11}
United Kingdom	1.5×10^{11}
France	1.5×10^{11}
Japan	1.3×10^{11}
Latin America	0.4×10^{11}
China	0.2×10^{11}

- Why do some countries consume so much more energy than others?

Where does all the energy go?

Figure 12.9 shows how the energy consumed by an average family in Britain is used. Notice how much energy is used for heating – remember the high power rating of heating systems.

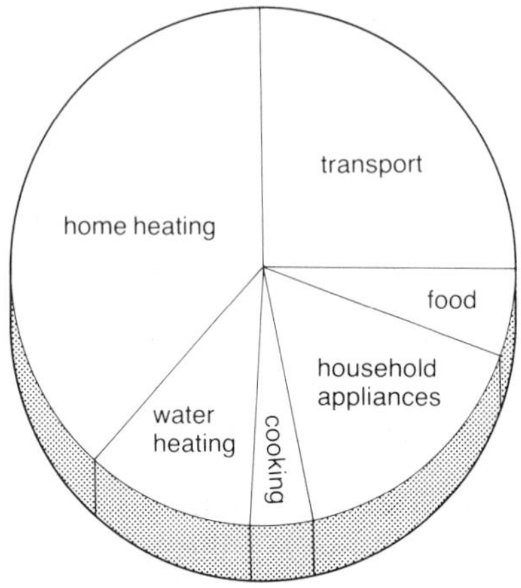

Figure 12.9 (Right) How an average family uses energy.

Now look at table 12.4, which shows how the energy consumption for Britain as a whole is split up between different sectors. Notice the following points.

- Although we use a great deal of energy in our homes, this accounts for less than a fifth of all the energy used.
- Industry uses most of our energy. Industry uses energy to turn raw materials like iron ore into useful things like cars.
- The biggest single user of energy is the fuel industry itself. Refining oil, mining coal and generating electricity all need (and waste) large amounts of energy. Much of the fuel consumed in Britain is used to generate electricity. Power stations are only about 30% efficient. 70% of the energy in the fuel is lost as heat, often through cooling towers.

Table 12.4
Energy consumption in Britain by different sectors (1983)

Sector	*Percentage of total*
agriculture	1%
iron and steel	4%
transport	18%
fuel industry	30%
other industries	18%
public services	5%
domestic (homes)	20%
miscellaneous	4%
total	100

12.3 The Sun, our provider

Nearly all our energy sources can be traced back to the energy of the Sun (figure 12.10). The Sun provides the energy needed for photosynthesis (section 20.10), which enables plants to grow. Not only does this provide us with firewood, it is also the origin of the energy in coal and oil (see below).

- The Sun evaporates the sea, giving rain to fill the rivers that provide hydroelectric power.
- The Sun causes differences in air temperature which give rise to the winds, another useful source of energy.
- The Sun and Moon cause the sea to move around the Earth, the source of tidal power.
- The only energy sources that do not originate in the Sun are geothermal energy (energy from the Earth's hot interior) and nuclear energy.
- In theory we could satisfy all our energy needs by gathering the Sun's radiation. In practice however, **solar energy** is difficult to use because the Sun does not always shine and solar cells are expensive.

Coal and oil; fossil fuels

Green plants carry out photosynthesis to make their food. Using the Sun's energy, plants turn carbon dioxide and water into carbohydrates like glucose and starch. In the process oxygen is formed.

$$\text{carbon dioxide} + \text{water} \xrightarrow[\text{energy}]{\text{light}} \text{carbohydrate} + \text{oxygen}$$

In this way plants store the Sun's energy for later use, or for use by any animals which eat the plants. When energy is needed, the carbohydrate reacts with oxygen, releasing energy. This is the reverse of photosynthesis. When plants and aimals die and decay, this oxidation process normally turns all the carbohydrate back to carbon dioxide and water. If the dead plants and animals are deprived of oxygen when they decay, the carbohydrates are not oxidised, but turn into other energy-rich compounds.

This is how coal and oil were formed. 400 million years ago the land was covered with dense forests of primitive plants and the seas were full of tiny organisms. When these living things died they were covered with mud and protected from oxidation. Gradually, over millions of years they

Figure 12.10 A summary of energy resources. (Reproduced by kind permission from BP Educational Service.)

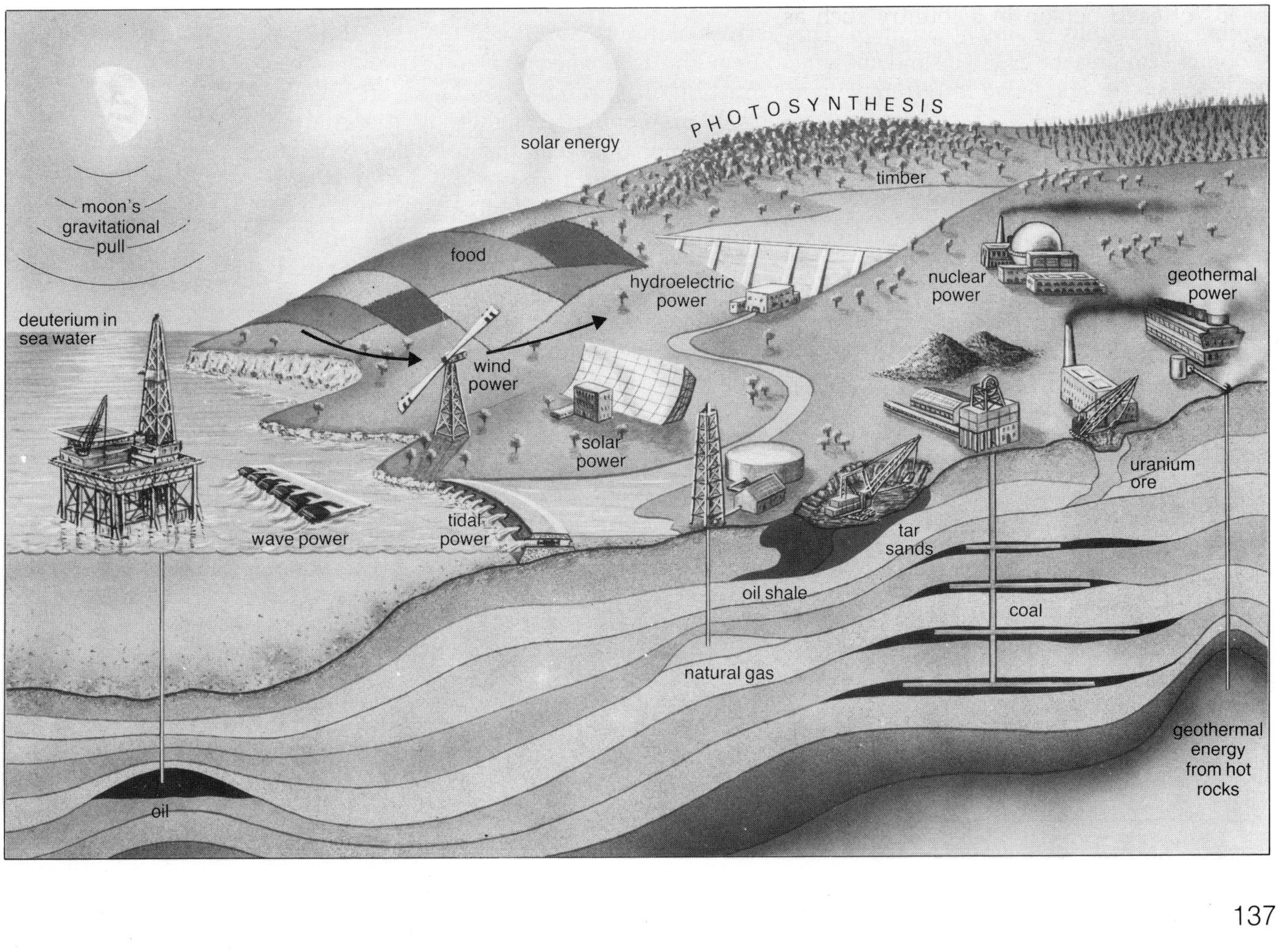

formed layers of energy-rich deposits buried beneath the land and under the sea bed. We call these deposits **fossil fuels**. Liquid fossil fuel, formed mainly from plants and animals that lived in the sea, is called **crude oil** or **petroleum**. It is often accompanied by a gaseous fuel, **natural gas**. Solid fossil fuel, **coal**, is formed mainly from land plants.

When we burn a fossil fuel like coal or oil, we release the Sun's energy trapped by organisms millions of years ago.

Using crude oil

Coal can be burned just as it comes out of the ground, without any further processing. This is how it is used in power stations and many homes. Crude oil however, is useless until it has been processed by **fractional distillation**.

Crude oil is a mixture of many different compounds, all of which contain carbon and hydrogen. Some of these compounds are very **volatile** (easily vapourised), which makes them useful for petrol engines. Others are less volatile and are no use in petrol engines, but can be used in large furnaces. The purpose of fractional distillation is to separate the compounds into groups or **fractions** of similar volatility. This is done by boiling the crude oil and allowing the fractions to condense at different temperatures.

The laboratory distillation of crude oil is illustrated in figure 12.11.

- What pattern is found in the colour of the fractions?
- What pattern is found in the **viscosity** (stickiness) of the fractions?
- Why do the fractions become harder to ignite with increasing boiling point?

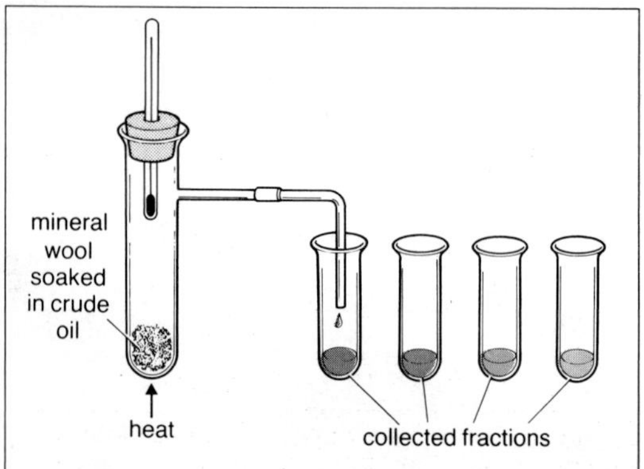

Figure 12.11 Laboratory distillation of crude oil.

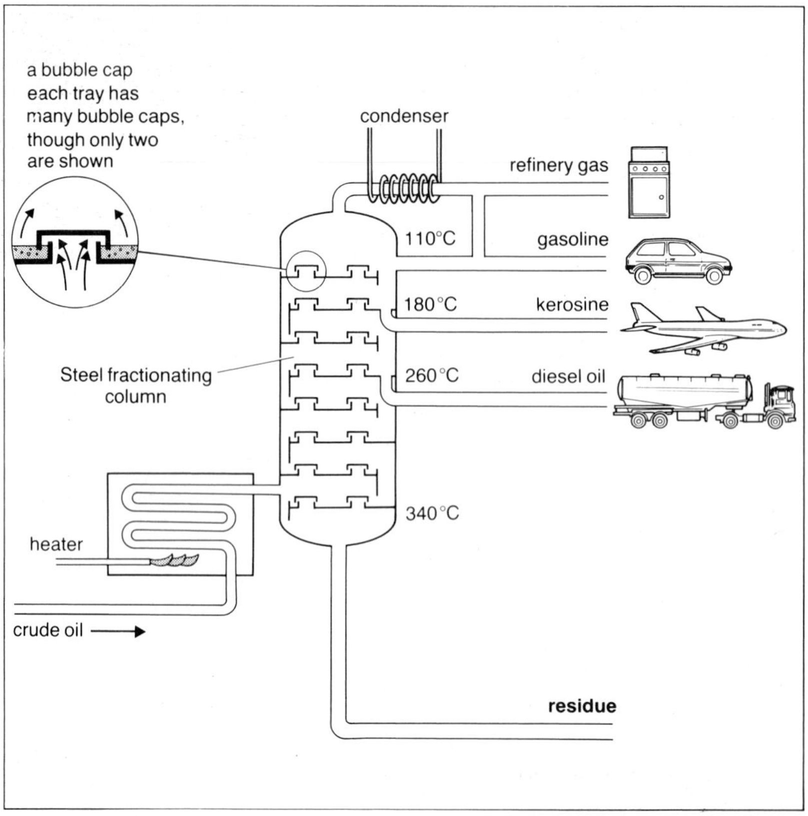

Figure 12.12 Distillation of crude oil in a refinery.

At an oil refinery, crude oil is distilled on a large scale. A steel fractionating column over 30 metres tall is used (figure 12.12). This column is very hot at the base and cool near the top. The crude oil separates into fractions according to boiling point. Volatile fractions condense higher up the column and come out near the top. Less volatile ones condense and run out lower down. Trays of *bubble caps* (figure 12.12) allow vapour to rise up the column but prevent liquid from running down again. Liquids condensed from a range of boiling points are collected from each tray. Table 12.5 shows how the different fractions are used.

Table 12.5
Uses of petroleum fractions

Boiling range	*Fraction*	*Percentage of crude oil*	*Uses*
below room temperature	refinery gas	1–2%	gaseous fuel, e.g. bottled gas making chemicals
30–160 °C	gasoline (petrol)	15–30%	motor car fuel making chemicals
160–250 °C	kerosine (paraffin)	10–15%	heating fuel jet fuel
220–350 °C	diesel oil	15–20%	diesel engine fuel for lorries, trains etc.
above 350 °C	residue	40–50%	fuel for power stations, ships etc. some is distilled further to give lubricating oil, waxes, bitumen etc.

> *Look at table 12.5.*
> - Why is gasoline a more dangerous liquid to store than diesel oil?
> - Why is kerosine of little use as a lubricant?
> - Is crude oil just a source of fuels? Explain.

The alkanes, a family of compounds

Crude oil is a mixture of many different compounds. Most of these compounds are made from the same two elements, carbon and hydrogen – they are **hydrocarbons**.

Carbon is a remarkable element. Each carbon atom can form four bonds to other atoms. Carbon can also form strong bonds to other carbon atoms. This allows it to form chains of carbon atoms, with other atoms attached to the side. The simplest type of chain has hydrogen atoms in these side positions. Compounds containing these simple hydrocarbon chains are called **alkanes**. They include most of the compounds present in crude oil. Table 12.6 shows some examples.

The alkanes form a *family* of compounds. There are many members of the family, because the chains can vary in length. All members of the alkane family have names ending in -**ane**.

The alkanes all have similar properties, and in particular they all burn readily in air. That is why they are such useful fuels. When an alkane burns in a plentiful supply of air, carbon dioxide and water are formed, and heat is given off.

alkane + oxygen → carbon dioxide + water

The combustion of alkanes is covered in more detail in section 14.1. Although the alkanes are all similar, some of their properties change gradually as the carbon chain gets longer. For example, as the chain lengths increase the boiling points increase and the compounds become more **viscous** (sticky). This explains the differences we noticed between the crude oil fractions in figure 12.11. The lightest fractions, with the lowest boiling points, contain the alkanes with the shortest chains. The heaviest fractions with the highest boiling points contain alkanes with long chains. For example, methane, the simplest alkane, is present in the refinery gas fraction (it is also the main component of North Sea gas). Octane, a liquid with boiling point 125°C, forms part of the gasoline fraction.

What do all of these objects have in common?

> - Draw the structural formula of pentane, C_5H_{12}.
> - Pentane is a volatile liquid, boiling point 36°C. In which crude oil fraction would you expect to find pentane?
> - Suggest a name for the alkane whose formula is $C_{10}H_{22}$.

As well as being useful fuels, the alkanes in crude oil are an important source of chemicals. Plastics, dyes, drugs, paints and a host of other important goods are made from chemicals obtained from crude oil.

Table 12.6
Some alkanes

Name	*Molecular formula*	*Structural formula*
methane	CH_4	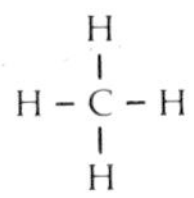
ethane	C_2H_6	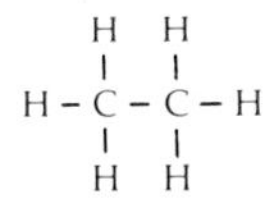
hexane	C_6H_{14}	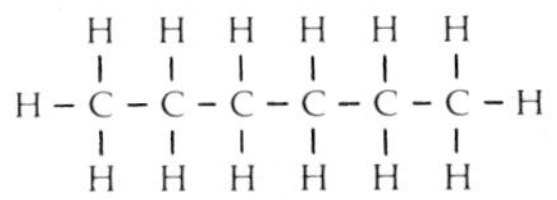
octane	C_8H_{18}	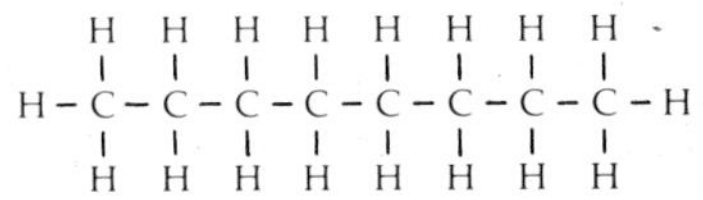

The molecular formula gives the number of each type of atom present. The structural formula shows how these atoms are joined together. Carbon atoms are represented by C, hydrogen atoms by H.

(*Above*) Burning gas at an oil refinery. All alkanes burn in air.

12.4 Other energy sources

For the past 150 years or so, industrialised countries such as Britain have relied on fossil fuels to supply their growing energy needs. This is still true today, as figure 12.13 shows.

Figure 12.13 The contribution of different energy sources to Britain's energy supply in 1983. Remember that a large part of the fuels are used to generate electricity.

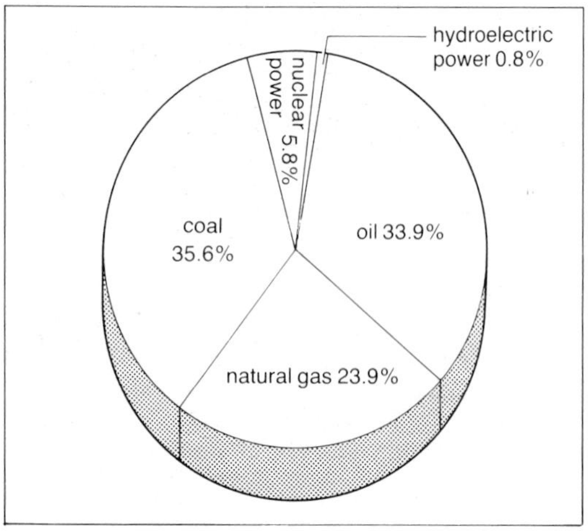

However, fossil fuels will not last forever. The reserves of oil and coal took millions of years to form but it will not take long to use them up. Figure 12.14 shows an estimate of how long our fossil fuels will last if we continue to use them at present rates. Although coal supplies are plentiful, oil is likely to run out before the middle of the next century. And at present oil is the fuel on which we are most dependent, particularly for transport and chemicals. What will we do for energy when the fossil fuels run out?

Energy resources – savings and income

The Earth's energy resources are rather like money. Imagine a person who has income from a job and also savings in the bank. Such a person can live off the income and leave the savings untouched. If the person wants lots of money he or she can dig into the savings as well.

Fossil fuels are like energy savings. They represent energy stored up over millions of years, so they are sometimes called **non-renewable resources**. Once used, they are gone for good. For the past 150 years we have been living off our energy savings, and they will soon run out. But we do have some energy income as well, and some of these **renewable sources** are shown in figure 12.15. Every day the sun shines (somewhere!), the wind blows, the rain falls and the tide comes in. Solar power, wind power, hydroelectric power and tidal power are therefore renewable sources, part of our energy income. We may have to use them more in the future as our fossil fuel savings run out.

Figure 12.14 An estimate of how long World supplies of different fossil fuels will last at present rates of use.

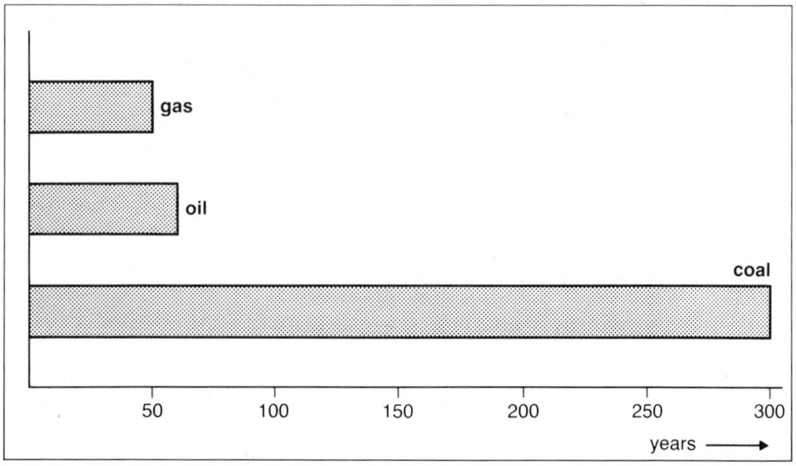

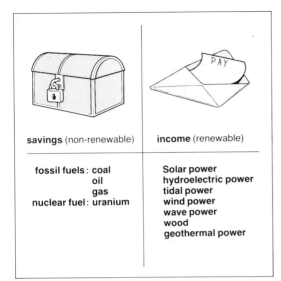

savings (non-renewable)	**income** (renewable)
fossil fuels: coal **oil** **gas** **nuclear fuel: uranium**	**Solar power** **hydroelectric power** **tidal power** **wind power** **wave power** **wood** **geothermal power**

Figure 12.15 Energy 'savings' and 'income'.

Solar power

The most sensible way to solve our energy problems is to use directly the source of all our energy, the Sun. There are two ways to do this. The Sun's energy can be collected and used to heat water and homes, or it can be used to make electricity in **photocells**. At the moment there are problems (for one thing, the Sun does not always shine everywhere), but solar energy is likely to be a major source in the future.

Tidal power

Every day the sea rises and falls with the tides. A tidal power station traps the high tides behind a dam or barrage across an estuary. As the tide falls the water flows though turbines which generate electricity. Few tidal power stations have yet been built, though there is a successful one across the River Rance near St. Malo in northern France. None has yet been built in Britain, but it has been suggested that a tidal barrage might be put across the Severn Estuary near Bristol.

Wind power

Wind, like water, has been used as a source of power for thousands of years. Some scientists believe the wind could be used to generate electricity on a large scale, using giant windmills. There are problems: the windmills (or wind *turbines* as they are called) have to be very large, and of course the wind does not always blow. But it may be that wind turbines off the coast of northern Britain will be generating some of our electricity in the future.

(*Above*) This bank of photocells in Senegal makes electricity to drive an underground irrigation pump.

Will wind power be used in the future to generate electricity? A 2000 kW experimental turbine in North Carolina, USA.

Hydroelectric power

People have used water power for thousands of years. For example, watermills have been used to grind flour. More recently water power is being used to generate electricity. Figure 12.16 shows how the water of the Earth goes through a cycle of evaporation and rainfall, driven by the Sun. This **water cycle** is the source of fresh water for all life on land, and it can be also used to generate hydroelectricity. In hydroelectric power stations, falling water drives the turbines which generate electricity.

- Solar, tidal and wind power are often called *alternative energy sources*. What other alternative energy sources can you think of?
- Draw a diagram to illustrate the energy changes involved in generating hydroelectricity.
- What problems do you think might arise in building a tidal barrage across the River Severn?
- Which alterntive energy sources do you think have the greatest chance of success in Britain?

Figure 12.16 The water cycle.

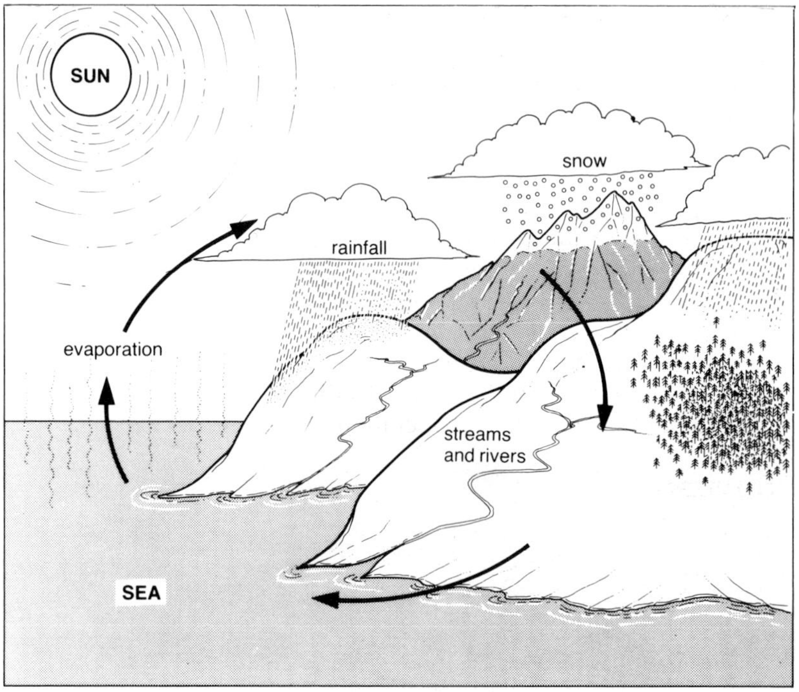

Hydroelectricity is an excellent energy source. Once the power station has been built, the energy is absolutely free. However, it does need water falling from a height. In Britain there is not much opportunity for generating hydroelectricity, but some countries use it a great deal. For example, Norway has so much hydroelectricity that until recently electricity was given away free.

Solar, tidal and wind power are **alternative energy sources** that will probably provide more and more of our energy as fossil fuels run out. However, one energy source that is increasingly used to generate electricity and will almost certainly be of great future importance is **nuclear energy**. This uses uranium as a fuel. Nuclear energy has many advantages, but there are also many people who feel it is unsafe. The whole question of nuclear energy is discussed further in sections 27.6 and 27.7.

12.5 Energy in the future

Until the early 1970s few people worried much about our future energy supplies. Industrialised countries like Britain and the USA had got used to plentiful supplies of energy, particularly oil. But in 1973, oil producers in the Middle East suddenly cut back production and increased their prices. Since most of the World's oil reserves are in the Middle East, Western countries began to realise that cheap energy would not necessarily last for ever. People began to talk about the *energy crisis*, and to look for new sources of energy.

Since the seventies, several things have happened. People have become more energy conscious, and have tried to save energy, for example by running smaller cars and by insulating buildings. As oil became more valuable, petroleum companies began to look at those oil reserves that had not been worth using before. These included offshore oilfields beneath the sea bed, like those in the North Sea, and oil shales, oily rocks found in parts of North America. Oil companies realised that one day these might prove a useful, though expensive source of energy. At the same time research

Figure 12.17 (Below) How energy sources might develop in the future. This assumes energy demand continues as at present.

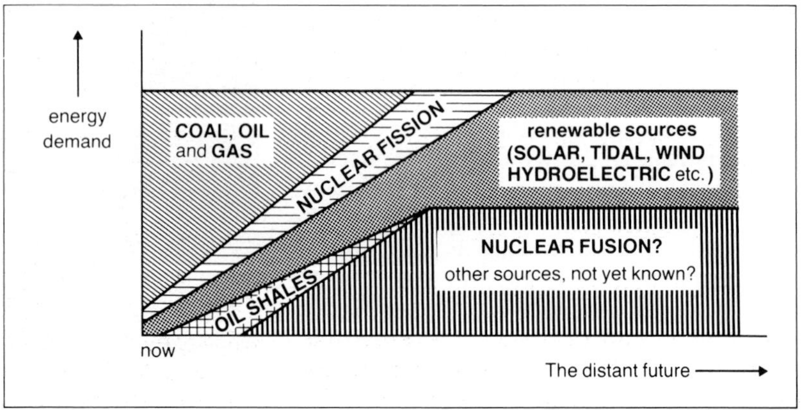

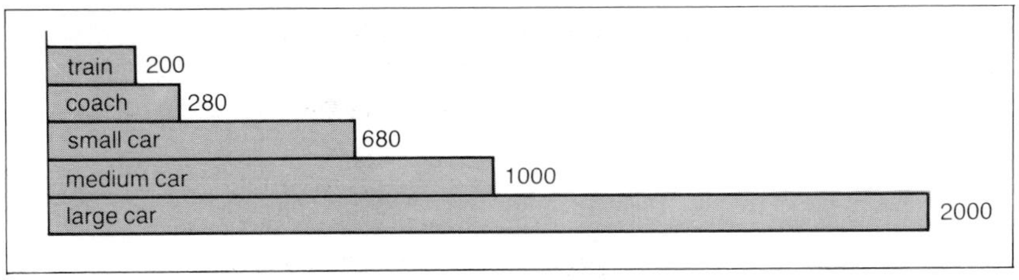

Figure 12.18 The energy used by different vehicles travelling at 100 km/h. Each vehicle is assumed to be carrying its full load of passengers. The figures are in kJ per passenger per km.

was being done into the alternative energy sources already mentioned.

All these developments have helped, but the energy problem is by no means solved. It is still difficult to see how we will replace fossil fuel supplies once they run out. Figure 12.17 shows one way things might develop.

Some people believe that one day the energy problem will be solved for good by nuclear fusion. Unlike **nuclear fission** (section 27.6), which uses uranium as a fuel, **nuclear fusion** uses deuterium ('heavy hydrogen'). There is a virtually unlimited supply of deuterium in the water and seas of the Earth. Nuclear fusion is the source of the Sun's enormous energy, but before we can generate electricity from nuclear fusion there are enormous scientific and technical problems to overcome (section 27.7).

Energy conservation

Figure 12.17 assumes that our demand for energy will stay the same in the future. This is unlikely: the demand will probably *increase* as developing countries become more industrialised. But one way of solving the energy problem is to *decrease* demand by conserving and saving energy.

If you remember the law of conservation of energy (section 12.1) the idea of 'energy conservation' seems unnecessary. The law says that energy is never destroyed, so why should it need conserving? The trouble is, although energy is never completely lost it tends to become more *spread out*. This is what happens when a hot body cools down; its heat gets spread out. Now, energy is at its most useful when it is concentrated rather than spread out. A little hot water is more useful than a lot of lukewarm water. Fuels are so useful because they are concentrated sources of energy that can be released when needed. When we talk of 'conserving' energy, we mean keeping it concentrated.

Saving energy in the home

Since a large part of domestic energy goes on heating, it makes sense to reduce the energy demand in heating our homes. This can be done in several ways. For example, turning down the thermostat by two or three degrees makes a big difference. Insulation can greatly reduce heat loss. Home insulation is considered in section 17.6.

Saving energy in transport

About one sixth of the energy used in Britain goes on transport. Figure 12.18 shows the energy used per passenger for different vehicles travelling at 100 km/h. Clearly, in energy terms, travelling by train or coach is much more economical than using cars, which often carry only one passenger. But if cars are used, it makes sense to keep them as small as possible, and to design them to use fuel economically, for example by aerodynamic styling. A great deal of fuel can also be saved by driving a car steadily, avoiding sudden braking or acceleration.

Summary

1 The law of conservation of energy says energy cannot be destroyed, only converted into other forms.

2 Whenever one form of energy is converted to another, some energy is lost, usually as heat.

3 Modern society depends heavily on energy to provide warmth, to drive machines and to change raw materials into useful products.

4 Most of our energy sources originate from the energy of the Sun. Fossil fuels like coal and oil come from organisms which stored the Sun's energy hundreds of millions of years ago.

5 Before crude oil can be used it must be separated into fractions by distillation.

6 The alkanes are a family of compounds containing carbon and hydrogen and occuring in crude oil.

7 As reserves of fossil fuels run out we will need to look for new energy sources and to conserve energy better.

8 Future energy supplies may depend on renewable, alternative sources like solar, tidal, hydroelectric and wind power.

Study questions

1 a) State the law of conservation of energy.
b) A person pedals a bicycle which has a dynamo attached. The dynamo supplies electricity to the bicycle lights. Draw an energy flow diagram like the one on page 134 to show the energy changes occurring.
c) Only a very small fraction of the energy given to the dynamo actually gets converted to light energy. Has the law of conservation of energy been broken? If not, what happens to the rest of the energy?

2 A load of bricks weighing 500 N has to be raised 20 m to the top of a building, using a rope and pulley. There are two ways of doing this:
A A man can pull the rope. It takes him two minutes to raise the bricks this way.
B An electric motor can winch the rope. It also takes two minutes.
a) If the man is paid at the rate of £3 an hour, what is the cost of the two minutes he takes to raise the bricks?
b) How much energy is needed to raise the bricks this distance?
c) Electricity is sold in units called kilowatt hours (section 10.8). 1 kilowatt hour = 3600 000 J. How many kilowatt hours of electricity are needed to raise the bricks?
d) What is the cost of the electricity needed to raise the bricks? (Take the price of the electricity as 5p per kilowatt hour.)
e) Which is cheaper: manpower or electrical power?
f) Why have machines steadily replaced people as a source of mechanical work over the last 150 years?

3 At 6 p.m. one February the Jones family were occupied as follows:
Jane was boiling the kettle to make a cup of tea.
Kevin was watching the colour television.
Mr Jones was vacuum cleaning the sitting room.
Mrs Jones was driving home in the car.
Lights were on in all the seven rooms of the house and the central heating was on.
a) Use table 12.2 to work out the total power of all the machines and appliances working for the Jones family at that instant.
b) Assuming the average power of a human to be 0.1 kW, calculate the number of 'energy slaves' working for the Jones family at that instant.
c) Suggest the likely energy source of each of the machines or appliances mentioned.
d) What energy-saving measures could a family like the Jones's take?

4 a) What is meant by *fossil fuels*?
b) The Sun is the original source of most of our energy. Explain how each of the following energy sources can be traced back to the Sun:
i) firewood,
ii) hydroelectric power,
iii) wind power,
iv) coal.
c) Explain the difference between *renewable* and *non-renewable* sources of energy.
d) Classify each of the energy sources in part (b) as renewable or non-renewable.

5 *Biogas* is an alternative source of energy, widely used in some parts of the world, e.g. China. Biogas is made by allowing waste materials such as dead vegetation, animal excrement and waste food to be decomposed by bacteria in a special container. A flammable gas is given off which can be used as a fuel. The gas is mostly methane. Methane is the simplest member of the family of carbon compounds called the alkanes.
a) What are alkanes?
b) Give the molecular formula and the structural formula of methane.
c) What substances are formed when methane burns in air?
d) For what purposes might biogas be most useful?
e) Why is biogas a particularly cheap source of energy?
f) Why would it be difficult for a British household to satisfy all its energy needs using biogas?

6 In each of the following cases, give one example of a machine or device that carries out the energy conversion mentioned.
a) Electrical energy to heat.
b) Electrical energy to sound energy.
c) Sound energy to electrical energy.
d) Kinetic energy to electrical enegy.
e) Chemical energy to light energy.
f) Chemical energy to potential energy.

7 a) Explain how gasoline (petrol) is obtained from crude oil.
b) Write the structural formula for one alkane you might expect to find in gasoline.
c) Crude oil provides many of the fuels used in transport. List some of these fuels, and the type of transport using them.
d) What energy sources may replace crude oil for the transport of the future?

13 Chemical reactions

Chemical reactions are important in the home, in industry and in living things. They occur whenever we toast a slice of bread and when a metal rusts. Chemical reactions also provide the energy to keep us warm and the chemicals to make us grow. What is more, they enable us to turn useless things like iron ore into useful things like iron and steel.

13.1 What is a chemical reaction?

When bread is toasted, steam rises from it and the surface becomes brown. If the bread is toasted for a long time, it may start to burn forming carbon dioxide as well as water vapour (steam). Eventually the toast is burnt to a brittle black deposit of carbon. Water, carbon dioxide and carbon, which form when toast is burnt, are very different from bread. New substances have been produced by heating (toasting) the bread.

Changes, like this, which result in the formation of new substances are called **chemical reactions** or **chemical changes**. The most important characteristic of a chemical reaction is the *formation of a new substance*.

The starting materials in a chemical reaction are called the **reactants**, and the new substances formed during the reaction are called the **products**.

We can describe what happens in a chemical reaction by writing a **word equation**. Chemists use equations to summarise their experiments in the same way that mathematicians use equations to summarise their results and calculations. Here is the word equation describing what happens when bread is toasted:

bread(s)
→ carbon(s) + water(g) + carbon dioxide(g)

(*Left*) Chemical reactions produce the dazzling effect in fireworks.

Notice the small letters in brackets after the name of each substance. They are called **state symbols** and show the state of the substance: solid, liquid or gas.

(s) is used for solid,
(l) for liquid,
(g) for gas or vapour and
(aq) for an aqueous solution, i.e. a solution in water.

Thus, the state symbol after water in the equation above is (g) and not (l) because the water is produced as a gas (steam) and not as a liquid.

When aluminium articles, like pans and window frames are first made, they look shiny. Over the next few months, though, the articles become dull as a thin layer of aluminium oxide forms on the surface.

- What evidence is there that a chemical reaction has occurred on the aluminium?
- What are the reactants?
- What is the product of the reaction?
- Write a word equation, including state symbols, for the reaction.

The rusting of iron and steel objects is a similar process to the tarnishing of aluminium. Rusting is discussed fully in section 14.9.

13.2 Energy changes in chemical reactions

The chemical reaction which turns bread into burnt toast or carbon is caused by heat (energy) from the cooker or toaster. Many important chemicals are produced in reactions caused by heat. One of the most important of these reactions is the manufacture of iron from iron ore (iron oxide). The iron ore is mixed with coke and heated to about 1500 °C in large blast furnaces which hold up to 2000 tonnes of material (section 24.7).

The iron oxide reacts with the coke (carbon) forming carbon monoxide which escapes as a gas and molten iron which trickles to the bottom of the furnace.

iron oxide(s) + carbon(s)
(iron ore) (coke)
→ iron(l) + carbon monoxide(g)

Reactions like this which take in energy (heat) when they occur are described as **endothermic** whereas reactions which give out energy are described as **exothermic**.

Exothermic reactions occur when fuels burn, when animals and plants respire, and when acids are neutralised. Fossil fuels, like coal, oil and natural gas, are mixtures of compounds containing mainly carbon and

Roasting chestnuts. What is the black substance on a roasted chestnut? What elements do you think chestnuts contain?

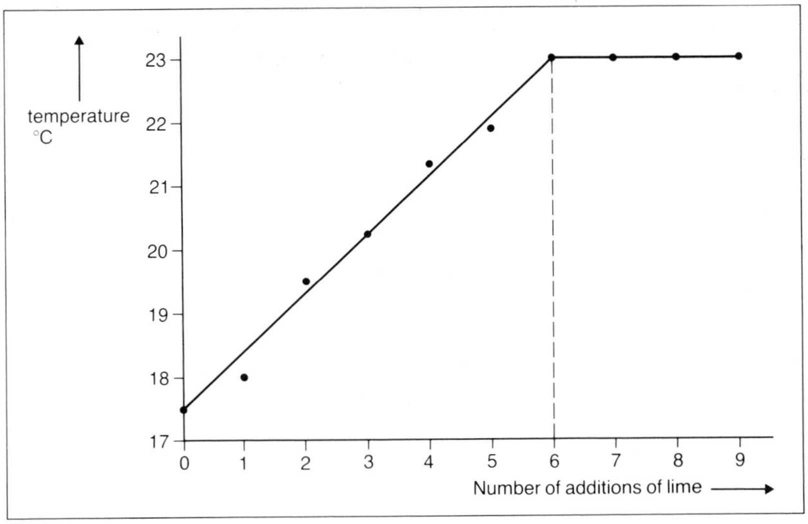

Figure 13.1 (Above) Neutralising vinegar (acetic acid) with lime.

hydrogen. When they burn, they react with oxygen producing a lot of heat plus carbon dioxide and water.

fuel (containing C and H) + oxygen → carbon dioxide + water

Burning and respiration are covered more fully in chapter 14.

Figure 13.1 shows the changes in temperature when small amounts of lime (calcium hydroxide) are added to 10 cm^3 of vinegar (acetic acid). Each addition of lime was one flat spatula measure (about 0.05 g).

- Is the reaction exothermic or endothermic?
- Why does the temperature rise about the same amount for each addition of lime?
- Why does the temperature stop rising after the sixth addition of lime?
- Why is this called a neutralisation reaction?
- Why do farmers and gardeners sometimes add lime to the soil?

Chemical reactions usually involve energy changes and this will cause the temperature to rise or fall. Exothermic reactions, which give out heat, produce a temperature rise. Endothermic reactions, which take in heat, cause a fall in temperature. Because of this, *temperature changes are often used as evidence that a chemical reaction has occurred.* Most chemical reactions which occur of their own accord are exothermic. Endothermic reactions are much rarer.

From the law of conservation of energy (section 12.1), it makes sense that if a reaction is exothermic in one direction, it must be endothermic in the opposite direction. Thus, the reaction of aluminium with oxygen to form aluminium oxide is exothermic, but the manufacture of aluminium by electrolysis of aluminium oxide is endothermic (section 9.5).

aluminium(s) + oxygen(g) ⇄ aluminium oxide(s) + energy
(forward: tarnishing (exothermic); reverse: electrolysis (endothermic))

When substances react, chemical bonds are made and broken. This is where the energy changes in chemical reactions come from. Energy is needed to *break* a chemical bond between atoms or ions but energy is given out when a bond is *made*. Thus:

Bond breaking is endothermic whereas bond making is exothermic.

Consider the reaction between aluminium and oxygen. Energy is first needed to break the bonds between Al atoms in the aluminium metal and between O atoms in the oxygen molecules (O_2). These two stages are endothermic. After this, bonds are formed between aluminium and oxygen to form aluminium oxide and this stage is exothermic. More energy is given out in the exothermic stage than is taken in during the endothermic stages. The overall reaction is therefore exothermic (figure 13.2).

Figure 13.2 (Below) Bond breaking, bond making and energy changes in the reaction between aluminium and oxygen.

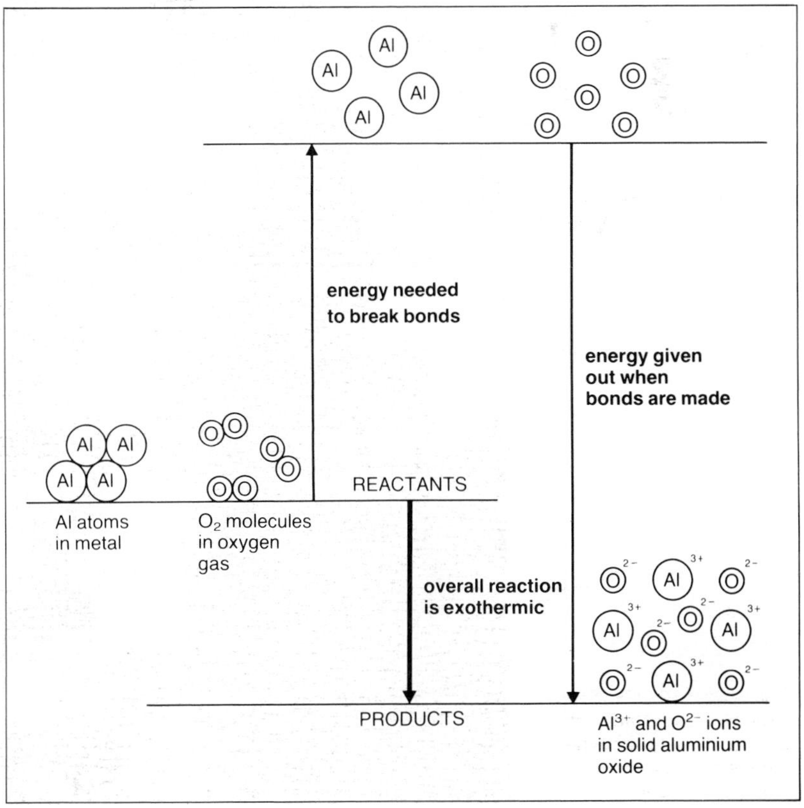

13.3 Investigating chemical reactions

Some reactions occur as soon as the reactants are mixed. Other reactions will only occur on heating. If you are interested in cooking, you will have seen many reactions which depend on heating substances. Even if your cooking skills are limited to frying an egg, you will have noticed some interesting changes occurring as the egg white turns from a clear, jelly-like liquid to a white solid. We can investigate reactions of this kind by recording the changes in appearance and in mass when substances are heated. Table 13.1 shows the effect of heating some common substances.

Look at the results in table 13.1.
- Which of the substances change state on heating?
- Write a word equation for one of these changes of state.
- Which substances change colour on heating?
- Which substances decrease in mass on heating?
- Why does water decrease in mass on heating?
- Why does hydrated copper sulphate decrease in mass on heating?
- Which substances are unaffected by heating?

A fire eater uses fuel in his act. What sort of fuel do you think he uses?

When some substances are heated, it is obvious that a chemical reaction has occurred because a new substance appears with a different colour from the starting materials. It is easy to see the new substances forming when sugar or hydrated copper sulphate are heated.

On heating, blue copper sulphate crystals turn white. A vapour is given off which condenses to a clear liquid on the cooler parts of the test tube. Tests show that the clear liquid is water. Adding water to the white solid re-forms the blue substance and the test tube gets hot. The white solid is called anhydrous copper sulphate. *Anhydrous* means without water. We can summarise the action of heat on hydrated copper sulphate in a word equation:

$$\underset{\text{(blue)}}{\text{hydrated copper sulphate(s)}} \xrightarrow{\text{heat}} \underset{\text{(white)}}{\text{anhydrous copper sulphate(s)}} + \text{water(l)}$$

Water is the only substance which reacts with anhydrous copper sulphate to form blue copper sulphate. Any liquid which contains water will therefore turn anhydrous copper sulphate blue. Because of this, *anhydrous copper sulphate is used as a test for water*.

Hydrated copper sulphate splits up on heating to form anhydrous copper sulphate and water. A reaction like this, in which one substance splits up into two or more simpler substances, is called **decomposition**. Some water vapour escapes from the test tube so there is a decrease in mass when the blue crystals are heated. Decomposition also occurs when baking powder or limestone is heated.

The decomposition of limestone is an important process in the manufacture of lime. Lime is used in making cement and in neutralising acidity in the soil. After quarrying and crushing, the limestone (calcium carbonate) is heated in huge kilns, when it decomposes into lime (calcium oxide) and carbon dioxide.

$$\underset{\text{(limestone)}}{\text{calcium carbonate(s)}} \rightarrow \underset{\text{(lime)}}{\text{calcium oxide(s)}} + \text{carbon dioxide(g)}$$

Table 13.1
Investigating reactions which take place on heating

Substance heated	*Appearance before heating*	*Effect of heating*	*Appearance on cooling*	*Change in mass*
copper	shiny pink metal	becomes red hot	surface is dull black	increase
baking powder (sodium hydrogen-carbonate)	white powder	clear liquid condenses on cooler parts of tube	white	decrease
water	clear liquid	liquid boils, steam forms	water condenses on cooler parts of tube	decrease
sand (silicon(IV) oxide)	fine brown powder (white if pure)	no visible change	fine brown powder	none
sugar	white crystals	melts to a pale brown liquid which darkens, steam is given off, finally a black solid forms	black solid remains	decrease
hydrated copper sulphate	blue crystals	clear liquid on cooler parts of tube, solid turns white	white solid remains	decrease
salt (sodium chloride)	white crystals	no visible change	white solid	none
limestone (calcium carbonate)	white powder	no visible change	white powder	decrease
cooking oil	pale yellow liquid	liquid boils, catches fire on strong heating	yellow liquid	decrease

When blue copper sulphate crystals are heated, they break up forming anhydrous copper sulphate and water. If, however, water is added back to the white solid, blue copper sulphate is re-formed. Two simpler substances, water and anhydrous copper sulphate, have joined together forming a more complex substance in blue, hydrated copper sulphate. A reaction like this in which two or more simpler substances join together forming a single product is an example of **synthesis**.

Synthesis is the opposite of decomposition. Synthesis is a 'building up' process, whereas decomposition is a 'breaking down' process. Thus:

$$\underset{\text{(blue)}}{\text{hydrated copper sulphate(s)}} \underset{\text{synthesis}}{\overset{\text{decomposition}}{\rightleftharpoons}} \underset{\text{(white)}}{\text{anhydrous copper sulphate(s)}} + \text{water(l)}$$

> *When copper metal is heated in air it becomes dull black and increases in mass.*
> - Has the copper lost or gained something on heating?
> - Which has occurred, decomposition or synthesis?
> - Where has the increase in mass come from?
> - Write a word equation for the chemical change.

13.4 Chemical reactions in living things

Chemical reactions involving both the 'break down' (decomposition) and the 'build up' (synthesis) of large molecules are important in living things. Most of the food that we eat is broken down into smaller units during digestion. The break-down processes are usually exothermic. The energy which they provide helps us to move about and keep warm. Once the food has been broken down into smaller units, these can be used to synthesise the chemicals that our bodies need.

One of the commonest foods that we eat is **starch**. This is present in many foods including potatoes, bread and rice. Molecules of starch are composed of long chains of glucose units. Each starch molecule can contain five hundred or more glucose units (figure 13.3).

When we chew bread or potatoes, the starch in them begins to react with water

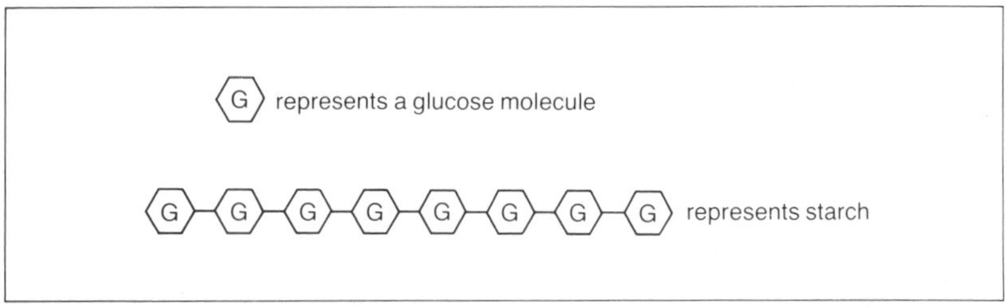

Figure 13.3 (Above) A simple model for the structure of starch.

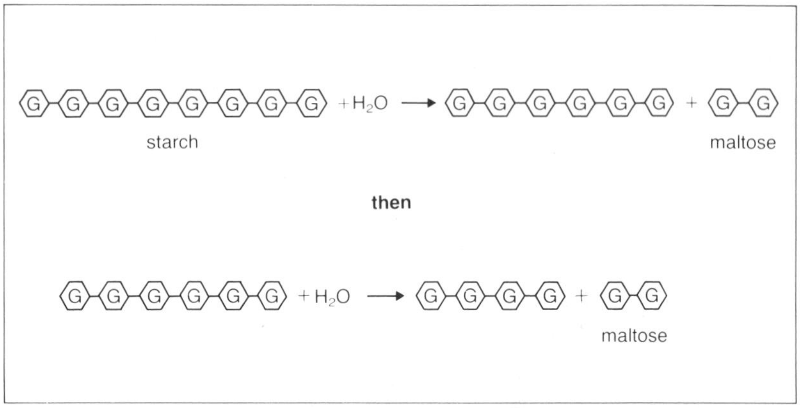

Figure 13.4 When we chew starch, it reacts with water and splits off maltose molecules.

forming maltose (figure 13.4). Maltose molecules, each made of two glucose units, are stripped off from the ends of the starch molecule one after another. This process is an example of **hydrolysis**, a reaction in which a substance reacts with water and splits up (*lysis* means *splitting*). Hydrolysis also occurs when maltose molecules are further broken down to glucose by digestive juices (figure 13.5). Hydrolysis is very important in plants and animals. It occurs during the breakdown of proteins and fats as well as starch.

Figure 13.5 (Right) Maltose is hydrolysed by digestive juices to glucose.

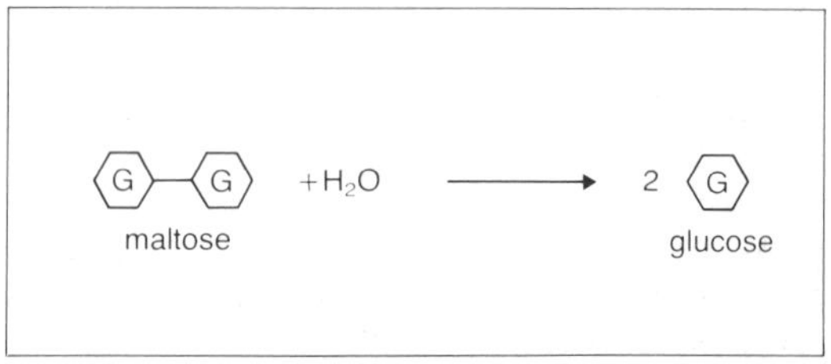

Plants and animals both use glucose molecules to synthesise more complicated chemicals. Plants use glucose to produce either starch or cellulose. The starch acts as a store of energy (food) for the plant, whereas cellulose chains support the plant and act as a structural material (figure 13.6). Notice that alternate glucose units in the cellulose are aligned in opposite ways. Animals can also synthesise a substance from glucose which is very similar to starch. This acts as an energy store and is called glycogen.

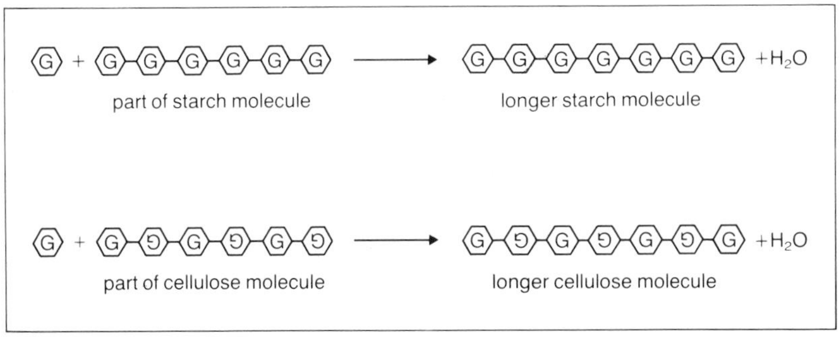

Figure 13.6 (Above) Plants produce starch and cellulose from glucose by condensation reactions.

These reactions which produce starch, cellulose and glycogen are the reverse of hydrolysis. Smaller units react together to form complex molecules and water. Processes like this are very important in living things and they are called **condensations**. Condensation also occurs when amino acids join together forming proteins and when fats are synthesised. Notice how *condensation is the reverse of hydrolysis*. Condensation is a 'building up' process which also produces water, whereas hydrolysis is a 'breaking down' process which uses up water.

These chemicals in foods and the simple units from which they can be synthesised are studied further in sections 15.3 and 15.4.

13.5 Changes in mass on heating

Sometimes it is impossible to tell whether a chemical change takes place when a substance is heated. Baking powder, sand, salt and limestone do not *appear* to change on heating. We can, however, check whether anything has happened by weighing the substance before and after heating. Any mass changes will help us to decide whether the substance has undergone synthesis or decomposition. When substances are tested in this way, they can be divided into three classes.

- Substances which do not change in mass on heating, e.g. salt and sand. These substances do not react on heating.
- Substances which lose mass on heating. Some of these substances, such as water and cooking oil, lose mass because they vapourise on heating.

  cooking oil(l) → cooking oil(g)

  Other substances, like baking powder, sugar, hydrated copper sulphate and limestone, lose mass because they decompose on heating to form gases which can escape.
- Substances which gain mass on heating, e.g. copper, magnesium. These substances react with oxygen in the air forming solid oxides. This is synthesis.

  copper(s) + oxygen(g) → copper oxide(s)

Many substances change in mass when they are heated. Some gain something from the air and increase in mass. Others lose something to the air and decrease in mass. But what happens if the total mass of the reacting substances *including the air is* taken into account?

In order to see if there is any change in the total mass during a chemical reaction, the following experiment was carried out. Shiny copper foil was heated strongly in oxygen in a sealed flask (figure 13.7). On cooling, the copper had darkened and had lost its shine. The sealed flask and its contents were weighed before and after the copper was heated. *The mass of the flask was exactly the same before and after the reaction.*

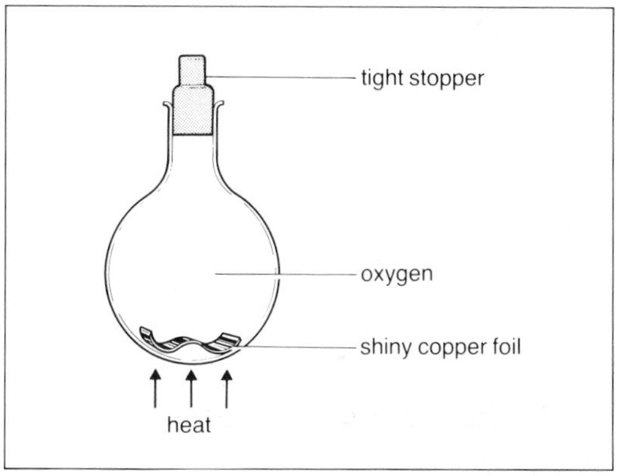

Figure 13.7 (Right) Heating copper in oxygen.

- Why is it important to keep the flask sealed during the experiment?
- Why does the copper become darker on heating?
- Has the total mass of the chemicals changed during the reaction?
- Is it possible to create mass in a reaction? Is it possible to get something from nothing?
- Is it possible to destroy mass in a reaction?

During the last century, many scientists carried out experiments similar to this one.

Provided all the reactants and products are taken into account, the mass of the reactants always equals the mass of the products.

In other words, mass is conserved. This result is called the **law of conservation of mass**.

13.6 Representing chemical reactions by equations

So far, we have used word equations to summarise reactions. For example,

calcium carbonate (limestone) → calcium oxide (lime) + carbon dioxide

It is, however, more convenient to use the formula of a substance instead of its name when we write equations. So, we could write CO_2 for carbon dioxide, CaO for calcium oxide and $CaCO_3$ for calcium carbonate. The chemical equation for the reaction would then be:

$$CaCO_3 \rightarrow CaO + CO_2$$

Thus, *an equation is a summary of the reactants and the products in a chemical reaction*. Scientists use equations to summarise reactions in the same way that typists use shorthand to summarise letters.

A **balanced equation** shows:

- the formulae of the reactants and products,
- the number of moles of the reactants and products involved in the reaction.

This means that, before we can write an equation for a reaction, we must know the formulae of the reactants and products and also the number of moles of each involved in the reaction.

Writing an equation for the burning of magnesium

Magnesium burns in air with an extremely bright white flame producing a fine white powder. The magnesium burns even more fiercely in pure oxygen. Because of this, magnesium is used as a light source for photography. Flash bulbs contain magnesium (or aluminium) foil surrounded by oxygen. When the flash bulb is used, an electric current passes through the metal. The metal heats up and suddenly flares into reaction with oxygen.

Experiments show that when magnesium burns, it reacts with oxygen forming magnesium oxide. In section 4.4, we found that the formula of magnesium oxide was MgO. So, when magnesium burns in oxygen, we know that: the reactants are magnesium (Mg) and oxygen (O_2) and the product is magnesium oxide (MgO). The obvious equation for this would be

$$Mg + O \rightarrow MgO$$

but oxygen exists as O_2 molecules and not as a single O atoms, so the correct equation is

$$2Mg + O_2 \rightarrow 2MgO$$

The O_2 is two O joined together, but 2MgO is MgO + MgO. In the last equation, there are two Mg and two O on *both* sides of the arrow, so the equation is correctly balanced. A balanced equation has equal numbers of atoms of each element on both sides.

- Why are the next two equations not balanced?

$$Mg + O_2 \rightarrow MgO$$
$$Mg + O_2 \rightarrow 2MgO$$

- Why must the equation not be written as

$$Mg + O_2 \rightarrow MgO_2?$$

Magnesium is used to make light-weight alloys. These are used particularly in aircraft parts and in household goods. Although pure magnesium is brittle and weak, these disadvantages can be overcome by alloying it with aluminium and zinc.

The most commonly used compounds of magnesium are magnesium oxide (MgO) and magnesium hydroxide ($Mg(OH)_2$). Magnesium oxide is used as a lining for high-temperature furnaces because of its exceptionally high melting point and low reactivity. Magnesium hydroxide is a very weak alkali. Because of this, it is put in toothpastes to neutralise the acids which cause tooth decay. A suspension of magnesium hydroxide in water (commonly called *milk of magnesia*) is used to treat acid indigestion.

13.7 Predicting equations

Clearly, it is impossible to carry out an experiment to find the equation for every reaction we study. Provided we know the names of the reacting substances and the names of products, we can work out their formulae and then *predict* an equation for the reaction. There are three stages in writing an equation.

1 *Write a word equation*:

hydrogen + oxygen → hydrogen oxide (water)

2 *Write symbols for elements and formulae for compounds*

Remember that the common gases (hydrogen, oxygen, nitrogen and the halogens) exist as molecules containing two atoms (when they are not combined with other elements). They are, therefore, represented in equations as H_2, O_2, N_2, Cl_2, Br_2 and I_2. This gives:

$$H_2 + O_2 \rightarrow H_2O$$

All other elements are regarded as single atoms when we write equations (i.e. Zn for zinc, S for sulphur, C for carbon, etc.). The formulae of ionic (metal/non-metal) compounds can be obtained by balancing the charges on ions (section 9.4).

3 *Balance the equation with respect to atoms*
There are two oxygen atoms in O_2 on the left of the last equation and only one on the right. Therefore, H_2O on the right must be doubled ($2H_2O$).

$$H_2 + O_2 \rightarrow 2H_2O$$

There are now four H atoms in $2H_2O$ on the right, so four H atoms ($2H_2$) must be shown on the left. The balanced equation is, therefore:

$$2H_2 + O_2 \rightarrow 2H_2O$$

Remember that *formulae can never be altered to make an equation balance*. This would create an entirely different substance. Equations can only be balanced by putting a number in front of a formula, thus doubling or trebling the whole formula. Figure 13.8 represents the last equation in terms of the particles involved.

Here are two more examples to show how equations are written.

1 *The reaction between natural gas (methane) and oxygen*. This reaction takes place when a gas cooker is used.
Write the word equation

methane + oxygen → carbon dioxide + water

Write symbols for elements and formulae for compounds

$$CH_4 + O_2 \rightarrow CO_2 + H_2O$$

(*Above*) In a gas cooker, methane reacts with oxygen, forming carbon dioxide and water.

Figure 13.8 (Below)

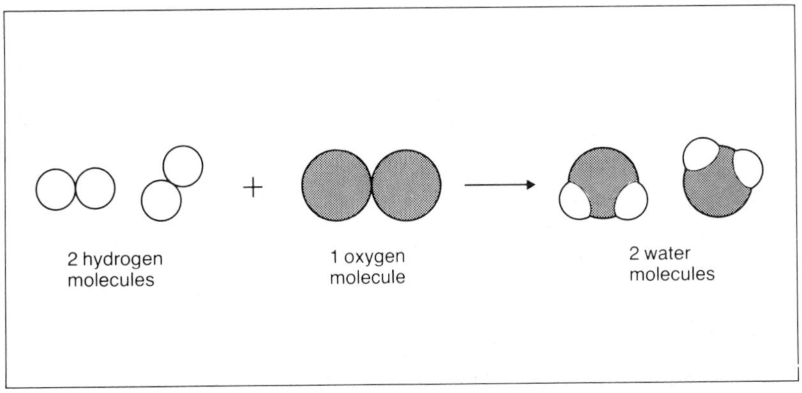

Balance the equation. Carbon balances already, one atom on the left and one atom on the right. There are four H atoms on the left and only two on the right, so we must write $2H_2O$. This gives:

$$CH_4 + O_2 \rightarrow CO_2 + 2H_2O$$

We now have two O atoms on the left and four O atoms on the right (two in CO_2 and two in $2H_2O$). By writing $2O_2$, the equation balances as

$$CH_4 + 2O_2 \rightarrow CO_2 + 2H_2O$$

2 *The reaction between magnesium and sulphuric acid*
Write the word equation

magnesium + sulphuric acid
→ magnesium sulphate + hydrogen

Write symbols for elements and formulae for compounds

$$Mg + H_2SO_4 \rightarrow MgSO_4 + H_2$$

Balance the equation. The equation already balances. Check this for yourself.

- Write balanced equations for the following reactions.
  a) aluminium with oxygen giving aluminium oxide, Al_2O_3,
  b) calcium with water giving calcium hydroxide, $Ca(OH)_2$, and hydrogen,
  c) sodium hydroxide with hydrochloric acid giving sodium chloride and water,
  d) heating hydrated copper sulphate ($CuSO_4.5H_2O$) to give anhydrous copper sulphate.

13.8 Reaction rates

Different chemical reactions take place at different rates. Some reactions, like explosions, are so fast that they are almost instantaneous. One explosion that you may have seen is the reaction between hydrogen and chlorine. When a burning splint is put into a mixture of equal volumes of these two gases there is a very loud bang and hydrogen chloride is produced.

$$H_2(g) + Cl_2(g) \rightarrow 2HCl(g)$$

Other reactions, like the weathering of limestone on buildings, may take centuries before we notice any changes.

$$\underset{\text{calcium carbonate in limestone}}{CaCO_3(s)} + \underset{\text{in rain water}}{CO_2(aq) + H_2O(l)} \longrightarrow \underset{\text{calcium hydrogencarbonate which is soluble in rain water}}{Ca(HCO_3)_2(aq)}$$

Most reactions take place at moderate rates, somewhere between those described in the last two paragraphs. The burning of coal, the rusting of steel and the chemical reactions which take place when food is cooked are examples of reactions which occur at steady rates.

Making reactions go faster

It takes about ten minutes to fry chips, but twenty minutes or so to boil potatoes. Larger potatoes may take even longer.

- Why do larger potatoes take longer to cook than smaller ones?
- Why can chips be cooked faster than boiled potatoes?
- Why can boiled potatoes be cooked faster in a pressure cooker?

Temperature

One of the reasons why chips can be cooked faster than boiled potatoes is because the chips are fried in fat at a much higher temperature than boiling water.

When molecules react, bonds must first break in the reactants and then other bonds can form to make the products. Breaking bonds requires energy. At higher temperatures, the average energy of the molecules increases so bonds are more likely to break and the reaction goes faster.

When potatoes are cooked, the starch in them is partly hydrolysed by reaction with water contained in the potatoes. Using ⟨G⟩ to represent glucose, we can write an equation for this as:

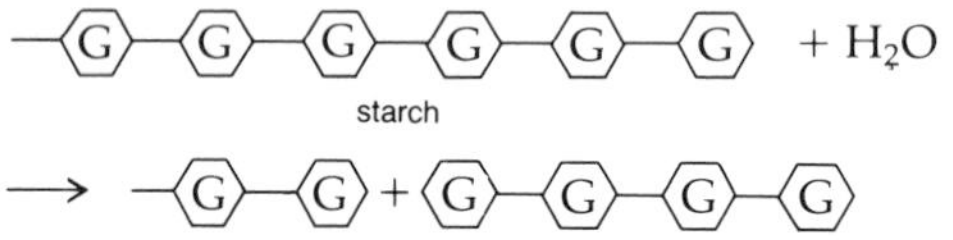

This reaction takes place faster in the hot fat which is at a higher temperature than boiling water.

Chemical reactions which take place when food 'goes off' occur more quickly at higher temperatures. Thus, milk turns sour very quickly if it is left in the sun, but it can be kept for several days in a refrigerator. A deep freezer is ideal if perishable foods like meat, fish and soft fruit are to be stored for long periods. The temperature inside a deep freezer is about −18 °C, while that inside a refrigerator is about 5 °C.

Surface area

Another reason why chips can be cooked faster than boiled potatoes is because they are smaller, with a greater surface area for the same mass. In general, the smaller the pieces of solid, the greater is the total surface area exposed. With more surface exposed, the reaction goes faster.

Figure 13.9

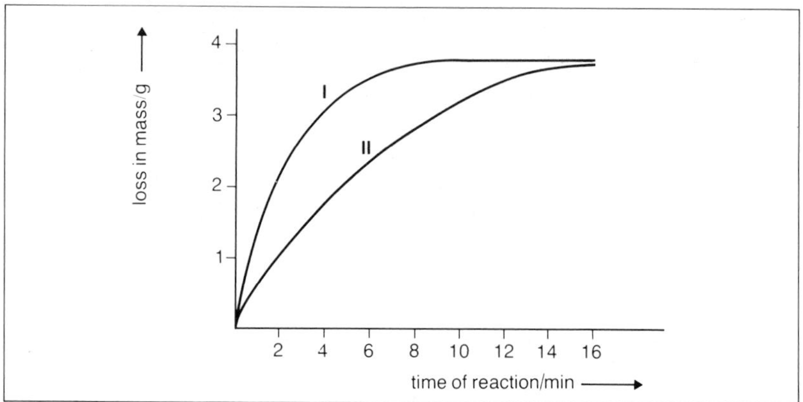

The graphs in figure 13.9 show the results of two experiments to investigate the effect of surface area on reaction rate. The reaction studied was that between marble chips and dilute hydrochloric acid (figure 13.10).

$$\underset{\text{calcium carbonate in marble}}{CaCO_3(s)} + 2HCl(aq) \rightarrow CaCl_2(aq) + H_2O(l) + CO_2(g)$$

The marble chips lose mass because carbon dioxide is produced and escapes into the air.

- *In experiment I,* 30 *small* marble chips, weighing 10 g reacted with 100 cm^3 of dilute hydrochloric acid.
- *In experiment II,* 6 *large* marble chips weighing 10 g reacted with 100 cm^3 of the same hydrochloric acid.

In each experiment, the marble chips are in excess: there is more than enough for the acid to react with. This means that the acid will be used up first.

- Why is the final decrease in mass the same in both experiments?
- Why do the graphs become horizontal?
- Which graph shows the larger decrease in mass per minute at the beginning of the experiment?
- Which experiment begins at the faster rate?
- Why does the reaction rate differ in the two experiments?
- Why does a pile of firewood burn faster than a tree trunk?

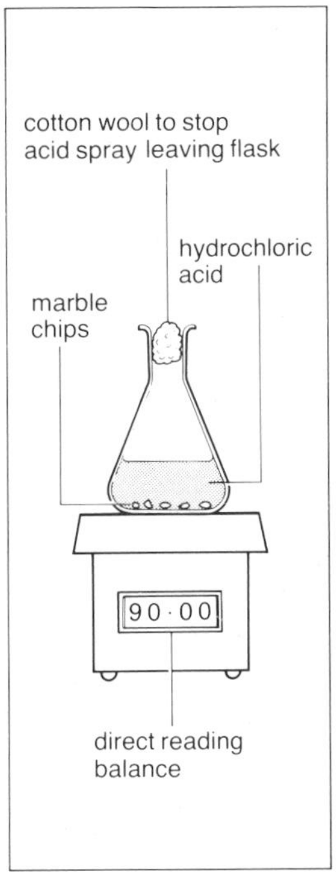

Figure 13.10

Concentration

Substances that burn in air burn much more vigorously in pure oxygen. In oxyacetylene burners, acetylene burns in pure oxygen. These burners produce such high temperatures that the flame will cut through sheets of metal.

$$\underset{\text{acetylene}}{2C_2H_2(g)} + 5O_2(g) \rightarrow 4CO_2(g) + 2H_2O(g) + \text{heat}$$

Chemical reactions occur when particles of the reacting substances collide with each other. Collisions between acetylene molecules and oxygen molecules occur more often when oxygen is used in place of air. Thus, the reaction occurs faster and gives off more heat when the concentration of oxygen is increased by using the pure gas.

Pure oxygen can also be used to speed up chemical changes in the body. This can help the recovery of hospital patients, such as those suffering from extensive burns.

Catalysts

Catalysts are substances which alter the rate of a reaction without being used up. Most catalysts are used to speed up reactions, but a few catalysts can be used to slow them down. These substances are called negative catalysts or inhibitors. Under normal conditions, hydrogen peroxide decomposes slowly to give water and oxygen. The rate of reaction increases greatly on adding a small amount of manganese dioxide.

$$2H_2O_2(aq) \xrightarrow[\text{catalyst}]{MnO_2} 2H_2O(l) + O_2(g)$$

On the other hand, glycerine is sometimes added to hydrogen peroxide as a *negative* catalyst to *slow down* its rate of decomposition.

Many reactions involving gases are catalysed by platinum, nickel and other transition metals. Margarine is manufactured from edible vegetable oils, such as palm oil, using a nickel catalyst. The nickel catalyses a reaction between the oil and hydrogen to form a fatty solid which is margarine. By controlling the extent of the change, the margarine can be made as soft or as hard as required.

Catalysts allow the chemicals to react more easily. Bonds break more easily when a catalyst is present and so the reaction goes faster.

These workmen are using an oxy-propane torch to cut metal. Propane burns in oxygen with a very hot flame like acetylene.

Why are reaction rates important?

There are many reactions in our bodies which would never occur if the reacting substances were just mixed together. At this very moment, thousands of different chemical reactions are going on in your body to keep you alive and moving. Each reaction is helped along by its own specific catalyst. These catalysts in biological processes are called **enzymes**. Without enzymes the reactions in your body would stop and you would die. One important enzyme that we all rely on is **amylase**. Amylase is present in saliva. It catalyses the initial breakdown of starch in foods such as bread, potatoes and rice. Enzymes are proteins which are usually very large molecules. Their structure is easily disrupted by changes in temperature. If this happens the enzyme cannot act as a catalyst. This helps to explain why cells and organisms cannot survive if the temperature gets too high or too low.

Enzymes are used in biological washing powders to break down foods and blood and other stains on clothing. 'Biological' powders work better than ordinary washing powders because they contain enzymes as well as soaps and detergents.

- Gardeners add fertilisers to the soil to help their plants grow. Do the fertilisers make the plants grow faster?
- Are the fertilisers used up by the plant?
- Are fertilisers catalysts?

Chemists are not satisfied with merely turning one substance into another. They want to carry out processes faster and more cheaply. In industry, it is often necessary to speed up slow reactions so that they are more economical. Time and money are all important. For this reason, catalysts are immensely important in the chemical industry.

The key reaction in the manufacture of sulphuric acid is the **contact process**. This involves converting sulphur dioxide and oxygen to sulphur trioxide.

$$2SO_2 + O_2 \rightarrow 2SO_3$$

At normal temperatures, this reaction will not happen. Chemical enegineers have, however, found that the reaction takes place quickly at 450°C in the presence of a catalyst of platinum or vanadium(V) oxide. By speeding up the reaction in this way, sulphuric acid can be made quickly, and therefore cheaply. This is essential because sulphuric acid is perhaps the most important of all industrial chemicals. More details of the contact process are given in section 25.2.

Summary

1 In a chemical reaction, a new substance is always formed.

2 The starting materials in a chemical reaction are called the reactants and the substances formed during the reaction are called the products.

3 Chemical reactions usually involve energy changes.

4 Reactions which give out energy are described as exothermic, those which take in energy are described as endothermic.

5 Bond breaking is endothermic whereas bond making is exothermic.

6 Decomposition occurs when one substance splits up into two or more simpler substances.

7 Synthesis occurs when two or more substances join together forming a single product.

8 The law of conservation of mass says that matter cannot be destroyed; the total mass of products always equals the mass of reactants.

9 An equation is a summary of the reactants and products in a chemical reaction.

10 A balanced equation shows:
  a) the formulae of the reactants and products,
  b) the number of moles of the reactants and products.

11 The stages in writing an equation are:
  a) write a word equation,
  b) write symbols for elements and formulae for compounds,
  c) balance the equation.

12 The rate of a chemical reaction can usually be increased by:
  a) increasing the temperature,
  b) increasing the surface area of a solid reactant,
  c) increasing the concentration of a reactant,
  d) using a suitable catalyst.

13 The catalysts in biological reactions are called enzymes.

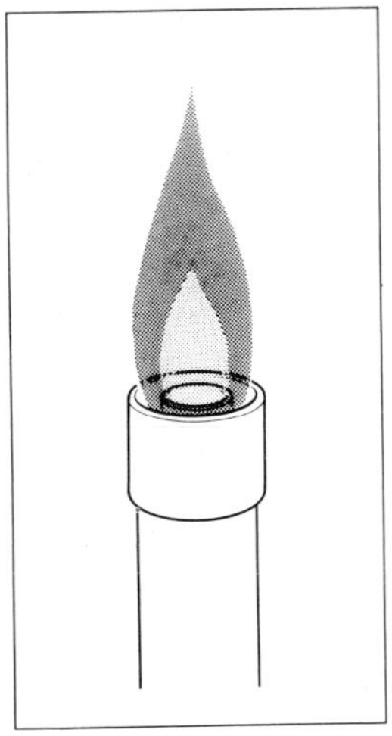

Figure 13.11

Study questions

1 When green nickel carbonate is heated, a black solid is produced and a gas is given off.
  a) How would you find out if the gas produced is (i) carbon dioxide, (ii) water vapour or, (iii) oxygen?
  b) What experiments would you carry out to see if this reaction is reversible?
  c) Is the reaction an example of synthesis or decomposition? Explain your answer.
  d) The formula of nickel carbonate is $NiCO_3$. Write an equation, with state symbols, to summarise what happens when $NiCO_3$ is heated.

2 Table 13.2 shows what happens when various substances are heated in air.
  a) What gases are produced when the following are heated in air: (i) Epsom salts, (ii) soil, (iii) red mercury oxide?
  b) Which substances are decomposed on heating?
  c) Which substance undergoes synthesis on heating?
  d) Which substance is not changed on heating?
  e) Write a word equation for the action of heat on Epsom salts.
  f) Write balanced equations to summarise the action of heat on (i) iron wire and (ii) red mercury oxide, HgO.

Table 13.2

Substance heated	*Appearance before heating*	*Effect on heating*	*Appearance after heating*	*Change in mass*
Epsom salts (hydrated magnesium sulphate)	clear crystals	turns white, moisture on sides of test tube	solid remains white	loss
soil	dark grey solid	moisture on sides of tube, gas produced turns lime water milky	grey solid	loss
iron wire	shiny grey metal	becomes red hot	surface becomes grey black	gain
red mercury oxide	red powder	silver liquid forms, gas produced relights glowing splint	silver liquid remains	loss
sand (silicon (IV) oxide)	pale brown powder	none visible	pale brown powder remains	none

3 Some glues are thought to react with the air during the setting process. Devise a method of testing whether a particular glue reacts with the air when it sets.

4 i) **A** is a green powder. When **A** is heated, it gives off a colourless gas **B**, and leaves a black powder **C**.
  ii) **B** turns limewater ($Ca(OH)_2(aq)$) milky.
  iii) When **B** is passed over heated carbon, it forms another gas **D**.
  iv) **D** burns in air with a blue flame forming **B**.
  v) When hydrogen is passed over heated **C**, a red-brown solid **E** is formed which conducts electricity. A gas **F** is also formed, which condenses to a colourless liquid on cooling.
  a) Identify **A**, **B**, **C**, **D**, **E** and **F**.
  b) Write balanced equations for the chemical reactions in stages (i) to (v).

5 Figure 13.11 shows a flame of burning natural gas (almost 100% methane, CH_4).
  a) Redraw figure 13.11 and mark on your drawing (i) the hottest part of the flame, and (ii) a region of the flame containing unburnt gas.
  b) What are the products when methane burns completely?
  c) Write a balanced equation for the complete burning of methane.
  d) How would you test for the products you have suggested in part (b)?

6 Three separate samples of copper were heated in (i) an open flask, (ii) a sealed flask, (iii) an evacuated flask.
  a) Write a word equation for the reaction of copper when heated in air.
  b) Will the open flask and its contents change in mass on heating? Explain.
  c) What reaction, if any, occurs in the sealed flask?
  d) Will the sealed flask and its contents change in mass on heating? Explain.
  e) What reaction, if any, occurs in the evacuated flask?

7 For each of the following pairs of reactants *complete the word equation* if necessary and then write a balanced chemical equation.
  a) aluminium + oxygen →
  b) lead oxide + hydrogen →
  c) silver oxide + zinc →
  d) calcium + water → calcium hydroxide + hydrogen
  e) magnesium + hydrochloric acid → magnesium chloride + hydrogen
  f) copper oxide + sulphuric acid →
  g) petrol (C_8H_{18}) + oxygen →
  h) lime (CaO) + water →

14 Burning, breathing and rusting

Burning, breathing and rusting may not seem to have much in common. Yet they all involve the same basic process – reaction with oxygen.

14.1 What happens when fuels burn?

What are fuels?

When the word *fuel* is used, you probably think of petrol, coal, wood, gas and the like. You are maybe less likely to think of candle wax as a fuel, and certainly you might not class foods like potatoes as fuels. Yet all these materials can be *oxidised to produce energy*. This is what we mean by a fuel.

Oxidation means combining with oxygen, and this is usually done by burning the fuel in air. Coal, wood, gas and candle wax all burn to release heat and some light energy. When petrol burns in an internal combustion engine, the heat energy it gives out is partly converted to mechanical energy. Foods like potatoes *could* be burned, but when we eat foods their energy is released by a more controlled sort of oxidation (section 14.5).

In spite of some differences, all the fuels we have mentioned have several things in common.

- They all react with oxygen.
- They all produce energy, usually heat, when they react with oxygen. The reaction is exothermic.
- They all produce carbon dioxide and water when oxidised.

We can easily show that carbon dioxide and water are produced by using the apparatus shown in figure 14.1.

(*Left*) This Turkana woman is using the oxidation of fuel to release heat for cooking. Later, when the food is eaten, oxidation of food will release energy inside human bodies.

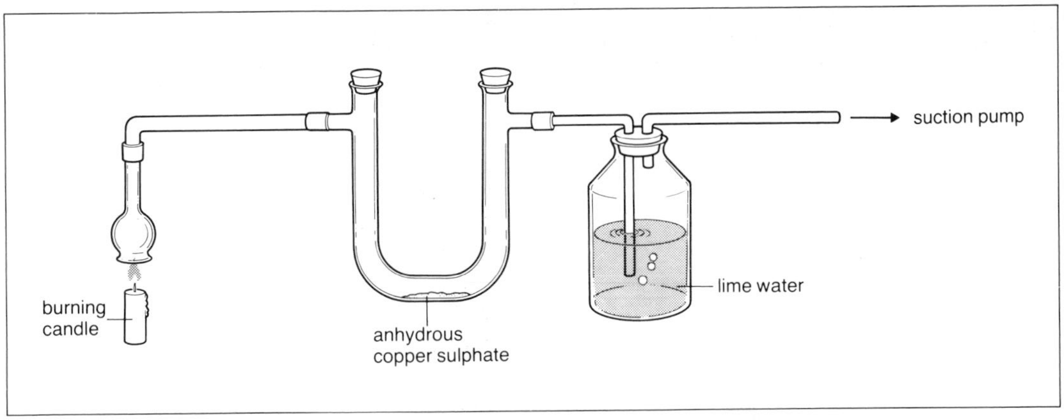

Figure 14.1 An experiment to show that water and carbon dioxide are produced when a candle burns.

Look at figure 14.1.
- What happens if water is produced by the burning candle?
- What happens if carbon dioxide is produced by the burning candle?
- If carbon dioxide *and* water are produced by the burning candle, what elements *must* be present in candle wax? What other element *might* be present?

Writing equations for the combustion of fuels

Most fuels are a mixture of different compounds. But the compounds are usually made of carbon and hydrogen and sometimes oxygen. When they burn they form carbon dioxide and water, provided there is a good supply of air. It is quite easy to write a chemical equation showing what happens when a fuel burns.

Take propane, for example, the main component of bottled gas such as Calor Gas. The formula of propane is C_3H_8, and in a plentiful supply of air it burns to form carbon dioxide and water.

$$C_3H_8 + 5O_2 \rightarrow 3O_2 + 4H_2O$$

- Write an equation for the combustion of methane, CH_4, the main component of household gas.

Important fuels

We use fuels for many things. We burn them to keep us warm, or we may convert the heat they give into electrical energy in a power station. Fuels like petrol and diesel oil are used to provide kinetic energy in cars and lorries. Food fuels give living things the energy they need. Some of the important fuels we use are listed in table 14.1.

Table 14.1
Important fuels

Fuel	*Composition*	*Where it comes from*	*Energy produced when 1 g burns*	*How we use it*
wood	very complex contains C, H, O	trees	20–25 kJ	burned on domestic fires
coal	very complex mainly C, plus H and O	decomposed remains of vegetation	30–40 kJ	burned on domestic fires and in power stations used to make coke for steelmaking
oil	very complex mainly hydro carbons	decomposed remains of marine life	50 kJ	distilled to make petrol, diesel oil, fuel oil, etc.
natural gas	mainly methane, CH_4	decomposed remains of marine life	55 kJ	burned for domestic heating and cooking, and as an industrial fuel

- Which fuel in table 14.1 must be processed before it can be used?
- Which fuel or fuels are used to generate electricity?
- Which fuel or fuels are commonly used to provide mechanical energy?
- Which fuel or fuels produce carbon dioxide and water when they burn?

Fuel cells

The chemical energy in fuels is normally converted to electrical energy in a two-stage process. The fuel is first burnt, giving heat, and the heat is then used to boil water, providing steam to drive turbines. But this is an inefficient process – only about 30% of the fuel's energy gets converted to electrical energy.

Scientists are working on fuel cells which oxidise fuels in an electric cell, producing electrical energy directly without going via heat. Simple fuel cells, using hydrogen or methanol as the fuel, have been developed. Scientists are now trying to make fuel cells which use abundant fuels like methane.

14.2 Air

Fire extinguishers

Fire fighters use several different methods to put out fires, but they all use the same principle. They all work by preventing the fuel getting the oxygen it needs to burn.

- *Water* wets the surface of the fuel, cooling it and preventing air reaching it.

  Water cannot be used with some fires. Oil floats on water, so water will not put out an oil fire, because the burning oil floats on top. Water conducts electricity, so it cannot be used on electrical fires.

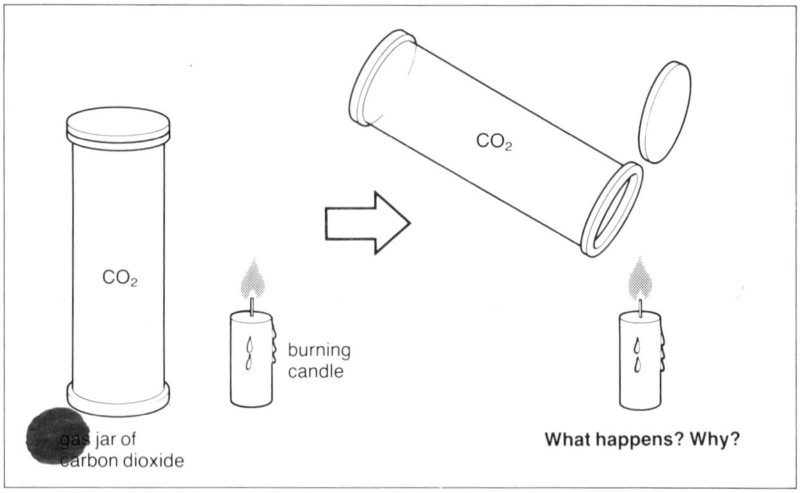

Figure 14.2

- *Carbon dioxide* is a heavy, non-flammable gas. It can prevent air reaching the fuel, so smothering the fire (see figure 14.2).
- *Foam.* Some fire extinguishers produce a foam which contains bubbles of carbon dioxide. The foam smothers the fire.

These firemen are using foam to control a fire. The burning tanks contained waste oil.

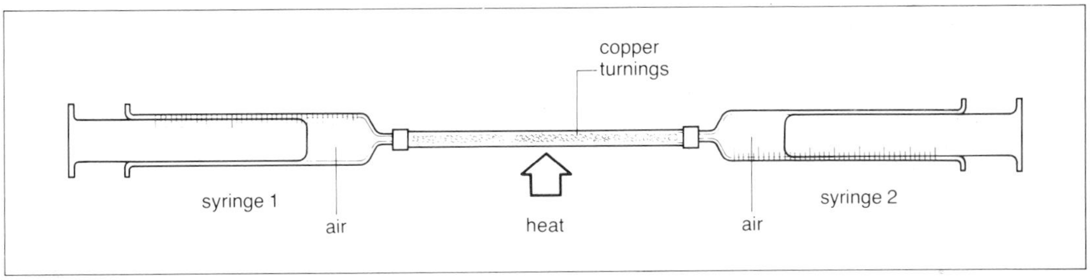

Figure 14.3 Finding the percentage of oxygen in air.

How much of the air is used up when fuel burns?

We know that fuels need oxygen to burn, and that this oxygen comes from the air. How much of the air is oxygen? We can find out by reacting the oxygen with heated copper in the apparatus shown in figure 14.3.

At the start of the experiment there is 100 cm^3 of air in the apparatus. The copper is heated and the air is pushed backwards and forwards over the hot copper. Oxygen combines with copper, forming solid copper oxide:

$$2Cu(s) + O_2(g) \rightarrow 2CuO(s)$$

The oxygen is used up and the volume of gas gets less. The apparatus is allowed to cool and the new volume of gas is measured. In one experiment the final volume was found to be 80 cm^3.

- What volume of oxygen was there in the original 100 cm^3 of air?
- What percentage of the air is oxygen?
- What gas remains after the experiment?
- Why was the apparatus allowed to cool before measuring the final volume of gas?

Air is a mixture of gases, and its composition varies very little. About four-fifths of it is nitrogen. Oxygen makes up about one fifth and the rest is water vapour, carbon dioxide and noble gases. Table 14.2 gives the percentage composition of pure air.

Table 14.2
Percentage composition of air by volume

Gas	*Percentage*
nitrogen	78
oxygen	21
noble gases (mainly argon)	0.9
carbon dioxide	0.01–0.1
water vapour	variable

14.3 What happens when elements burn in oxygen?

Most of the fuels we use are compounds of carbon and hydrogen, but we sometimes burn elements. Pure hydrogen is used as a rocket fuel and in oxyhydrogen torches, used for cutting metals under water. Charcoal and coke are nearly pure forms of carbon.

- What is formed when hydrogen burns?
- What is formed when carbon burns?
- Carbon and hydrogen are both non-metals. What other non-metals do you know which burn in air?

Some metallic elements will burn in air. You have probably seen magnesium burn with a brilliant white light. It was once used for photographic flash bulbs.

- What is formed when magnesium burns?

If a substance will burn in air, it will burn even better in pure oxygen. We can investigate the burning of elements in oxygen

The fuel used for barbecues, charcoal, is almost pure carbon.

using the method shown in figure 14.4. Once the element has burned, we can examine the product.

Table 14.3 shows the results obtained when some elements are burned in oxygen.

> *Look at table 14.3.*
> - Which elements form oxides which are liquids or gases at room temperature?
> - Which elements form oxides which are solids at room temperature?
> - Which elements form acidic oxides?
> - Which elements form alkaline oxides?
> - What general rules can you make about the properties of the oxides of metals and the oxides of non-metals?

Table 14.3 shows only a small number of elements, so we must be careful about making general rules based on these results alone. By looking at the properties of many more elements, though, we can make two general rules. (Periodic table, below.)

- ■ The oxides of metals are always solids. The oxides of non-metals are usually liquids or gases.
- ■ The oxides of metals are alkaline or insoluble in water. The oxides of non-metals are usually acidic.

Which areas of the periodic table contain metallic elements? Which contain non-metallic elements?

Table 14.3
Burning elements in oxygen

Element	*How it burns*	*Product*	*Appearance of product*	*Acid/alkaline nature of product in water*
carbon	glows bright red	CO_2	colourless gas	weak acid
sodium	brilliant yellow flame	Na_2O	white solid	alkali
magnesium	brilliant white flame	MgO	white solid	weak alkali
hydrogen	blue flame	H_2O	colourless liquid	neutral
sulphur	blue flame	SO_2	colourless gas	acid
iron	red hot sparks	Fe_3O_4	black solid	insoluble
copper	glows red	CuO	black solid	insoluble

Figure 14.4 (Below)
Burning elements in oxygen.

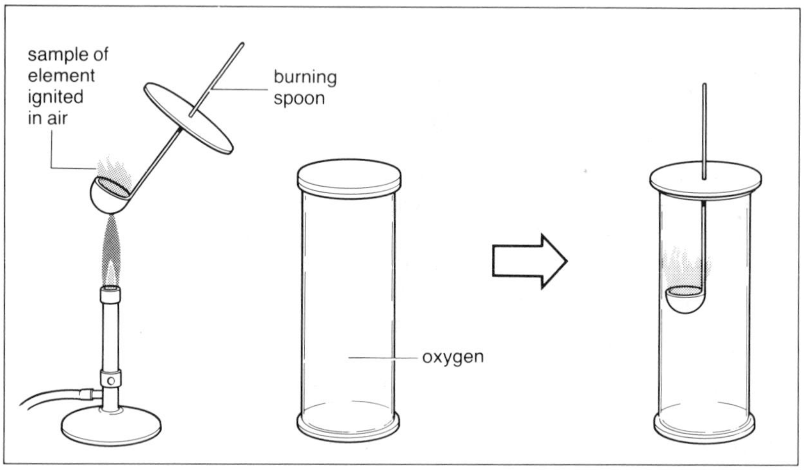

Figure 14.5 (Below)
Properties of the oxides of elements in the periodic table.

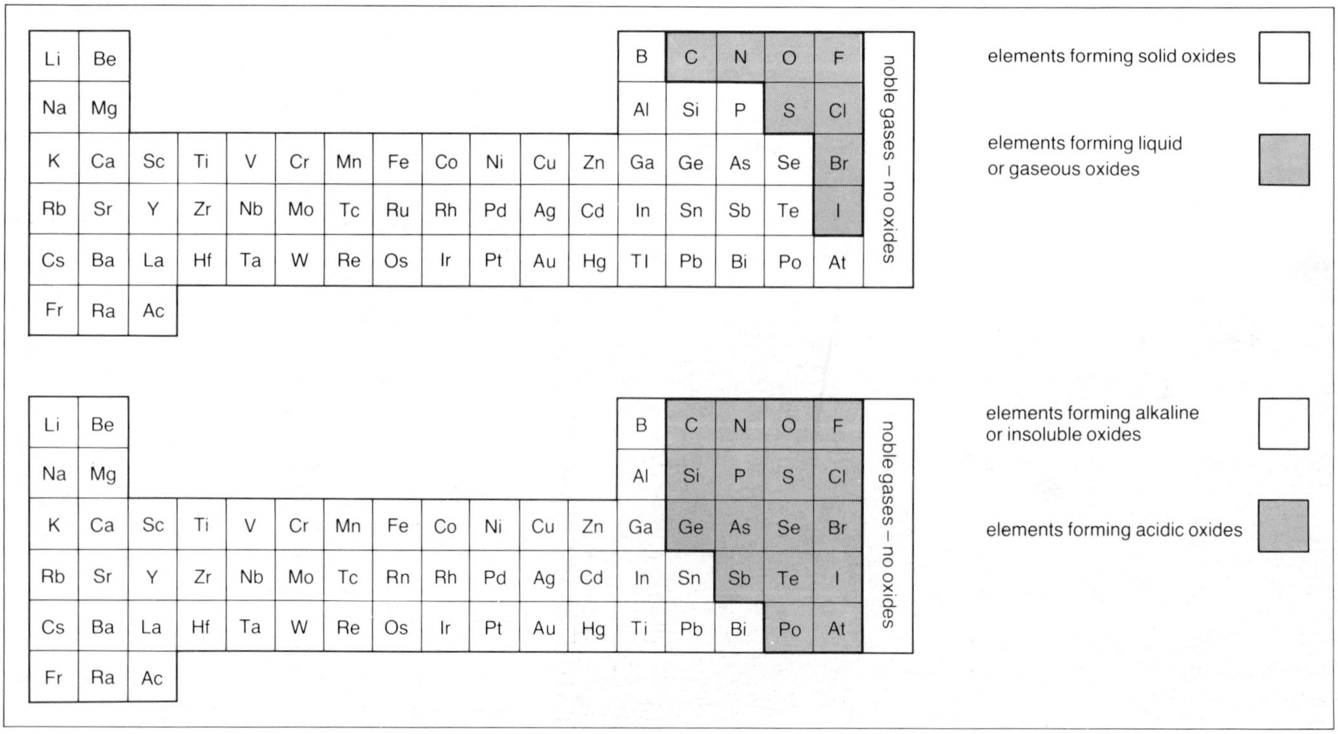

14.4 Where does all the waste go?

The products of burning fuels

When a hydrocarbon fuel burns completely, only carbon dioxide and water are formed. But there are usually many other products as well. If the air supply is poor, carbon monoxide and soot (carbon) may form instead of carbon dioxide. Most fuels contain traces of sulphur, which forms sulphur dioxide when the fuel burns. Some of the fuel may not burn at all, so unburnt hydrocarbons may be discharged into the air. Oxides of nitrogen (NO and NO_2) may also be produced, due to the combination of oxygen and nitrogen from the atmosphere. All these gases are pumped into the atmosphere and cause **pollution**.

What is pollution? A pollutant is a substance produced as a result of human activities and released into the environment, where it causes harm to living things. Sometimes pollutants may also damage non-living structures. Every pollutant has a *source*; it might be a factory, a farm or a burning fuel. It follows a *pathway* (in air, or water, or on land) to a *target* where it does its damage.

The targets might be human beings, farm animals, wild animals or plants. Living things depend on one another in a complicated way in what is called an ecosystem (section 2.4). Because of this a pollutant that affects only one organism directly can have an indirect effect on several others. For example, a herbivore might eat a plant that has been treated with an insecticide, and then get eaten by a carnivore. In this way the insecticide is passed from one organism to the next (section 24.4).

Scientists believe that the large-scale clearing of forests to make way for agriculture may result in disastrous changes in the weather. But these poor farmers in Brazil need the land to feed their families.

Pollution of the atmosphere

Because gases diffuse (spread out) freely, atmospheric pullution can affect wide areas. Canada suffers from atmospheric pollutants produced by industry in the USA. The Scandinavian countries complain about the damage done to their fisheries and forests by acid rain caused by pollutants in Britain and West Germany. Scotland suffers from pollution produced further south in England.

Oxides of carbon

Carbon monoxide, CO, is a very poisonous gas. It combines with haemoglobin in the blood and stops it carrying oxygen round the body. It is present in dangerous quantities in car exhaust and cigarette smoke. Sometimes it is found in the fumes produced by gas heaters or paraffin heaters, if their air supply is poor. Fortunately, the levels of carbon monoxide in the atmosphere as a whole are low, so it is not a major pollutant.

Carbon dioxide, CO_2, is produced in much larger quantities when fuels burn. Carbon dioxide is not, of course, poisonous. Indeed, it is produced by living organisms during respiration (section 14.5). Vast amounts of carbon dioxide are used by green plants in photosynthesis (section 20.10). However, the extra carbon dioxide produced by burning fuels has caused the level of the gas in the atmosphere to rise steadily since the Industrial Revolution. What is more, people have cleared forests to make room for farms, industries and cities, and this has reduced the amount of carbon dioxide absorbed by photosynthesising plants. Before the Industrial Revolution, the carbon dioxide concentration in the atmosphere was about 270 parts per million (ppm). By 1976 it was 325 ppm, and it has been suggested that it may rise to 450 ppm by the year 2050. These are relatively small amounts, but scientists are worried about the *greenhouse effect* of carbon dioxide.

Carbon dioxide lets most of the energy from the Sun pass through, but absorbs some of it as it is reflected back from the Earth's surface. This tends to make the Earth get warmer, and this greenhouse effect could increase average temperatures by 1.5°C by the year 2050. Scientists are unsure of the full effects of this, but they believe that agriculture would be affected, and that the sea level might rise due to increased melting of the polar ice caps.

Smog in Los Angeles, California, USA.

Sulphur dioxide

This gets into the air from burning coal and fuel oil. Sulphur dioxide in the atmosphere can be converted to sulphuric acid in rainfall. This is called acid rain. Even though the acid is dilute, it can do considerable damage to stone and metal in buildings, and can kill plants and animals. There is more about acid rain in section 25.2.

Smoke

This is a fine suspension of solid particles produced by burning coal and other fuels. It makes the air dirty and in winter can cause smoke-fogs called 'smogs'. In Britain the 1956 Clean Air Act controlled the use of smoky fuels, and smogs are now much less common. Average smoke levels in cities like London and Glasgow are now less than a quarter of their level in 1958. This has given a 60% increase in winter sunshine.

Oxides of nitrogen

These are poisonous and, like sulphur dioxide, they can cause acid rain. Scientists believe they also damage the upper atmosphere, where they combine with ozone (O_3). Ozone absorbs the Sun's harmful ultraviolet rays. When oxides of nitrogen remove this ozone, more ultraviolet rays reach Earth. Ultraviolet rays can damage skin cells. In small amounts they only cause sunburn, but in large doses they may cause skin cancer.

Another group of pollutants which are thought to damage the ozone layer are the chlorofluorocarbons in aerosol sprays. Every time you use an aerosol pack, these chlorofluorcarbons are pumped into the atmosphere, and they may eventually reach the ozone layer and interfere with it.

14.5 Food as a fuel

Fuels like oil and natural gas are sources of energy – energy for movement, energy for heating, energy for lighting. Living things need a source of energy too, and their energy comes from the food they eat.

Breathe in, breathe out

Figure 14.6 shows a simple experiment. The experiment is used to compare the amount of carbon dioxide in exhaled (breathed out) air with the amount in ordinary, atmospheric air. A person breathes gently in and out several times through the mouthpiece. The lime water in tube B soon turns milky, but in tube A it stays clear for a long time. Obviously, then, exhaled air contains more carbon dioxide than the atmospheric air inhaled in the first place.

Table 14.4 gives the composition of exhaled and inhaled (atmospheric) air.

Table 14.4
Percentage composition by volume of exhaled and atmospheric air

	Atmospheric air	*Exhaled air*
nitrogen	79	79
oxygen	21	17
carbon dioxide	0.03	4

Look carefully at the figures in table 14.4.
- Which gas is used up during breathing?
- Which gas is produced during breathing?
- Try to explain what is happening to these gases between entering and leaving the lungs.

Figure 14.6 (Right)
Comparing the CO_2 content of exhaled air and atmospheric air.

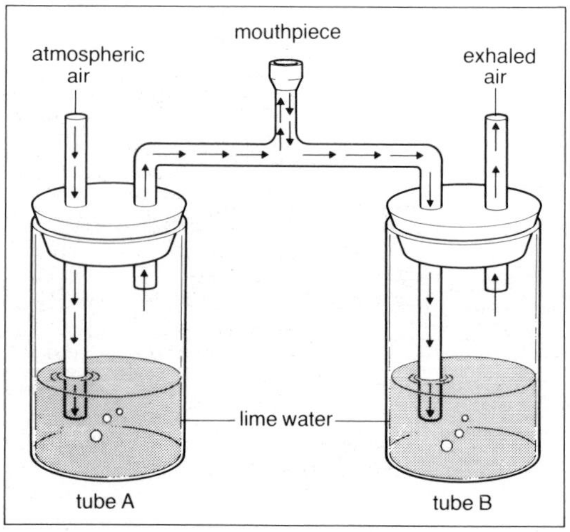

Respiration

When we breathe we use up oxygen and produce carbon dioxide and water. The same thing happens when a hydrocarbon fuel burns.

Our bodies use many different foods as fuels, but an important and simple one is **glucose**, $C_6H_{12}O_6$. Glucose can be burned in air. If the air supply is good, carbon dioxide and water are formed, and 2898 kJ of energy is given out for each mole of glucose burned (figure 14.7).

$$\underset{\text{glucose}}{C_6H_{12}O_6(s)} + 6O_2(g) \rightarrow 6CO_2(g) + 6H_2O(g) + 2898\,\text{kJ}$$

The same *overall* reaction happens in our bodies, when glucose is oxidised to give carbon dioxide and water, providing energy. The process of breaking down chemicals to provide energy for a living organism is called **respiration**. The word respiration is also sometimes used to refer to the act of breathing. In this book, *respiration* is used to refer only to the chemical reactions which take place in the cells, releasing energy.

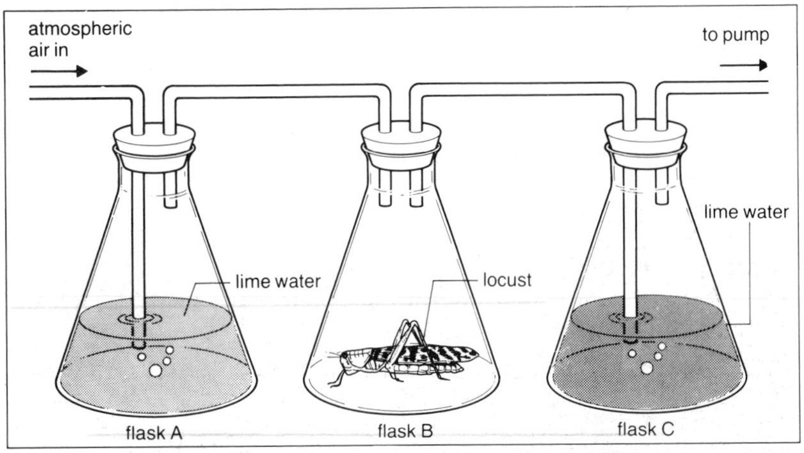

Figure 14.8 (Above) An experiment to show that living things produce carbon dioxide.

Figure 14.7 (Below) Complete oxidation of 1 mole of glucose produces 2898 kJ of heat.

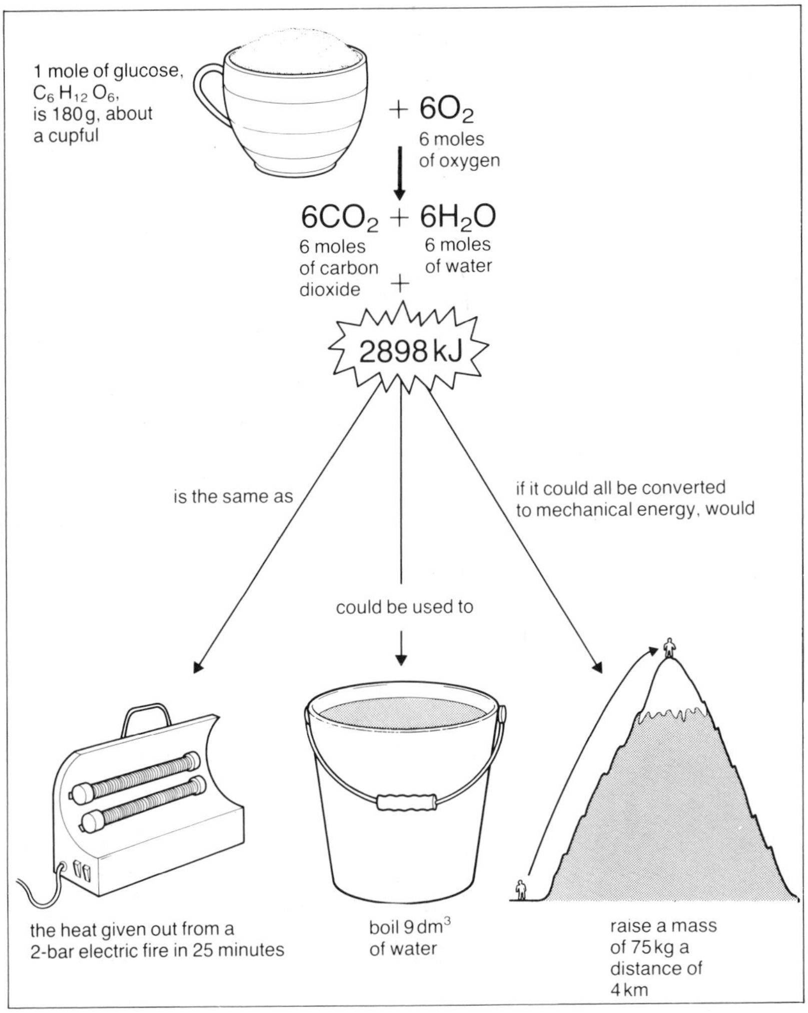

Burning and respiration are similar processes. Both use up oxygen, produce carbon dioxide and water, and release energy. But there are important differences. When an energy food like glucose is oxidised in the cells of your body, there are obviously no flames, and the process is much more controlled than burning. In fact the oxidation of glucose in the body occurs via a large number of separate chemical reactions. Around fifty separate reactions take place as glucose is oxidised to carbon dioxide and water. About half of the energy from these reactions is released as heat. The rest of the energy is transferred to a compound called adenosine triphosphate, ATP for short. The ATP then passes this energy to muscle fibres to enable them to contract.

In this complicated, but controlled, way the energy produced by the oxidation of glucose is used to contract muscles and so move your limbs. Even so, half of the 2898 kJ of energy given by a mole of glucose gets 'lost' as heat. This is why you get hot when you are running or working hard.

Respiration in other living things

All living things respire. We can show this experimentally in a number of ways. Figure 14.8 shows an experiment that can be used to show that small living organisms produce carbon dioxide. Air is drawn through the apparatus using a vacuum pump. The experiment is then repeated under exactly the same conditions, but with no locust in flask B.

- What would you expect to happen to the lime water in flasks A and C in the first experiment?
- The second experiment acts as a control. What does this mean? Why is it necessary?

Different living things can be tested in this way, including plants. If green plants are used, though, the experiment must be carried out in the dark, otherwise photosynthesis will occur (section 20.10). Since photosynthesis uses up carbon dioxide and produces oxygen, it would complicate the results.

When seeds germinate and begin to sprout, they respire rapidly as they use their food reserves to produce energy for the growing shoot. Figure 14.9 illustrates one experiment which can be used to show that heat is produced by germinating barley. Two vacuum flasks are filled with barley grains. Flask A contains grains that have been soaked in water for twenty-four hours. Flask B contains grains that have been killed by boiling them in water for 10 minutes, and then allowed to cool.

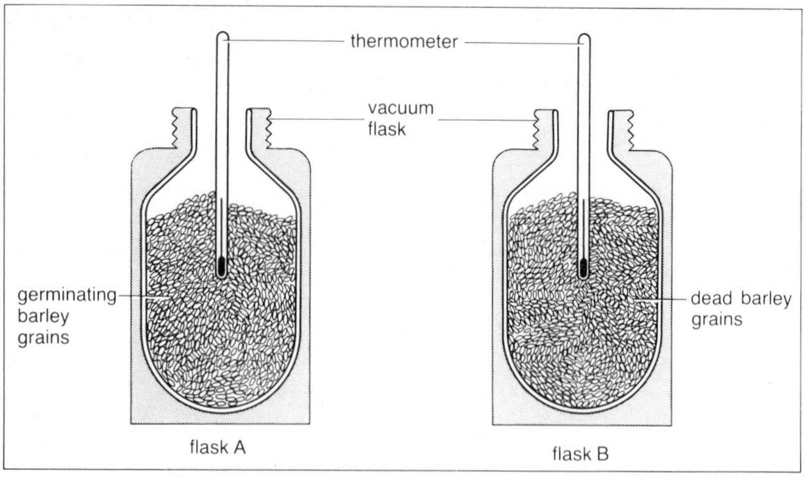

Figure 14.9 Production of heat by germinating barley.

- What would you expect to happen to the temperature of each flask over the course of a few days?
- What is the purpose of flask B?

So far we have talked about respiration with particular reference to the oxidation of glucose. Many other food molecules can be oxidised to produce energy. This kind of respiration, involving oxidation by air, is called **aerobic respiration**. We shall see in the next section that respiration is also possible when no oxygen is available. This is called **anaerobic respiration**.

14.6 Getting energy when there is no air

You will have heard of yeast, particularly if you know how to make bread or wine. In this section we will see why yeast is so useful to bakers and brewers.

Yeast is a living organism, a tiny, single-celled fungus. Under the microscope, yeast cells look like little spheres.

Like human cells, yeast cells can respire aerobically. Put some yeast in a solution of glucose and it quickly begins to convert the glucose to carbon dioxide and water. In this way it obtains energy for growth. At first the yeast uses oxygen dissolved in the water. However this dissolved oxygen soon gets used up. But the yeast goes on respiring, using up glucose and obtaining energy, without needing oxygen. The products of this *anaerobic* respiration are no longer carbon dioxide and water. Carbon dioxide and ethanol are formed instead.

$$\underset{\text{glucose}}{C_6H_{12}O_6(aq)} \xrightarrow{\text{yeast}} \underset{\text{ethanol}}{2C_2H_5OH(aq)} + \underset{\text{carbon dioxide}}{2CO_2(g)} + \underset{\text{energy}}{84\,kJ}$$

Ethanol is usually just called *alcohol*. Notice that the equation does not involve oxygen at all; the respiration is anaerobic. This anaerobic respiration of yeast is often called **fermentation**.

Anaerobic respiration does not give the yeast as much energy as it would get from aerobic respiration. Compare the 84 kJ given out in this reaction with the 2898 kJ when glucose is oxidised aerobically. If we separated out the ethanol, it could be burned in air, giving carbon dioxide and water, and more energy. But in the absence of air, the yeast cannot oxidise the ethanol, so the reaction stops at this point.

We have good reason to be grateful to yeast. Without yeast our bread would be heavy and hard. Bakers mix yeast into their dough. Anaerobic respiration of the yeast produces bubbles of carbon dioxide in the dough, which makes it rise. You can see these bubbles in the solidified dough when you cut a loaf of bread.

- What is unleavened bread?
- What happens to the alcohol produced when yeast ferments dough? Why do we not get drunk when we eat bread?

Bakers are interested in the carbon dioxide produced by yeast, but brewers are more interested in the alcohol. Alcoholic drinks are made by fermenting a sugary solution. Table 14.5 shows the starting materials for some alcoholic drinks.

Yeast cannot live in a solution of alcohol stronger than about 14%. When the alcohol reaches this strength fermentation stops. Stronger drinks like brandy and whisky, can be made by distilling the alcohol solutions.

In small amounts, alcohol makes people relaxed and may help digestion. Larger amounts have a serious effect on mental and physical performance. Excessive drinking can be very dangerous, particularly for car drivers. Alcohol is addictive if taken regularly in large amounts and it can damage the liver. After all, alcohol is really a drug – a drug which just happens to be socially acceptable. But suppose alcohol had only just been discovered, instead of having been used for thousands of years. It would probably be banned by most governments as a dangerous drug.

Yeast is not the only organism that can respire anaerobically. Other microorganisms, particularly bacteria, can do so as well. Some can *only* respire this way – they cannot respire aerobically. Human muscle cells are able to respire anaerobically for short periods. When this happens a substance called lactic acid is produced. If a lot of lactic acid is produced by the muscles, it makes them ache. When your muscles work hard for a short period, for example in a sprint race, they quickly run out of oxygen. For a while, the muscle cells respire anaerobically and the concentration of lactic acid builds up. The muscles begin to ache and you have to rest. As you rest, the blood brings fresh oxygen to the muscles, which go back to normal aerobic respiration and use up the lactic acid. The ache then goes away.

- Which form of respiration, aerobic or anaerobic, is the more efficient way of getting energy?
- Why do organisms find it useful to be able to respire anaerobically?
- Why does fermentation of dough stop when the dough is baked?

Table 14.5
Sources of sugar for some alcoholic drinks

Drink	*Source of sugar for fermentation*
wine	grapes
beer	malt (made from barley)
cider	apples
perry	pears

14.7 How do living things obtain oxygen?

Most living things get their energy by aerobic respiration. This means that they use up oxygen and produce carbon dioxide, so they need some way of exchanging these two gases with the atmosphere.

Diffusion

As we saw in chapter 3, a gas always diffuses from a region where its concentration is high to a region of lower concentration. So it should not be too difficult for an organism to obtain oxygen from the air. Oxygen will tend naturally to diffuse from the atmosphere, where its concentration is high, into the organism, where oxygen is being used up and its concentration is lower. This is just what happens, but once inside the organism the oxygen will only diffuse slowly through the liquid part of the cytoplasm inside the cells. Thus, unless the distance from the organism's surface to the point where the oxygen is wanted is small, a **transport system** will be needed to carry the gas round the organism. Similar arguments apply to the removal of carbon dioxide from the organism.

Examples of organisms which do not need a gas transport system, and rely on simple diffusion through their surface, are shown in figure 14.10. Note that these organisms are either

- small, so that their surface area is large compared to their volume, and the gas does not have far to diffuse (e.g. *Amoeba*), or
- shaped so that their surface area is large (e.g. the leaves of a plant).

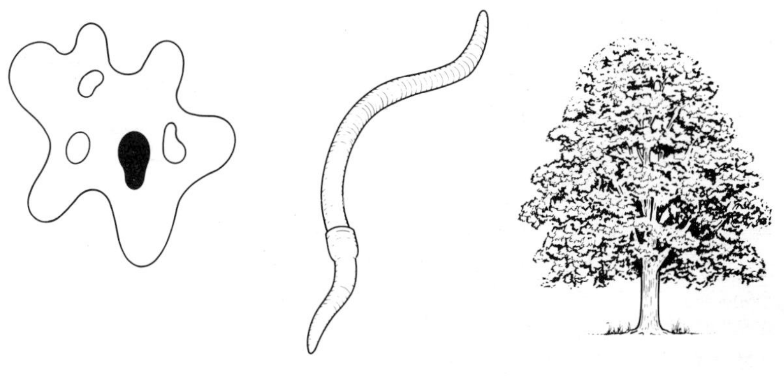

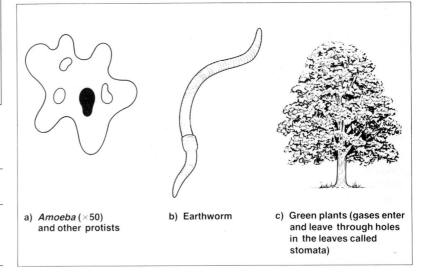

a) *Amoeba* (×50) and other protists
b) Earthworm
c) Green plants (gases enter and leave through holes in the leaves called stomata)

Figure 14.10 Organisms which exchange gases by direct diffusion through their surfaces.

Insects

Insects are very active organisms. They need large amounts of oxygen, particularly in flight. Their surface area is too small compared to their volume to provide this oxygen by direct diffusion through their surface. To get over this, insects have a system of branching air-filled tubes. These distribute oxygen to the tissues, particularly to the muscles (figure 14.11). These tubes, called **tracheae**, have openings, called **spiracles**, on the surface of the body. The tracheae form a branching network which ends in very fine tubes called **tracheoles**, which reach all parts of the insect's body. Tracheoles are permeable so gases can diffuse through them to the cells (figure 14.12).

Movements of the thorax and abdomen of the insect help the air to pass through the system. Air sacs in the main tracheal trunk improve the movement of air by acting like bellows.

- The insect's flight muscles have an especially dense network of tracheoles. Why do you think this is?

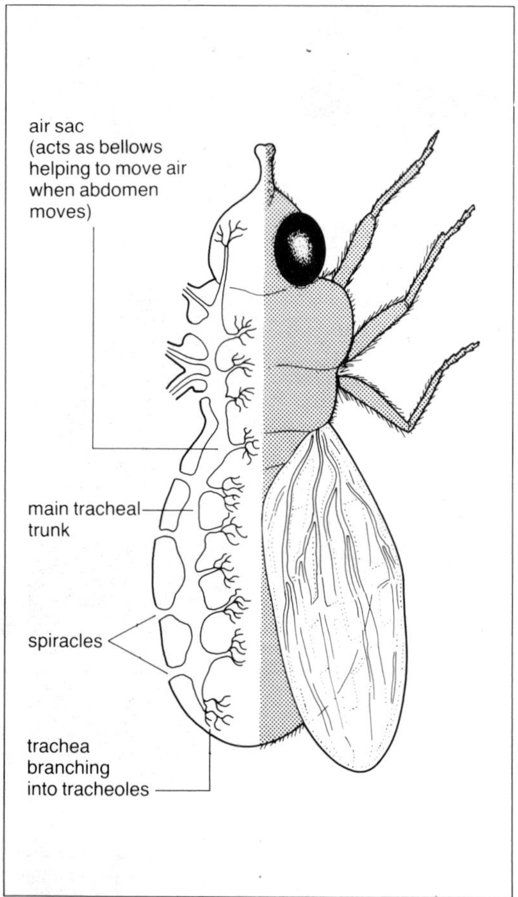

Figure 14.11 Tracheal system for distributing oxygen around an insect's body.

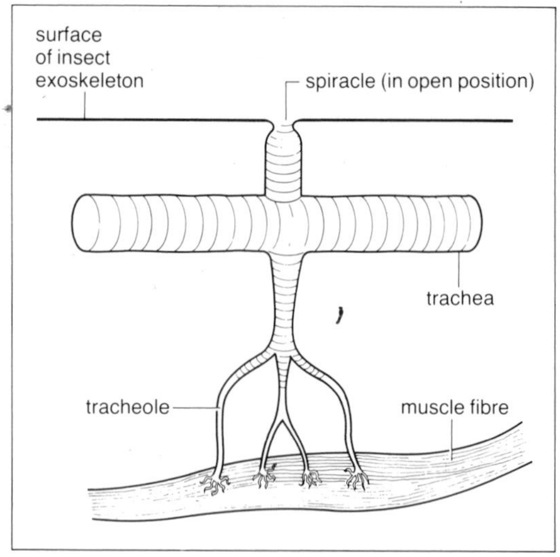

Figure 14.12 Tracheae and tracheoles supplying oxygen to the muscle of an insect.

Fish

Larger animals like fish, reptiles, birds and mammals, carry oxygen round their bodies in their blood (section 5.2). To do this, they need a **respiratory surface** where oxygen can be absorbed by the blood. In birds, reptiles and mammals, **lungs** provide the respiratory surface. In fishes, the respiratory surface is in the **gills**.

All respiratory surfaces have several things in common (figure 14.13). On the outside (the exterior) they are exposed to a source of oxygen. In the case of lungs, this is air, in the case of gills it is water containing dissolved oxygen. On the inside (the interior), very close to the surface, they have a dense network of blood capillaries to carry away dissolved oxygen. The surface is thin so oxygen can pass through readily. The respiratory surface usually has a very high surface area.

The concentration of dissolved oxygen in water is low, so gills need to be very efficient at extracting the gas. In fact they can extract up to 80% of the dissolved oxygen.

Figure 14.13 A generalised respiratory surface.

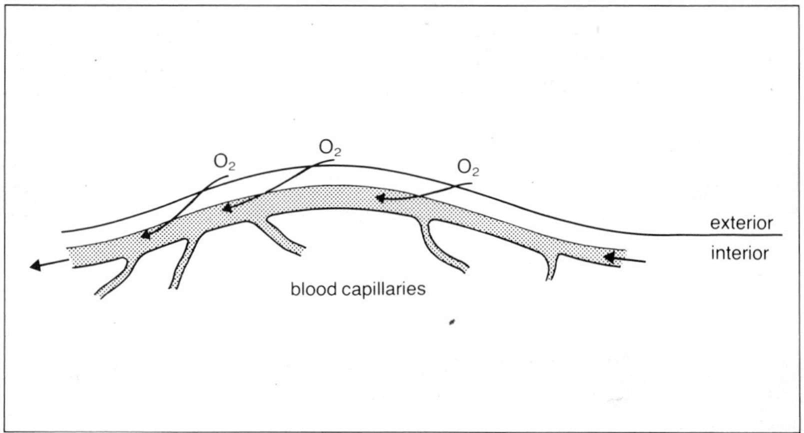

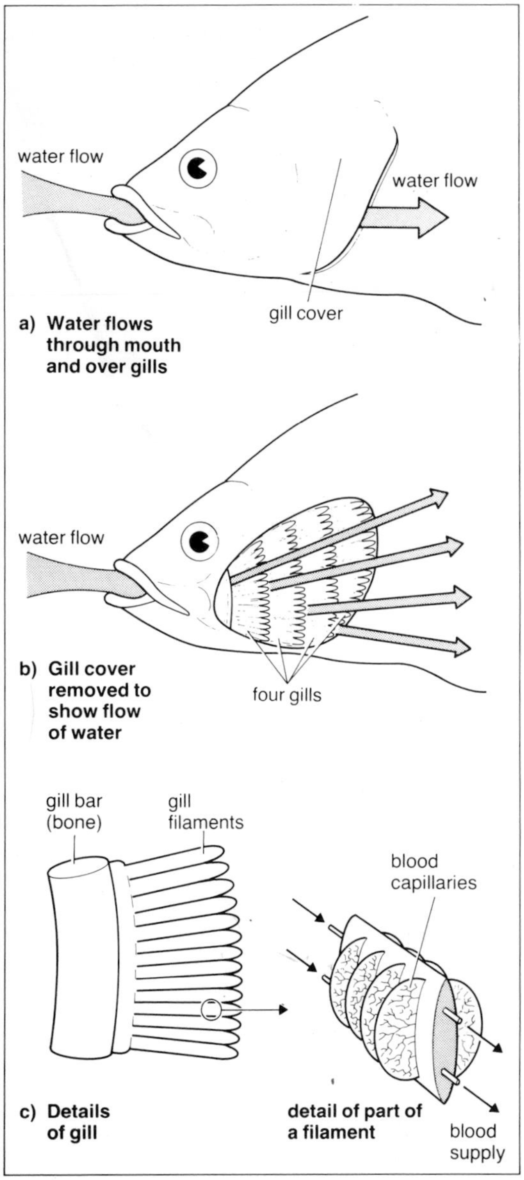

Figure 14.14 (Left) Structure and function of gills.

Figure 14.14 shows the structure and arrangement of gills in a typical fish. There are four gills on each side of the head. By opening and closing its mouth and gill cover, the fish pumps water over its gills. Gills are feathery structures with a very high surface area and many blood capillaries. As water flows over the gills, dissolved oxygen diffuses into the capillaries where it is carried away by red blood cells. Gills are very efficient in water, but in air they stick together. This reduces their surface area so the fish cannot obtain enough oxygen to live.

Mammals

The way in which mammals, particularly humans, obtain oxygen is considered in the next section.

14.8 How do we breathe?

Smoking and health

In the last thirty years doctors have collected figures on the connection between cigarette smoking and certain diseases, particularly lung cancer. Among other things these figures show:

- Lung cancer kills thirteen times as many cigarette smokers as non-smokers.
- Smokers are twice as likely to suffer a coronary thrombosis (heart attack) as non-smokers.
- A smoker who gives up smoking halves his or her risk of death from lung cancer within two years.
- Most people who take up smoking do so below the age of twenty. Anyone who reaches twenty without smoking is unlikely to begin.
- Non-smokers can suffer from the smoke produced by others.

(Below) As well as having increased risks of cancer and heart disease, smokers find breathing harder. Anyone reaching twenty without smoking is unlikely to begin.

Doctors are now certain that smoking causes several diseases. These include:

- Lung cancer. An uncontrolled cancerous growth of part of the lung tissues. Most of the people who develop lung cancer eventually die from it.
- Cancer of the mouth and throat.
- Emphysema. Thinning and breaking down of parts of the lung tissue leading to breathing difficulty.
- Chronic bronchitis. Clogging of breathing passages by excess mucus (cattarh). This makes breathing difficult and causes coughing.
- Coronary thrombosis. Heart attack caused by blocking of arteries that supply blood to the heart.

As well as causing these and other diseases, smoking has other effects:

- It reduces the sense of taste and smell.
- It makes the smoker's breath and clothes smell unpleasant.
- Pregnant women who smoke often have smaller babies than non-smokers, and their babies have a higher chance of being born dead, or dying shortly after birth.

All this raises two questions. Why is smoking so harmful? And why do people go on smoking knowing it is so dangerous? The second question is difficult to answer, but in this section some answers can be given to the first.

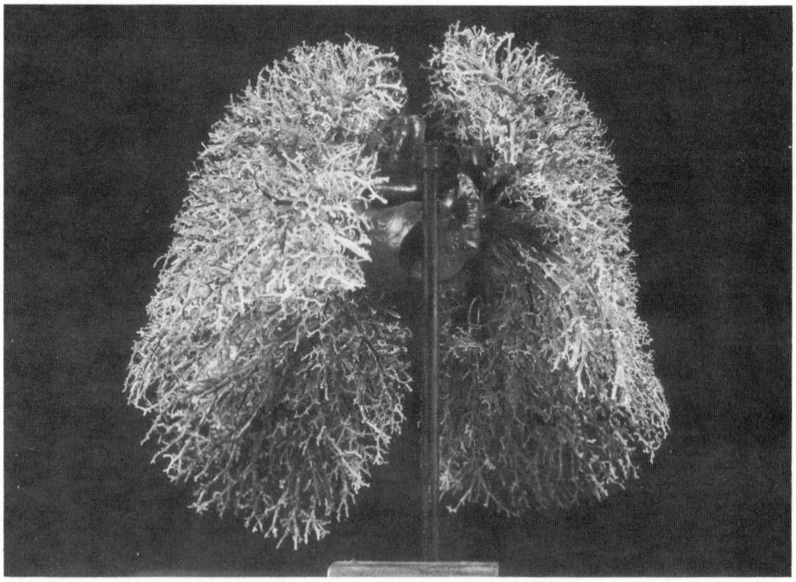

(*Above*) A plastic casting of the bronchial tree from human lungs.

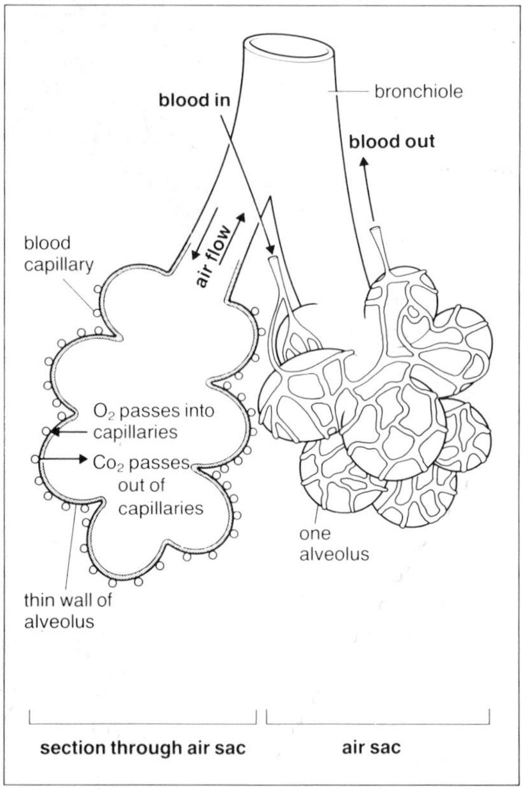

Figure 14.15 (Left) The respiratory surface of lungs – air sacs and alveoli.

Lungs

Your lungs are two bags with a huge surface area. Spread out, they would cover a tennis court. Each lung contains fine tubes called **bronchioles**, forming a branching system rather like the branches and twigs of a tree. In fact this network is called the **bronchial tree**. The photograph shows a plastic casting of the bronchial tree, made from human lungs.

Each bronchiole ends in an air sac (figure 14.15). Each air sac is rather like a bunch of grapes, the 'grapes' being bubble-like pockets called **alveoli**. Each alveolus is only about 0.2 mm in diameter, and there are about 300 million alveoli in a pair of lungs, so although the lungs are shaped like bags their consistency is rather like foam rubber.

The alveoli form the respiratory surface of the lungs. Air is constantly pumped in and out of the lungs. Their walls are thin (about a thousandth of a millimetre). Their inner side is covered in a film of moisture, and oxygen dissolves in this moisture and passes through the alveolus wall. The outer surface of the alveolus is covered with a dense network of blood capillaries. Oxygen passes into these capillaries and is carried away by red blood cells to different parts of the body where it is needed. A similar process occurs with carbon dioxide, which is brought by the blood to the alveoli, passes through the walls and is carried away in the air flow.

In emphysema, the walls separating the alveoli become thin and break down. This is often caused by corrosive substances in cigarette smoke. This reduces the surface area of the alveoli, making oxygen absorption less efficient and leading to breathing difficulty.

Inflating the lungs: the chest as a pump

For efficient exchange of oxygen and carbon dioxide with the blood, the air in the alveoli must be constantly replaced. The lungs can be inflated (blown up) and deflated by increasing and decreasing the volume of the **thorax**, the chest cavity containing the lungs (figure 14.16). Remember that although they have a spongy consistency, the lungs behave like a pair of large, elastic bags. These bags stretch and inflate when the thorax volume is increased. Section 7.7 gives details of how the chest acts as a pump.

When the lungs expand, the pressure of the air inside them falls and air flows in. The total capacity of a man's lungs, fully inflated, is about $5\,dm^3$ (five litres). During quiet breathing only $0.5\,dm^3$ of air is exchanged per breath. During exercise, breathing is deeper and about $2.5\,dm^3$ are exchanged. The air passes through the mouth or nose then through the **larynx** ('voice box') to the trachea.

The trachea, or windpipe, branches into two **bronchi**, one for each lung. Rings of cartilage strengthen the trachea and bronchi and prevent them collapsing. The whole respiratory passage is lined with fine hairs called **cilia**, which continuously move to and fro. The passages also secrete **mucus**, a sticky liquid. Mucus has two purposes. Firstly, it keeps the respiratory surfaces moist because it is slow to dry out. Secondly, it traps dust and other fine particles, stopping them reaching the lungs. The movements of the cilia continuously sweep the mucus up the respiratory passage towards the mouth, where it is eventually swallowed or spat out as cattarh.

Smoking irritates the respiratory surfaces and makes them produce extra mucus. It also stops the cilia beating, so mucus builds up in the respiratory passages and clogs them. The result is chronic bronchitis.

Certain chemicals in cigarette smoke, particularly in cigarette tar, are **carcinogenic**. The means they make cells in the lungs reproduce in an uncontrolled way, producing growths. This is lung cancer, and it almost always kills.

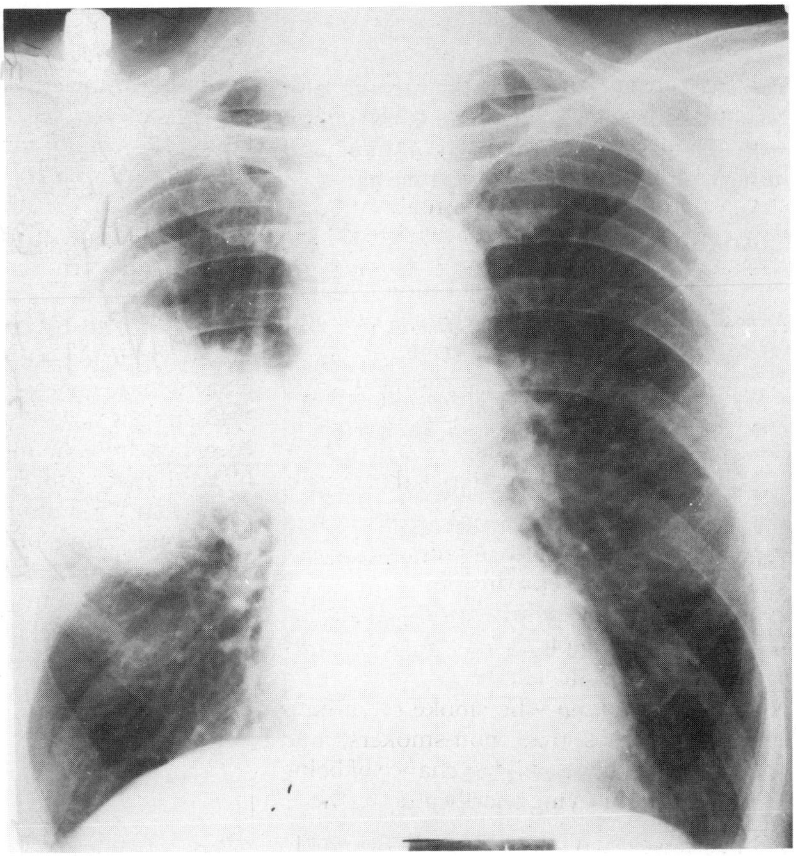

(*Above*) This X-ray photograph shows that this person has lung cancer. The cancer is the white patch in the middle of the lung on the left.

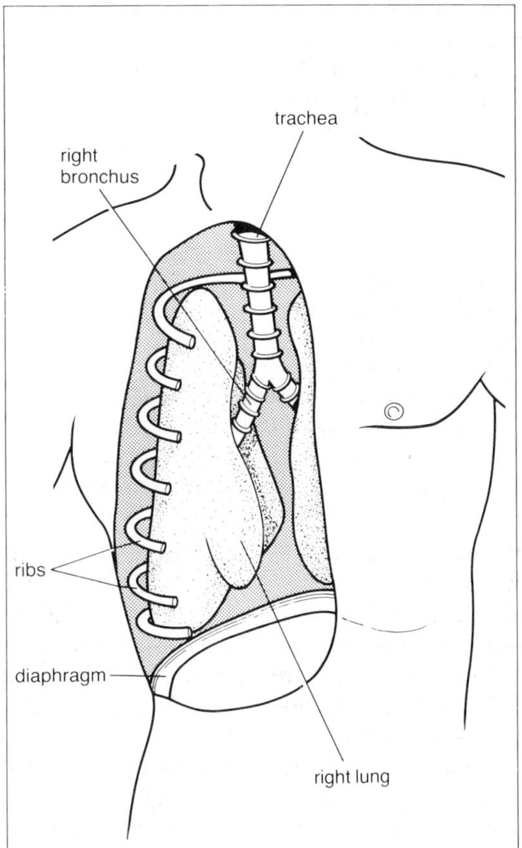

Figure 14.16 Part of the thorax (chest cavity) of human (heart not shown).

14.9 Rusting

We already know that both burning and respiration involve oxidation – combination with oxygen. Another very common and important oxidation process is **rusting**.

Corrosion of metals

When the exposed surface of a metal loses its bright, shiny look and becomes dull and tarnished, it has started to corrode.

> *For the following list of metal articles:*
> - Which would corrode quickly if left outside?
> - Which would corrode slowly?
> - Which would not corrode at all?
>
> an iron nail
> a galvanised iron dustbin
> a bright new penny
> aluminium foil
> a stainless steel knife

Some metals, like the copper in a new penny, corrode very slowly because they are rather unreactive. Aluminium is a fairly reactive metal (see the reactivity series in table 14.6) yet it hardly corrodes at all. This is because it quickly forms a thin, but very strong, layer of aluminium oxide which protects it from further corrosion. Unprotected iron corrodes (rusts) very quickly. But there are ways of protecting iron from rusting. It can be coated with zinc (galvanised), or mixed with another metal such as chromium to give a stainless steel alloy.

Rusting is a very serious problem which costs hundreds of millions of pounds a year. Nevertheless, iron is such a cheap, strong metal that we build bridges, cars, railways, ships and many other structures from it. Steel, an alloy of iron and carbon, is even more useful than iron. But because iron and steel rust so quickly, we have to replace them as they corrode, or spend money protecting them from rust.

Table 14.6 Reactivity series of metals

Na	*most reactive* ↑
Mg	
Al	
Zn	
Fe	
Sn	
Cu	*least reactive*

Rusting costs hundreds of million of pounds each year.

What causes rust?

Iron rusts quickly if it is wet. Salt helps rusting too. Metal structures on ships or near the seaside rust at an alarming rate. What other factors cause rusting? Figure 14.17 shows an experiment that can be used to investigate this.

Look at figure 14.17.
- Examine tubes 1 and 2. What is needed, besides water, to cause rusting?
- Why does the nail in tube 4 rust, whilst the one in tube 5 does not?
- Why does the nail in tube 6 not rust?

Rusting is an oxidation reaction. Both oxygen and water must be present for iron to rust. Rust is iron(III) oxide, Fe_2O_3. Rusting is a complicated reaction, involving several stages. During rusting, tiny electric currents flow in the metal. If the iron is in contact with water containing salt, or other ionic substances, it rusts faster, because the water conducts electricity better.

(*Left*) This ship isn't just being painted to make it look good! The paint stops air, water and salt getting to the iron in the hull, saving it from rusting.

Preventing rust

There are several ways of preventing rust.

Protection by oil or paint

A protective layer of oil, grease or paint, or a plastic covering, keeps air and water away from the iron and stops it rusting. This only works as long as the layer is complete. As soon as the paint peels or the oil rubs off, rusting starts again.

Alloying

Some metals, like aluminium, form a tough layer of oxide which protects them from further corrosion. Unfortunately rust is porous and flaky and does not protect iron. But iron can be mixed with certain metals, like chromium or nickel, which do form a protective oxide coat. These alloys are called stainless steels, and might contain up to 20% chromium or nickel.

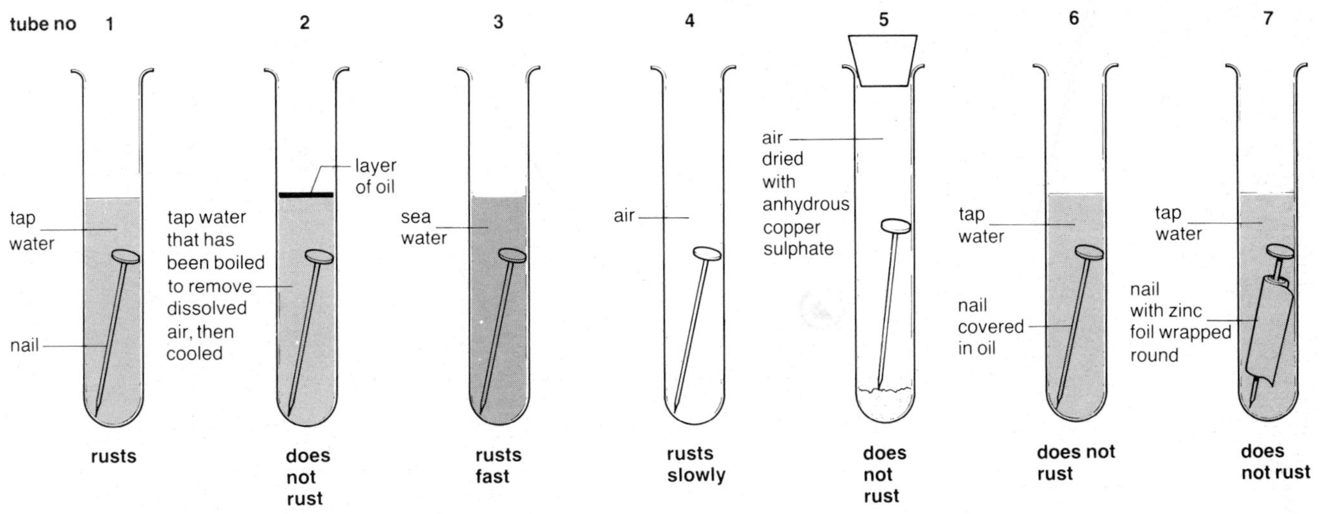

Figure 14.17 Investigation of rusting.

Plating

Iron is sometimes covered with a thin layer of another metal, such as chromium or tin, which is unreactive and does not corrode quickly. The metal protects the iron in the same way as a coat of paint would. This is called plating. Car bumpers are often chromium plated, but they soon corrode if scratched. 'Tinned' food is sold in steel cans, covered with a thin layer of tin, but these too rust quickly once the tin layer is removed.

Sacrificial coating

If iron is coated with a more reactive metal, such as zinc, it will not rust even if the coating is scratched off in places. Zinc is more reactive than iron, so it is oxidised in preference. The layer of zinc is more than just a protective coating, keeping out air and water. It actually saves the iron from corroding, by corroding itself. The zinc is 'sacrificed' for the sake of the iron, and it will go on protecting the iron as long as there is some zinc left. It is not even necessary to cover the whole surface of the iron, as long as some of the iron is in contact with zinc (see tube 7 in figure 14.17).

Zinc-coated iron is called **galvanised iron**. Many iron and steel articles that are used outdoors are galvanised. Dustbins, wheelbarrows and corrugated iron sheets are examples.

> *Look at the reactivity series in table 14.6.*
> - What metals besides zinc might be suitable for sacrificially coating iron?

Summary

1 Fuels are substances which can be oxidised to produce energy. Most common fuels contain carbon and hydrogen, and form carbon dioxide and water when they burn.

2 In fuel cells, fuels are oxidised to give electrical energy directly.

3 The percentages by volume of different gases in dry air are: nitrogen 78%, oxygen 21%, noble gases 0.9%, carbon dixoide 0.01–0.1%.

4 When elements burn in oxygen they form oxides.

5 The oxides of metals are solids, and those that dissolve in water give alkaline solutions. The oxides of non-metals are usually liquids or gases and give acidic solutions.

6 Burning fuels often produce air pollutants. These include oxides of carbon, sulphur and nitrogen.

7 Respiration is the process by which all living things obtain energy from food.

8 During aerobic respiration, glucose is oxidised to give carbon dioxide and water.

9 Anaerobic respiration occurs in the absence of air. When yeast respires anaerobically, ethanol (alcohol) and carbon dioxide are formed.

10 All but the smallest organisms need a transport system to carry oxygen to different parts of the organism.

11 Insects use a system of small tubes called tracheae and tracheoles to transport oxygen.

12 Fish obtain dissolved oxygen from water using their gills.

13 Mammals have lungs which they use to pass oxygen into the blood and to remove carbon dioxide.

14 Smoking prevents the lungs working properly, and affects health in a number of other ways.

15 Rusting is an oxidation reaction. Oxygen and water are necessary to cause rusting.

16 Rusting of iron can be prevented by a protective surface coating. Sacrificial coatings like zinc are particularly effective.

Study questions

1 The apparatus in figure 14.18 can be used to measure the percentage of oxygen in air. The phosphorus is touched with a red-hot wire, and the cork is quickly replaced. The phosphorus burns fiercely at first, forming solid phosphorus oxide, P_2O_5. The phosphorus then goes out, *before* it is used up. The water level rises in the jar, and after the apparatus has cooled the new level is read off. The results are:

Before burning takes place
volume of gas in jar = $1000\,cm^3$

After phosphorus has burned
volume of gas in jar = $820\,cm^3$

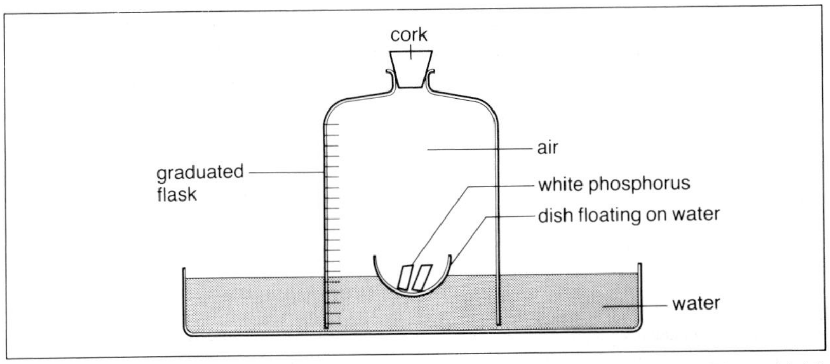

Figure 14.18

a) Why does the water level rise in the jar?
b) Why does the phosphorus stop burning before it is used up?
c) What volume of oxygen is used up by the burning phosphorus?
d) Calculate the percentage of oxygen in the air using these results.
e) Accurate experiments show that the percentage of oxygen in air is 21%. Compare your result with this value and give a reason for any difference.
f) What gases are left in the jar after the phosphorus has burned?
g) Why is it important, for this experiment, that phosphorus forms a solid oxide and not a gaseous one?
h) Why was the apparatus allowed to cool before reading off the final volume?

Table 14.7

Element burned	*Name of product*	*State of product (s, l or g)*	*Acid/alkaline nature of product, (acidic, alkaline or insoluble)*
potassium, K			
phosphorus, P			
calcium, Ca			
zinc, Zn			
selenium, Se			
aluminium, Al			

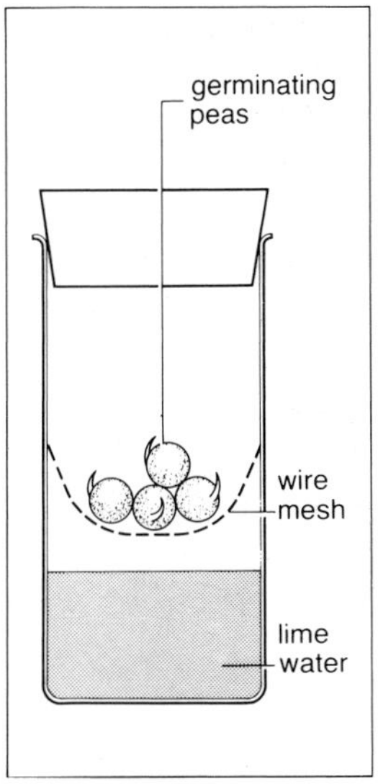

Figure 14.19

2 Table 14.7 refers to the products formed when different elements burn in oxygen. Copy out the table, then use the periodic table in figure 14.5 to make predictions about the products. Fill in your predictions.

3 Nonane, C_9H_{20}, is a hydrocarbon present in petrol.
a) What products would be formed when nonane burns under ideal conditions in a good supply of air?
b) Write a balanced equation for nonane burning in this way.
c) How many moles of oxygen are needed to burn one mole of nonane?
d) What is the mass of 1 mole of nonane? (C = 12, H = 1)
e) One litre ($1\,dm^3$) of nonane weighs 720 g. How many moles of nonane are there in one litre?
f) How many moles of oxygen are needed to burn one litre of nonane?

When one mole of nonane burns, 6200 kJ of heat are given off.

g) How much heat is given off when one litre of nonane burns?
h) What pollutants are likely to form when nonane burns in a car engine?

4 City air usually contains several substances that are dangerous to health. Name three such substances. For each one (a) say how the substance got into the air (b) say why it is harmful to health (c) suggest how levels of the substance in the air could be controlled.

5 Wood is a very complex material. In its simplest form its chemical formula is approximately CH_2O. Wood is often used as a fuel.

The formula of glucose is $C_6H_{12}O_6$, or CH_2O in its simplest form. Glucose is used as a fuel by living organisms.
a) What is the name of the process in which energy is obtained from a fuel like wood?
b) What is the name of the process by which a living organism obtains energy from glucose?
c) Give two similarities between the processes you have named in (a) and (b).
d) Give two differences between the processes you have named in (a) and (b).

6 Figure 14.19 shows an experiment to investigate whether germinating peas produce carbon dioxide.
a) What change would you expect to *see* in the tube, apart from germination of the peas?
b) What control experiment should also be carried out?
c) Mention one other change that would occur in the tube. Design an experiment to measure this change.
d) Will germination of the peas in the tube continue normally? Explain your answer.

7 a) Describe briefly how an insect obtains the oxygen it needs for respiration. Why would a similar system be unsuitable for humans?
b) A person will die if their lungs are filled with water. A fish will die if it is taken out of water. Explain the difference.
c) The interior surface of our bronchial tubes is covered with a layer of sticky mucus. Why is this? Why are fishes' gills not covered with mucus?
d) Frogs have very primitive lungs, and much of their gaseous exchange occurs through the skin. Why is it important that the skin of a frog is always wet?

8 a) Give three features of alveoli which make them efficient for gaseous exchange.
Table 14.8 gives the composition of atmospheric air, exhaled air, and alveolar air. Alveolar air is air actually inside the alveoli.
b) How could a sample of alveolar air be obtained for analysis?
c) Look at the figures for atmospheric air and exhaled air.
i) Why does exhaled air contain more carbon dioxide than atmospheric air? Where does the extra come from?
ii) Why does exhaled air contain less oxygen than atmosphere air? Where has the oxygen gone to?
d) Look at the figures for alveolar air and exhaled air. Why are the figures different? (Hint: remember exhaled and inhaled air follow the same route to the alveoli.)

Table 14.8

	Atmospheric air	*Exhaled air*	*Alveolar air*
nitrogen	79.01	79.5	80.7
oxygen	20.96	16.4	13.8
carbon dioxide	0.03	4.1	5.5

9 a) What is rust? What conditions favour rusting?
b) Why is the steel hull of an ocean-going ship especially likely to rust?
c) Why are blocks of zinc often bolted to a ship's hull?
d) A small child dropped an iron nail into a kettle. The nail was only discovered weeks later by the childs parent, but it had hardly rusted at all. A similar nail dropped in the garden pond had rusted badly in two days. Explain the difference.
e) Aluminium is a more reactive metal than iron. Aluminium hardly tarnishes at all when exposed to air and water, yet iron rusts in hours. Explain.
f) What do burning, breathing and rusting have in common?

Index